# Canadian Fire Alarm Association

# Fire Alarm Systems

# A Reference Manual

## 2010 Edition

**Canadian Fire Alarm Association**
**85 Citizen Court – Units 3 & 4**
**Markham, Ontario, Canada L6G 1A8**

**TEL: 1- (800) 529-0552**
**FAX: 1- (905) 479-3639**

**www.cfaa.ca**

**email: info@cfaa.ca**

# FIRE ALARM SYSTEMS

# A REFERENCE MANUAL

## 2010 EDITION

### A Module of the CFAA Fire Alarm Technology Program

ISBN: 978-0-9734001-3-7

**Printed in Canada**

## CFAA FORWARD

Fire alarm systems continue to be a major element for life safety in buildings. The subject of fire alarm systems is a unique discipline that has evolved with technological advances and is also linked with the legal requirements of Codes and Standards. This new edition of the manual is written as a reference resource for those taking Course 5 of the CFAA Fire Alarm Technician program, but also as an informative document to provide a better understanding of how things work, installation considerations and the multitude of fire alarm system requirements.

As stated in the previous edition, an understanding of basic electricity and basic electronics is necessary to achieve the maximum benefit. Knowledge of fire growth and progression is also helpful in addition to comprehension of the interdependent structure of the related codes and standards. *"Introduction to the Fire Detection and Alarm Industry"*, the Course 1 manual, is an excellent reference in this regard.

The new edition of *"Fire Alarm Systems: A Reference Manual"* is in a revised format with colour illustrations and photographs. The content of the thirteen chapters encompasses the fire topics of detection, signalling, control units, installation and testing. It has been built on the foundation of the previous edition and updated to include the advances in fire alarm system technology. Illustrations and photographs are intended to supplement the text and are not intended to promote a manufacturer's product. The text has been revised with information to reflect the changes in the Building Code, Fire Code and the latest edition of the Underwriters' Laboratories of Canada (ULC) standards.

Codes and Standards play a vital role in the fire alarm industry. The information in this text is provided for explanatory purposes but it is not a standards document. We thank ULC for their assistance in making some of the standards material available. The standards produced by ULC and the references to the specific sections of the Building Code and Fire Code as legislated in the various regions of Canada are necessary for a complete understanding of the requirements and should be consulted.

The text has been written in a manner suited to readers with diverse backgrounds who desire a better understanding of fire alarm systems in terms of design, installation, inspection and testing.

This book is the result of many volunteer hours by several members of the Canadian Fire Alarm Association. The list includes authors and those who spent hours reviewing the content. The rewriting of this book has had the technical advice and assistance of the CFAA Education Committee chaired by David Sylvester. David has provided both guidance in setting the format and many hours in review of this edition. We are particularly indebted to those contributors who drafted various chapters: Ken Baird, Dave Duggan, Mike Hugh, Andy Hewitson, Paul Jewett, Brad Pope, and Victor Repovz.

A special thank you goes to the editorial skills of Allen Hodson. Allen's persistence in completing the editing of the text, pulling the chapters together and providing a coherent style has resulted in this new edition: an edition that is both an easy to use reference and a text that will enhance your knowledge of fire alarm systems.

Carol Mather-Miles also deserves special thanks for the many hours she has spent compiling and formatting the chapters to make this publication possible.

You will find this new edition in its revised format a valuable asset to your library and a reference for understanding fire alarm systems.

Dave Goodyear, Chair
Course 5 Manual Committee

# Chapter 1: Fire Alarm Systems - An Overview

## 1.1 Chapter Overview and Key Concepts

This manual is a reference book on Fire Alarm Systems. The material builds on the knowledge from the other CFAA courses including the following CFAA Technician Program manuals: Course 1 - *Introduction to the Fire Alarm Industry*, and Course 3 - *Basic Electricity for Fire Alarm Technicians*.

It is also highly recommended that the reader have immediate access to the applicable *Building Code*, *Fire Code*, and the three Underwriters' Laboratories of Canada companion standards: *CAN/ULC-S524 Installation of Fire Alarm Systems*, *CAN/ULC-S537 Verification of Fire Alarm Systems* and *CAN/ULC-S536 Inspection and Testing of Fire Alarm Systems*.

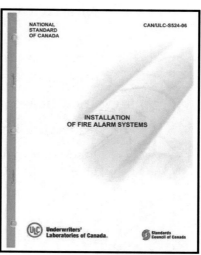

This chapter is intended to provide a summary of the various requirements contained in the codes and standards, and is for general information only. The reader must refer to the applicable codes and standards that apply in the particular jurisdiction for the precise requirements that apply to any given building or situation.

The *Building Code* generally tells us 'what' to do: the need for a Fire Alarm System, the requirements for detection devices, device zoning, audible and visible signalling, off-site monitoring, and the myriad of other specific details of a new Fire Alarm System.

The standards generally describe 'how' to do it: from installation to verification to periodic inspections and tests.

This chapter will describe how these documents all fit together, and how they are used by all participants in the industry.

## 1.2　　Learning Objectives

Upon successful completion of this chapter, the reader should be able to:

- understand why the Building Code is the primary reference document for system designers,

- explain the references from the Building Code to the ULC Standards

- differentiate between the various classifications of building occupancies

- know how to calculate the 'occupant load' for a given building

- understand how to determine building height

- discuss why different classifications of buildings require different levels of fire safety

©

## Language defined

Throughout the various codes and standards, certain words and phrases are used to identify specific items, situations, assemblies or processes. Before beginning a study of any of these documents, it is important that the definitions applicable to fire protection are clearly understood. Failure to understand the meaning of a defined term in a code requirement often leads to an incorrect interpretation of that requirement. Special terms that will be found in this chapter are listed below. Also refer to the Main Glossary at the end of this Manual.

| Term | Definition |
|---|---|
| **Authority Having Jurisdiction** | The organization, office, or individual responsible for approving equipment, an installation, or a procedure. Most often, it is the municipal Fire Department, although in some cases it may be the Building Department. |
| **Basement** | A storey or storeys of a building located below the first storey. |
| **Building Area** | The greatest horizontal area of a building above grade within the outside surface of exterior walls or within the outside surface of exterior walls and the centre line of firewalls. |
| **Building Height (in storeys)** | The number of storeys contained between the roof and the floor of the first storey. An elevator machine room, sitting atop an office building, would not generally be considered a storey in this application. |
| **Control Unit** | A device with the necessary circuits or components needed to provide acceptable operating power for a fire alarm system, receive signals from alarm initiating devices, cause audible alarm signals to operate, and electrically monitor the installation wiring and device placement against certain faults and/or removal. |
| **Exit** | A facility such as a door, stairs or ramp that leads from the floor area that it serves to an open public thoroughfare, or to a protected exterior open space that has access to an open public thoroughfare. Once in an exit facility, a person should have a continuous path leading to the building exterior. |
| **Fire Alarm System** | A system comprising both manually-operated devices and automatic fire detectors, alarm signalling devices and a control unit, all electrically interconnected in order to detect fire conditions and to warn the occupants of the building. |
| **First Storey** | The uppermost storey having its floor level not more than two metres above grade. In certain jurisdictions, it is the storey with its floor closest to grade and having its ceiling more than 1.8 m above grade. |

| Term | Definition |
| --- | --- |
| **Floor Area** | The space on any storey of a building between the exterior walls and required firewalls, including the space occupied by interior walls and partitions, but not including exits and vertical service spaces that pierce the storey. |
| **High Building** | A building where the floor level of the top storey of the building is above grade more than that allowed in 3.2.6 of the *Building Code* |
| **Major Occupancy** | The principal occupancy for which a building or part thereof is used, or intended to be used, and shall be deemed to include the subsidiary occupancies that are an integral part of the principal occupancy. |
| **Manual Station** | A device that initiates an alarm condition in a fire alarm system, when actuated manually. The station will remain in the operated condition until it has been reset to normal using a special tool. |
| **Occupant Load** | The number of people for which a building or part of a building is designed, on a square-metre basis for each person. This figure is set by the authorities, is different for different occupancies, and is quite likely different than the actual occupant load the building may eventually experience. |
| **Owner** | Any person, firm or corporation controlling the property under consideration. |
| **Storey** | That portion of a building which is situated between the top of any floor and the top of the floor next above it, and if there is no floor above it, that portion between the top of such floor and the ceiling (roof) above it. |

## 1.3    General

Properly designed, installed and maintained Fire Alarm Systems are a key element in the protection of life-safety, countering the destructive forces of fire. Early-warning, automatic Fire Detection and Alarm Systems provide a warning of fire danger so that occupant evacuation and fire suppression activities can quickly begin.

Early-warning fire detection systems protect both life and property. There is no single fire alarm system that is ideal for all buildings. Fire alarm systems range from simple systems that only sound audible alarm signals, to complex systems that utilize network configurations, and that interface to a variety of other building functions such as smoke control. It is important that fire alarm systems designers realize that each building has structural features and building layouts that create a different set of problems in terms of fire development, and therefore presents different levels of danger to the occupants. Each Fire Detection and Alarm System must be designed according to the specific building and its occupancy, so that in combination with other fire prevention measures, the effects of any fire can be kept to a minimum, and occupants protected from harm.

The time interval from the start of a fire to the safe evacuation of occupants is comprised of several chronological stages including: detection time, time to process the detection information, time to activate the signals, time for occupants to react, and time for the occupants to move out of the building. Fire Alarm Systems play a significant role in this process. Therefore, the people who design, install, verify, test and maintain automatic Fire Detection and Alarm Systems bear a great deal of responsibility both for the safety of the occupants and the contents of the buildings.

**Large residential building fire, Toronto, February 2008**

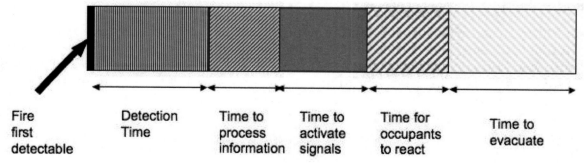

Fire first detectable — Detection Time — Time to process information — Time to activate signals — Time for occupants to react — Time to evacuate

The choice of detection devices, their sensitivity, the correct locations, and decisions regarding the installation materials and methods, as well as continuing maintenance of the system, ultimately determine the effectiveness and level of reliability of the fire alarm system.

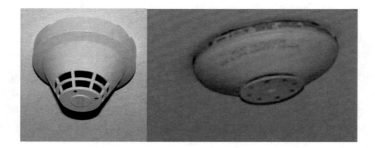

Just as important as detection, is the selection of signalling devices including both audible and visible devices. The ambient conditions must be evaluated, and the correct devices placed appropriately in order to achieve the audibility and visibility objectives.

Other fire-safety functions are likely to be controlled automatically by the Fire Alarm System and the successful interfacing of these systems requires a detailed systems approach to fire protection.

The system designer must understand the occupancy classification of the building, and how critical events within the building are to be managed, when selecting the appropriate Fire Alarm System design and operational features.

Fire Alarm Systems in larger complexes may incorporate visual signal appliances, annunciators, emergency telephones and other equipment required to provide voice communications capability. Voice communications systems that incorporate paging messages can assist in the evacuation process by providing the occupants with additional information about the alarm event.

Automatic extinguishing systems, such as sprinkler systems, kitchen-hood fire extinguishing systems, building air-handling systems and off-site alarm monitoring connections are often required to be interconnected into the building's Fire Alarm System.

The Underwriters' Laboratories of Canada standard *CAN/ULC- S524 Installation of Fire Alarm Systems* describes a Fire Alarm System as consisting of at least the following interconnected devices: a control unit, a manual station and an audible signal appliance.

Fire Alarm Systems come in several variations. Simple systems can be viewed as a black box (the control unit) with one or more initiating (input) circuits connected to the detection devices and one or more alarm signalling (output) circuits connected to signalling devices, or other circuits controlling ancillary equipment such as connections for fans for smoke control, or to an off-site monitoring company.

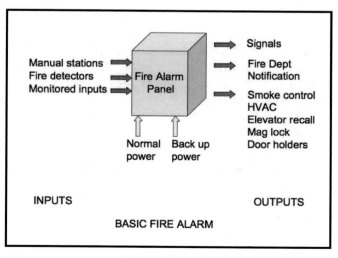

Initiating or detection circuits are for the connection of detection devices including manual stations, heat detectors and smoke detectors. An alarm condition is initiated when any device changes the current flow through the circuit. Many new systems use addressable detection devices. These devices (manual stations, heat detectors and smoke detectors) each have a unique code or address, and they individually communicate digitally with the fire alarm control panel. In these systems the type of detector and its location can be identified by the digital address. More complex Fire Alarm Systems may have multiple control panels, each having input and output circuits, with the control panels communicating digitally over a dedicated network or a Distributed Fire Alarm System.

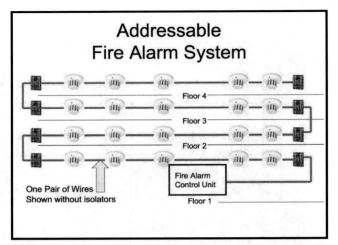

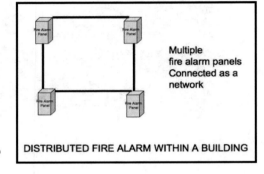

## 1.4    It Begins With *The Building Code*

Our industry is a code-driven industry! There are many codes, standards and other regulations related to the installation and maintenance of fire alarm systems. Fire alarm systems are almost always installed because of the requirements contained within the *Building Code* and to a lesser extent, the *Fire Code*. These requirements are written into the *Building Code* to ensure that each building that is constructed across Canada provides at least a minimum level of life safety for the occupants. A complete description of the applicable codes and standards is contained in Chapter 3 of the CFAA Course 1 Manual *Introduction To The Fire Detection & Alarm Industry*.

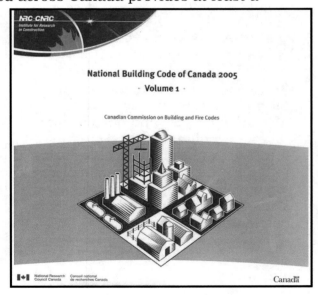

The *Building Code* contains the minimum requirements for the design of Fire Alarm Systems. The specific requirements depend upon the building classification, occupant load and the physical size of the building. *The Building Code* in turn also references other documents such as the ULC Standards that must also be followed.

©

Some owners of existing buildings voluntarily request that Fire Alarm Systems be installed, or they wish to upgrade an existing Fire Alarm System to provide a certain level of protection for their employees, as well as additional protection for both the building structure and the processes or contents of the building, even though not required by the codes. All fire protection features of a building, whether required by code or not, will be designed in accordance with good fire protection engineering practice, and that Fire Alarm System components will be installed in accordance with the standards.

So what is required of a Fire Alarm System? A system must be designed and installed so that through the appropriate choice, quantity and arrangement of fire detection devices, a fire is detected at the earliest possible moment, and audible and visible warning signals will be heard and/or seen, and recognized as an alarm signal.

Electrical supervision of field wiring, devices and power supplies ensures dependability of the fire alarm system by ensuring that it is functional at all times.

## 1.5    Interrelationship Of Codes And Standards

The *Building Code* regulates in which buildings a Fire Alarm System is required, and how it must function. It states where automatic detection devices are required, and details the monitoring of sprinkler systems. It defines the requirements for signalling including signal duration and audibility levels. It stipulates when off-site alarm monitoring is required. The *Building Code* also specifies the emergency power supply requirements for the Fire Alarm System. The annunciation requirements and zoning indications to be displayed, are defined by the *Building Code* as well as the requirements for Emergency Voice Communication Systems.

Note particularly that throughout the *Building Code*, references are made to many other codes and standards. The *Building Code* states that Fire Alarm and Voice Communication systems must be installed in accordance with *CAN/ULC-S524 Installation Of Fire Alarm Systems*. The *Building Code* also states that, once installed, Fire Alarm and Voice Communication Systems must be verified in accordance with *CAN/ULC-S537 Verification Of Fire Alarm Systems*. Since the *Building Code* is a legal requirement, each document referenced in the *Building Code* also becomes a legal requirement.

The latest edition of a code or standard is not always the edition that is the legally enforceable edition. Volume 1, Division B, Part 1, Section 1.3 of the *Building Code* provides the particular year or edition of the referenced code or standard that is to apply.

The *CAN/ULC S524 Standard* also references several equipment standards. Individual components of fire alarm systems must comply with the following standards all of which have been created for Fire Alarm Systems:

- CAN/ULC-S525, Audible Signal Devices including Accessories
- CAN/ULC-S526, Visible Signal Devices including Accessories
- CAN/ULC-S527, Control Units for Fire Alarm Systems
- CAN/ULC-S528, Manual Stations
- CAN/ULC-S529, Smoke Detectors
- CAN/ULC-S530, Heat Actuated Fire Detectors for Fire Alarm Systems
- CAN/ULC-S533, Egress Door Securing and Releasing Devices

**National Building Code (Model Document)**
- Changes made by the Province
- Enacted Legislation by Province into Law to become the Provincial Building Code
- States WHAT is required
- Refers to Standards

**ULC Installation of Fire Alarm Systems CAN/ULC S524**
- States HOW & HOW MANY to Install
- Refers to CEC, Part 2, Section 32
- Refers to EQUIPMENT Standards

**ULC Verification of Fire Alarm Systems CAN/ULC S537**
- States HOW to Verify

**Canadian Electrical Code (Model Document)**
- Changes made by Province
- Enacted/Legislated by Province into Law under Power Act to become Electrical Safety Code
- States WHAT to Install related to Wiring, Conduit and Electrical Safety

**National Fire Code (Model Document)**
- Changes made by Province
- Enacted/Legislated by Province into Law
- States WHAT is required
- Refers to Standard

**ULC Test & Inspection of Fire Alarm System CAN/ULC S536**
- States HOW to Test and Inspect

- CAN/ULC-S541, Speakers for Fire Alarm Systems, including Accessories

- CAN/ULC-S548, Devices and Accessories for Water Type Extinguishing Systems

- CAN/ULC-S561 Installation and Services for Fire Signal Receiving Centres And Systems

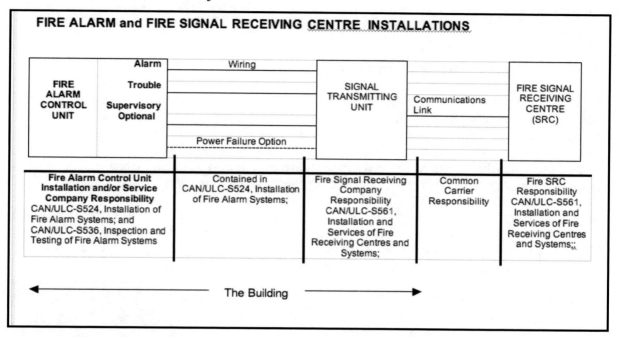

These ULC standards specify how the devices must be manufactured. While they are necessary for the product manufacturer, these standards are not usually necessary for the person installing, testing or maintaining fire alarm systems.

CAN/ULC-S561 *Installation and Services for Fire Signal Receiving Centres and Systems* is also referenced for requirements for connections to alarm monitoring stations. This standard also has requirements for equipment and the type of communication links installed at the building where a Fire Alarm System is installed, to ensure that connection to the monitoring station is reliable.

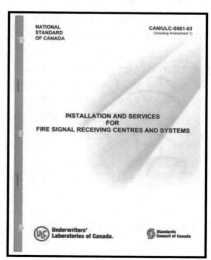

Unlike security systems, the installation of Fire Alarm Systems is considered to be the installation of electrical systems, and falls under the requirements of the applicable Canadian/Provincial electrical codes. The *Canadian Electrical Code* (CEC) is also referenced through CAN/ULC-S524, where it states that the installation of all field wiring is to be in accordance with the *Canadian Electrical Code, Part 1, Section 32*. An electrician is required to do this work.

Most provinces have adopted the CEC, sometimes with a specific supplement, which then serves as the provincial Electrical Safety Code, generally adopted as a legal document under the provincial Power Act.

After the building has been granted an Occupancy Permit, the *Building Code* has done its job, and now the *Fire Code* comes into effect and becomes a legal requirement for that building. The *Fire Code* contains requirements for Fire Safety Plans and acceptable levels of testing and maintenance of safety systems including the Fire Alarm System.

## 1.6    Plans and Specifications

The Authority Having Jurisdiction (AHJ) (usually the building department) requires acceptable plans and specifications for any Fire Alarm System, for approval, prior to installation. The municipal plans examination people then study the submitted documents to ensure that the Fire Alarm System has been designed in compliance with all applicable code requirements. These plans and specifications must be approved before a Building Permit is then issued and the work can begin.

These same plans and specifications may also be used as tender documents by an owner to receive bids from various contractors for the installation of the system. They must therefore contain all pertinent information including device layout, device specifications, riser diagrams and system operational descriptions.

These documents, in the majority of cases, must be prepared by a professional such as an Architect or Engineer and are generally required to be appropriately stamped. Some smaller buildings are exempted from this; it varies from province to province, and from municipality to municipality.

These requirements also apply to all 'material alterations', which affect the public health, fire safety or the structural sufficiency of the building in any substantial manner. On the other hand, such permit applications would not be required for minor alterations such as, for example, the change of a heat detector to another type of heat detector, as long as the same coverage is upheld, but may apply, for example, if all smoke detectors were to be changed to heat detectors. It would also apply if the Fire Alarm System operation were changed from a single-stage to a two-stage. The general expectation however is that any alteration to existing fire/life safety components is generally considered a material alteration, and must first be reviewed by the AHJ.

## 1.7    Requirements For A Fire Alarm System

The main determining factors in establishing if a Fire Alarm System is required by the *Building Code* are:

- the building's use (Group and Division Classification),

- the height of the building (number of storeys), and

- the occupant load of the building.

In order to clearly understand these code requirements, one first must understand the meanings of these terms, why they are necessary, and how they are used for Fire Alarm System applications.

The *Building Code* Subsection 3.2.4. 'Fire Alarm and Detection Systems' stipulates when a Fire Alarm System is required. These code requirements can apply to both new buildings and to existing buildings requiring a new Fire Alarm System, either as part of a required retrofit, a material alteration, or a repair. They will probably also apply to a voluntary installation.

Within the *Building Code,* the fire alarm requirements become more complex as the risk becomes greater. For example in multi-unit residential buildings (where people sleep) the requirements are greater than in office buildings of the same size. Where people are less mobile (such as in healthcare facilities) the risk, and therefore the requirements, are greater. Similarly higher buildings have greater requirements than lower buildings.

**Combustible Building –
Log Cabin Group C**

## 1.7.1 Classification of Buildings

In *Building Code* subsection 3.1.2, 'Classification of Buildings or Parts of Buildings by Major Occupancy', provisions are given for classifying buildings in accordance with how the building will be occupied or used.

Buildings are classified according to their use and inherent hazard, such as:

- density of population (occupant load),

- mobility and alertness of occupants (as affected by age, mental illness, or restraint of occupants),

- fire load content, and

- the presence of hazardous material, equipment or processes.

The *Building Code* therefore divides occupancies into six main groups (A, B, C, D, E, and F) with further divisions for more accurate treatment.

**Correctional Facility –
Group B, Division 1**

**Computer Room –
Group D**

| Group | Major occupancy | |
|---|---|---|
| **Group A** | Division 1 | Assembly occupancies intended for the production and viewing of performing arts |
| | Division 2 | Assembly occupancies not elsewhere classified in Group A |
| | Division 3 | Assembly occupancies of the arena type |
| | Division 4 | Assembly occupancies in which provision is made for the congregation or gathering of persons for the purpose of participating in or viewing open-air activities |
| **Group B** | Division 1 | Institutional occupancies in which persons are under restraint or incapable of self-preservation because of security measures not under their control |
| | Division 2 | Institutional occupancies in which persons because of mental or physical limitations require special treatment |
| **Group C** | | Residential |
| **Group D** | | Business & Personal Services |
| **Group E** | | Mercantile |
| **Group F** | Division 1 | High Hazard, Industrial |
| | Division 2 | Medium Hazard, Industrial |
| | Division 3 | Low Hazard, Industrial |

For example, the main hazard of Group A, Assembly Occupancies, is that they contain a large number of people, who are present only occasionally, in combination with variable fire loads. Within this Group A, there are different conditions involving other hazards that do not apply to all occupancies. Hence the group is divided into subgroups called Divisions. As an example, hazards due to large numbers of people in fixed seats in a theatre are different than unseated people in a museum. Outdoor assemblies are relatively much safer than indoor assemblies and consequently such structures require different (and not as restrictive) fire safety treatment.

Buildings containing sleeping quarters must be treated differently from a fire safety approach, because the occupants may not be as immediately alert or mobile. Buildings containing such sleeping accommodation occur in several different occupancy Groups and Divisions.

Each major occupancy is further defined in, Definitions, as well as being described in the Building Code Classification Table. This table shows

©

that not only whole buildings, but sections or areas within buildings may be classified as different major occupancies.

Furthermore, the definition of a major occupancy means the principal occupancy or part thereof as used, or intended to be used, and includes subsidiary occupancies which are an integral part of the principal occupancy. Thus a gymnasium can be considered an integral part of a school, or a cafeteria an integral part of an office building, and a paint booth an integral part of a repair garage. Such subsidiary occupancies do not change the classification of the building itself with regard to Fire Alarm System requirements, but may have other requirements, such as for fire separations.

## 1.7.2　Building Height

The need for a Fire Alarm System, when a building is three or four storeys high, may depend on the definition of storey. Storey means that portion of a building which is situated between the top of any floor and the top of the floor next above it, and if there is no floor above it, that portion between the top of such floor and the ceiling above it.

Rooftop enclosures provided for elevator machinery, stairways and service rooms, used for no other purpose than for service to the building, are generally not considered a storey.

Mezzanines, under certain conditions in calculating the building height, need not be considered a storey. This is true also for balconies and galleries in theatres or other such places.

Building height is the number of stories contained between the floor of the first storey and the roof. The first storey is the storey that is closest to grade, with the ceiling being more than 1.8 m above grade. Note that the determination of grade may be challenging, because the definition of grade within the meaning of the *Building Code* is quite different to the grade level used by various building trades and contractors.

**High Building**

## 1.7.3　Occupant Load

Once the first storey is known, and therefore the building height, the next step in determining the need for a Fire Alarm System is to calculate the occupant load.

The number of people for which a building or part of a building is designed, on a square-metre basis for a given occupancy, is the calculated occupant load. It is not the actual number of people that may occupy the building, as this figure in a new building is totally unknown, or in an existing building as it may change daily or seasonally. The occupant load is calculated in various ways:

- the number of seats in assembly occupancies, where fixed seats are used, or

- two persons per bedroom or sleeping area in dwelling units, or

- the number of persons for which the area is designed, or

- as given in Table 3.1.17.1 Occupant Load, which applies to a variety of occupancies other than those described above.

For the purpose of rooms or groups of rooms intended for two or more occupancies at different times, the value that gives the greatest number of persons must be used for calculation purposes.

## 1.8    When is a Fire Alarm System Required?

The *Building Code*, Subsection 3.2.4. Fire Alarm and Detection Systems, requires a system in any building, regardless of Group or Division Classification, containing:

- more than three storeys, including storeys below the first storey,

- a total occupant load more than 300, other than in open air seating areas,

- an occupant load more than 300 below an open air seating area,

- an occupant load of more than 150 above or below the first storey, other than in open air seating areas,

- a school, college, or child care facility, including a day care facility, with an occupant load more than 40,

- a contained-use area,

- an impeded-egress zone,

- a licensed beverage establishment or a restaurant, with an occupant load more than 150,

- a high hazard industrial occupancy, with an occupant load more than 25,

- a medium hazard industrial occupancy or a low hazard industrial occupancy with an occupant load more than 75 above or below the first storey, or

- a residential occupancy with sleeping accommodation for more than ten persons.

©

Note that a Fire Alarm System may also be required by some provincial jurisdictions when the building contains an interconnected floor space, or when the building provides care, or care and treatment for more than ten persons in a care, or care and treatment occupancy.

### 1.8.1 When is a Fire Alarm System Not Required?

A Fire Alarm System is not required in apartment buildings where not more than four dwelling units share a common means of egress, or in buildings three storeys or less in building height where each dwelling unit is served by an exterior exit facility leading to ground level.

A Fire Alarm System is not required in a hotel (or motel) three storeys or less in building height provided each suite has direct access to an exterior exit facility leading to ground level.

A Fire Alarm System is not required in certain storage garages provided there are no other occupancies in the building.

### 1.8.2 Voice Communication System

The Building Code stipulates that a Voice Communication System is required in any building where the height of that building measured between grade and the floor of the top storey, is more than 36 m, or in buildings containing a floor area or part of a floor area located above the third storey and designed or intended for use as a Group B, Division 2 occupancy (or Division 3 in some jurisdictions).

Voice Communication Systems as required by the *Building Code* for high buildings must consist of:

- a two-way system in each floor area, connecting to a Central Alarm and Control Facility (CACF). Emergency telephones are to be installed in each floor area near exit stair shafts,

- a system of loudspeakers, operated from the CACF, and which are heard throughout the building. This system must allow voice instructions to be transmitted selectively to any zone or zones while maintaining an alert signal or alarm signal to the other zones in the building. This arrangement is referred to as a three-channel system, whereby the Alert signal, the Alarm signal, and a Voice Message can be transmitted simultaneously to three different parts of the building.

The CACF is a separate room near the main entrance of the building. There are many specific requirements for Fire Alarm System design and operational features to be provided by the CACF:

- A fire alarm annunciator including individual sprinkler water flow and supervisory indicators,

- Indicators for alert and alarm signalling,

- Switches to manually activate alarm signalling selectively to any or all zones,

- Indication if signals are silenced,

- Connections to an alarm receiving station,

- Voice communication permitting paging selectively to any or all zones,

- Firefighter emergency telephone system connecting to all zones,

- A switch to release all electromagnetic hold open devices,

- Indication elevators have been recalled,

- Switches to control smoke exhaust and fans serving more than two stories

## 1.9    Additional Requirements for High Buildings

Recognizing the increased potential for hazards for occupants in high buildings, the *Building Code* contains several specific requirements that are intended to provide additional safety features within such high buildings. Some of the additional requirements related to fire alarm systems are as follows:

- the installation of smoke control measures,

- provision of areas of refuge,

- emergency operation of elevators,

- venting to aid fire fighting,

- additional sprinkler coverage,

- provision of a Central Alarm and Control Facility,

- provision of voice communication systems,

- protection of electrical conductors, and

- smoke movement and venting controls.

These requirements apply to:

- every building of Group A, D, E or F major occupancy that is more than (i) 36 m high, measured between grade and the floor level of the top storey, or (ii) 18 m high, measured between grade and the floor level of the top storey and in which the cumulative or total occupant load on or above any storey above grade, other than the first storey, divided by 1.8 times the width in metres of all exit stairs at that storey, exceeds 300,

- every building containing a Group B major occupancy in which the floor level of the highest storey of that major occupancy is more than 18 m above grade or every building containing a floor area or part of a floor area located above the third storey designed or intended as a

Group B Division 2 (and 3 in some provincial jurisdictions) occupancy, and

- every building containing a Group C major occupancy whose floor level is more than 18 m above grade.

## 1.10    Two More Things To Remember About the *Building Code*

The *Building Code* states that when a Fire Alarm System is required, it must be installed throughout the building. It cannot be installed in just one wing or on just some floors.

There can only be one Fire Alarm System installed in a building. Note that this does not mean only one control unit. There may be several control units operating together as one system. This occurs in the case of distributed Fire Alarm Systems.

## 1.11    Chapter Summary

1.    The *National Building Code of Canada* is the primary source of information relating to building design criteria

2.    The *Building Code* references other notable documents thereby making them 'required' documents

3.    Generally speaking – codes tell us what to do – standards tell us how to do it

4.    Codes and standards fit together, and are routinely interpreted and applied by designers, installers and authorities

5.    A well-designed and properly-installed Fire Alarm System is a major component in the overall fire safety within any building

6.    An effective Fire Alarm System must almost always comprise detection inputs, signalling outputs and ancillary systems controls.

7.    A set of specifications and plans help ensure that a new system will meet the objectives of the *Building Code*.

8.    Buildings are classified as to types of occupancies. This is done to provide the system designer with applicable system requirements leading to greater safety for those buildings/occupants at greater risk.

9.    For various reasons, high-rise buildings present a potentially serious fire concern. Among the many additional requirements in the *Building Code* for high-rise buildings is the need for Emergency Voice Systems.

10.    In any building, there must be only one Fire Alarm System.

## 1.12    Review Questions

| # | ? | Question | Section |
|---|---|---|---|
| 1-1 | | **The National Building Code of Canada contains:** | |
| | A | The maximum requirements for the design of Fire Alarm Systems. | |
| | B | The minimum requirements for the maintenance of Fire Alarm Systems. | |
| | C | The minimum requirements for the servicing of Fire Alarm Systems and smoke alarms. | |
| | D | The minimum requirements for the design of Fire Alarm Systems. | |
| 1-2 | | **Buildings are classified according to:** | |
| | A | Their use and inherent hazard | |
| | B | Density of population such as the occupant load | |
| | C | Fire load content | |
| | D | All of the above | |
| 1-3 | | **A Group F Industrial occupancy includes:** | |
| | A | High Hazard | |
| | B | Medium Hazard | |
| | C | Low Hazard | |
| | D | All of the above | |
| 1-4 | | **A 'voluntary' Fire Alarm System is required to meet minimum code requirements because:** | |
| | A | The installation of a non code required fire alarm system still requires that the system be provided in accordance with the applicable minimum requirements of the building code and the referenced standards. | |
| | B | The designer cannot select the legal requirements to follow and not to follow; the designer must comply with applicable Code requirements. | |
| | C | If a fire alarm system is installed it must comply to the applicable building code and referenced standard. | |
| | D | All of the above | |

| # | ? | Question | Section |
|---|---|----------|---------|
| **1-5** | | **A Fire Alarm System is not required:** | |
| | A | In a building where more than three storeys, including storeys below the first storey is provided | |
| | B | in apartment buildings where not more than four dwelling units share a common means of egress, | |
| | C | In a school, college, or child care facility, including a day care facility, with an occupant load more than 40 | |
| | D | In a licensed beverage establishment or a restaurant, with an occupant load more than 150 | |
| **1-6** | | **When a Fire Alarm System is required:** | |
| | A | It can be installed in the parking garage only. | |
| | B | It can be only installed in just one wing or on just some floors. | |
| | C | It can be installed on just one floor of a 50 storey building | |
| | D | It must be installed throughout the entire building | |
| **1-7** | | **The National Building Code of Canada is:** | |
| | A | The primary source of information relating to building design criteria. | |
| | B | The primary source of information relating to building fire protection system maintenance requirements | |
| | C | The primary source of information relating to marine vessel fire protection design criteria. | |
| | D | The primary source of information relating to special hazard computer room data centre fire protection risk assessments | |
| **1-8** | | **The National Fire Code of Canada is:** | |
| | A | The primary source of information relating to building design criteria. | |
| | B | The primary source of information relating to building fire protection system scheduled maintenance requirements following the closing of the building permit and the occupancy of a completed building. | |
| | C | The primary source of information relating to marine vessel fire protection design criteria. | |
| | D | The primary source of information relating to special hazard computer room data centre fire protection risk assessments | |

©

| # | ? | Question | Section |
|---|---|----------|---------|
| **1-9** | | **The latest edition of a code or standard:** | |
| | A | Is always the edition that is the fire department enforceable edition | |
| | B | Is always the edition that is the legally enforceable edition | |
| | C | Is always the edition that is the local AHJ enforceable edition | |
| | D | Is not always the edition that is the legally enforceable edition | |
| **1-10** | | **The Building Code also specifies the:** | |
| | A | Emergency power supply requirements for the Fire Alarm System | |
| | B | The annunciation requirements and zoning indications to be displayed | |
| | C | The requirements for Emergency Voice Communication Systems. | |
| | D | All of the above | |

# Chapter 2: Manual Stations

## 2.1    Chapter Overview and Key Concepts

A Manual Station is a device designed to initiate a Fire Alarm System signal when operated manually. In most cases, it is comprised of a hinged or levered pull handle controlling an electrical contact such as a pushbutton or switch.

Manual stations are the first line of defense in a normally occupied building. Manual stations provide building occupants with the opportunity of initiating an alarm when they identify an alarm condition possibly before the automatic detection has detected a fire. Stations should be located in places where building occupants can see, and use them, under potentially dangerous situations such as a fire condition. For this reason, the *National Building Code of Canada* requires that stations be installed near every exit from each floor area.

Stations must be electrically connected to a Fire Alarm Control Unit as an 'alarm initiating' device.

Because there are two very different types of systems (operationally – single-stage and two-stage), then it follows that there are two different types of manual stations - single-stage and two-stage.

## 2.2    Learning Objectives

Upon successful completion of this chapter, the reader should be able to:

- understand why manual stations are built the way they are
- know what is referred to as a 'shorting device'
- discuss manual station location requirements contained in the *Building Code*
- tell why stations cannot be reset without a special tool
- describe the purpose of the glass rod

## Language defined

Throughout the various codes and standards, certain words and phrases are used to identify specific items, situations, assemblies or processes. Before beginning a study of any of these documents, it is important that the definitions applicable to fire protection are clearly understood. Failure to understand the meaning of a defined term in a code requirement often leads to an incorrect interpretation of that requirement. Special terms that will be found in this chapter are listed below. Also refer to the Main Glossary at the end of this Manual.

| Term | Definition |
|---|---|
| **Access-To-Exit** | Those parts of a building, such as aisles, hallways or corridors that provide access to an exit serving that floor area |
| **Contained-Use Area** | A supervised area containing one or more rooms in which occupant movement is restricted to a single room by security measures not under the control of the occupant |
| **Control Unit** | A device with the necessary circuits or components needed to provide acceptable operating power for a fire alarm system, receive signals from alarm initiating devices, cause audible alarm signals to operate, and electrically monitor the installation wiring and device placement against certain faults and/or removal |
| **Exit** | A facility such as a door, stairs or ramp that leads from the floor area that it serves to an open public thoroughfare, or to a protected exterior open space that has access to an open public thoroughfare. Once in an exit facility, a person should have a continuous path leading to the building exterior |
| **Floor Area** | The space on any storey of a building between the exterior walls and required firewalls, including the space occupied by interior walls and partitions, but not including exits and vertical service spaces that pierce the storey |
| **Impeded egress zone** | A supervised area in which occupants have free movement but require the release, by security personnel, of security doors at the boundary before being able to leave the area, but does not include a contained use area. |
| **Manual Station** | A device that initiates an alarm condition in a fire alarm system, when actuated manually. The station will remain in the operated condition until it has been reset to normal using a special tool. Previous editions of standards used the terminology "Manual Pull Station". |

**Means Of Egress**    A continuous path of travel provided for the escape of occupants from any point in a building or contained open space to a separate building, an open public thoroughfare, or an exterior open space protected from fire exposure from the building and having access to an open public thoroughfare. Means of egress includes exits and access to exits

**Public Corridor**    A corridor that provides access to exit from more than one suite

**Suite**    A single room or series of rooms of complementary use, operated under a single tenancy, and includes:

(a)    dwelling units,

(b)    individual guest rooms in motels, hotels, boarding houses, rooming houses and dormitories, and

(c)    individual stores and individual or complementary rooms for business and personal services occupancies.

2: Manual Stations

## 2.3    Manual Station Design Standard

The design and construction of manual stations is governed by *CAN/ULC-S528 Standard for Manual Stations for Fire Alarm Systems including Accessories*. It follows therefore that all manual stations must be listed by a nationally recognized testing laboratory, such as ULC (so indicated by a label on the station) to be legally acceptable for use on Fire Alarm Systems. The fact that the station carries a label is our assurance that the station meets all the requirements of the standard. Although it is not necessary that we be fully aware of all of the design details contained in the S528 Standard, it is useful and indeed interesting to review some of the more common manual station design and construction requirements as follows:

1.      Stations must be red in colour.

2.      Manual stations are constructed so that they will be reliable and durable for their intended installation and use.

3.      Stations are manually operated by pulling down on a lever-type mechanism, or by pulling out on the faceplate. A conventional, non-addressable manual station consists primarily of a switch or push-button which provides a 'normally-open' contact when the station is at rest with the pull-handle in the normal closed, non-operated, position.  Activating the station (pulling the handle) causes the switch or push-button to operate, thereby closing (reversing) the electrical contact. This type of device is referred to as a 'shorting' device. Refer to Chapter 7 for a discussion of the connection of system field devices into Control Units.

4.      The tension on the lever or door must be such that the station cannot be accidentally activated by brushing up against it or by fumbling for a light switch in the dark.  Some station designs incorporate a spring clip or small glass rod (or similar breakable device) that must be replaced if the station is operated.

> Note: The absence of the breakable device is often a deficiency that is noted during an Annual Inspection

5.      Once activated, a station cannot be reset by simply lifting up the lever or closing the door. This means that a tool of some sort, or in some cases, a key, must be used to restore the station to its normal mode. Until this is done the station must maintain its appearance of being activated.

## 2.4    Building Code Requirements

The *Building Code* is the document that stipulates the required locations of manual stations within a building.

1.    Generally speaking, manual stations must be located at or near required exits; that provide means of egress from a 'Zone' of the building or from the building to the exterior. For example, in a multi-storey building, each floor is considered to be a fire zone. Manual stations must be located on each floor, adjacent to the doors exiting into the stairwell(s), and they will be connected along with the other detection devices on each floor. In this way any device that is activated on any given floor will cause that floor zone to be displayed on the Zone Annunciator.

    Note: Elevators, escalators and overhead shipping doors are not considered to be a means of egress. For this reason, manual stations are generally not installed near elevators.

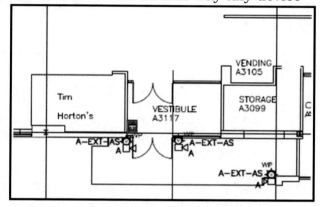

**Manual station on floor plan at
Vestibule Entrance Exit**

2.    A manual station must be located near the 'principal entrance' of a building. This will allow a person who has noticed a fire condition from the exterior of the building to warn the occupants of the danger. Similarly, a station is installed at the reception desk in a hotel. This location also is evident to a casual visitor who is aware of only the main entrance, and will exit the same way.

3.    Occasionally, building occupants (or visitors) will initiate nuisance false alarms by operating a manual station and running from the building. The following approach may be used if the nuisance alarm situation is untenable. If a suite of residential rooms has an exit to the exterior, a manual station is installed adjacent to that exit and a sign noting that 'FIRE ALARM MANUAL STATIONS ARE LOCATED IN APARTMENT UNITS', must be posted at every exit from public corridors. This requirement also applies to suites served by fire escapes.

4.    Manual stations must be installed in the stairwells of high-rise buildings, adjacent to doors giving access to certain floors referred to as 'cross over' floors.

## 2.5    Requirements of the Installation Standard

As a general rule, the *Building Code* indicates where manual stations are to be located, and *CAN/ULC-S524 Installation of Fire Alarm Systems* tells us how they are to be installed. *CAN/ULC-S524* describes the necessary installation materials and methods that must be used when installing manual pull stations. The more common considerations include:

1.  Stations must be installed between 1200mm and 1400 mm measured from the floor to the centre of the station.

2.  When conditions permit, the station must be installed on the latch side of the door, within 1500 mm of the opening.

3.  Stations must be visible at all times. This means, for example, that if a door is allowed to be held open, it will not block the station from view, when the door is open.

    Note: Quite often during a Fire Alarm System Inspection, it is noted that a station is hidden from view by shelving, merchandise etc. This must be recorded as a deficiency.

4.  In the case where a door is surrounded by glass panels, and mounting the station on the metal framing could be hazardous, then it may be installed on a wall surface as close as possible to the door.

5.  In the case where a door-system consisting of several aligned doors (e.g. an entrance to a shopping mall or theatre) exceeds 12m in width; stations may be installed at each side of the door system.

6.  *CAN/ULC-S524* makes reference to the *Electrical Code* with respect to installation requirements pertaining to wire type and size, physical protection, conduit, electrical boxes, bonding etc. that applies to the installation of all system devices including manual stations.

## 2.6    Types of Manual Stations

When we use the term 'type' when referring to a Fire Alarm System, we mean that the system to which the station is connected is either 'single-stage' or 'two-stage'.

1.  In a single-stage system, which is by far the most common, the activation of a manual station or any other alarm-initiating device, will cause the audible and visible signal devices to operate, initiate the ancillary functions (such as elevator recall, HVAC shutdown, door release) and, if required, send a signal to an off-site monitoring centre, or the Fire Department. This operation is called a 'single-stage' or 'evacuation' system.

©

2.    In a two-stage system, the activation of the handle of a manual station does not cause the evacuation process to begin. Instead, the system goes into its 'first stage' or 'alert' mode. In this mode, signalling devices sound at a slow pulsing rate – typically about 20 pulses per minute. Occupants do not evacuate, but they are aware of a potential danger, and they should prepare to evacuate if so instructed. However, building supervisory personnel are aware of the fact that a fire emergency could exist, and they should respond in a manner consistent with the Fire Safety Plan approved for the building.

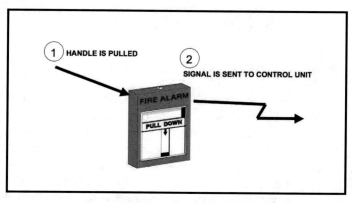

**Single-stage System**

3.    If, after a brief investigation by supervisory personnel, it is determined that a real fire emergency exists, then one of these designated people can insert a special key into any manual station and twist the key, thus initiating the second-stage, evacuation process. Two-stage manual stations are designed such that there is no access to the stage-two key switch until the handle of the station has first been actuated.

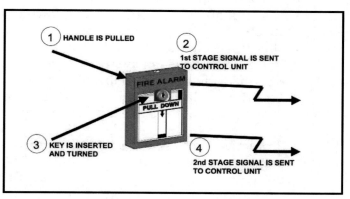

**Two-stage System**

4.    It is evident therefore that a two-stage manual station must incorporate two separate sets of contacts. One set will be activated when the station is pulled, thereby putting the system into first-stage, and a second set of contacts will be activated by the key switch.

5.    It follows that the connection of a two-stage manual station to the Fire Alarm Control Unit (FACU) will be slightly different. The alarm contacts will be connected onto an initiating circuit, such that the zone location of the station will be displayed on an Annunciator. This is the connection method for both types of station. The stage-two key switch, however, is connected to the FACU as a separate input.

6.    Some common sense rules apply to the use of two stage manual stations, the most obvious being that two-stage manual stations can only be installed on a two-stage fire alarm system, and only single-stage manual stations can

be used with single-stage fire systems. Such two-stage stations must be keyed alike.

## 2.7    Special Situations

1.    Key Stations:  Manual stations that are part of a Fire Alarm System in a 'contained use' area such as penal institutions obviously must be of a design that cannot be operated by the residents. In this case, the stations are of a type that can be activated only by a key that is carried by supervisory personnel. Electrically the key switch functions the same as the pull handle contact in a normal station.

2.    Coloured Stations:  Manual Stations used in Fire Alarm Systems must be red! Very often however, different coloured manual stations are found in buildings. Structurally they may look like manual stations – but be cautious! They may be painted blue or yellow or some other colour. The chances are very high that a yellow-coloured station will actually be a 'discharge' control station for a Carbon Dioxide extinguishing system. And blue-finished stations were often used as discharge control stations for Halon extinguishing systems. Fire Alarm Technicians must exercise caution when working in a building that contains special extinguishing systems. Test the station only after confirming that it is indeed part of the Fire Alarm System and not part of a different system.

3.    Protective Covers: To reduce the possibility of nuisance alarms caused by inappropriate activation of a station in public areas, a clear, plastic protective cover may be used.  This cover must be lifted or moved in order to gain access to the station.  In some cases, this cover will contain its own battery-powered horn that will sound when the cover is opened or moved, in an effort to discourage persons from causing an intentional nuisance alarm.  Note: Protective covers are required to be ULC-listed as accessories as described in the S528 Manual Station standard, and as such must bear their own ULC label.  Any non-labeled cover will be considered as a deficiency and must be removed and/or replaced with a suitably labeled device.

4.    Hazardous Locations - Manual stations may sometimes have to be installed in areas containing hazardous atmosphere where the possibility of an explosion exists.

In this case, stations must be labeled for acceptable use in such locations. They must be described and labeled as 'Explosion-Proof'.

**Explosion proof
Manual Station**

©

## 2.8    Chapter Summary

1.    Manual stations for use on Fire Alarm Systems must be constructed in accordance with CAN/ULC-S528 *Standard for Manual Stations for Fire Alarm Systems, including Accessories.*

2.    Some of the common requirements are that the station must be red, must contain an electrical switch, and must not be resettable without the use of a special tool.

3.    Stations must be installed such that they are readily visible at all times.

4.    There are two basic types of manual stations – those that are to be installed as part of single-stage systems and those that are to be installed as part of a two-stage system.

5.    Conventional stations are referred to, electrically, as a 'shorting device' on the alarm initiating device circuit.

2: Manual Stations

## 2.9     Review Questions

| # | ? | Question | Section |
|---|---|----------|---------|
| **2-1** | | **Manual stations that are part of a Fire Alarm System in a 'contained use' area such as penal institutions must be of a design that cannot be operated by the residents therefore:** | |
| | A | No manual stations are installed | |
| | B | The stations are of a type that can be activated only by a key | |
| | C | Only blue push down type manual stations are installed | |
| | D | A magnetically locked secure door will be released when the manual station is pulled in the contained use area. | |
| **2-2** | | **In a two-stage system, the activation of the handle of a manual station:** | |
| | A | causes the evacuation process to begin on all floors. | |
| | B | does not cause the evacuation process to begin. | |
| | C | causes the 3-3-3 temporal signal on all floors. | |
| | D | causes the emergency lighting to increase and the magnetically locked secure doors to re-arm. | |
| **2-3** | | **In a single-stage system, which is by far the most common, the activation of a manual station or any other alarm-initiating device, will** | |
| | A | cause the alert signal process to begin on all floors. | |
| | B | not cause the evacuation process to begin. | |
| | C | cause the 3-3-3 temporal evacuation signal on all floors. | |
| | D | causes the emergency lighting to increase and the magnetically locked secure doors to re-arm. | |
| **2-4** | | **The _____ indicates where manual stations are to be located, and _____ Installation of Fire Alarm Systems tells us how they are to be installed.** | |
| | A | Electrical Code, CAN/ULC-S536 | |
| | B | Fire Code, CAN/ULC-S537 | |
| | C | Building Code, CAN/ULC-S524 | |
| | D | Plumbing Code, CAN/ULC-S527 | |

©

| # | ? | Question | Section |
|---|---|----------|---------|
| **2-5** | | **Generally speaking, manual stations must be located** | |
| | A | At the principal entrance/exit of the building | |
| | B | at or near required exits; that provide means of egress from a 'Zone' of the building | |
| | C | on each floor, adjacent to the doors exiting into the stairwell(s) in a multi-storey building, | |
| | D | All of the above | |
| **2-6** | | **Manual stations are generally not installed near** | |
| | A | Elevators | |
| | B | Escalators | |
| | C | Overhead vehicle shipping doors | |
| | D | All of the above | |
| **2-7** | | **The design and construction of manual stations is governed by** | |
| | A | CAN/ULC-S524 | |
| | B | CAN/ULC-S527 | |
| | C | CAN/ULC-S528 | |
| | D | CAN/ULC-S537 | |
| **2-8** | | **Identify the sentence that is not true** | |
| | A | Manual stations must be red in colour. | |
| | B | Manual stations are manually operated by pulling down on a lever-type mechanism. | |
| | C | A conventional, non-addressable manual station consists primarily of a switch or push-button which provides a 'normally-open' contact when the station is at rest with the pull-handle in the normal closed, non-operated, position. | |
| | D | Once activated, a station can be reset by simply lifting up the lever or closing the door. | |
| **2-9** | | **A device that initiates an alarm condition in a fire alarm system, when actuated manually.** | |
| | A | Heat Detector | |
| | B | Manual Station | |
| | C | Sprinkler Flow Switch | |
| | D | Supervisory valve | |

| # | ? | Question | Section |
|---|---|----------|---------|
| **2-10** | | **A Manual Station is a device designed to initiate a Fire Alarm System signal when operated** | |
| | A | With a smoke detector. | |
| | B | Under remote control display command centre | |
| | C | Automatically | |
| | D | Manually | |

©

# Chapter 3: Fire Detectors

## 3.1    Chapter Overview and Key Concepts

Automatic fire detectors are devices that are connected to the initiating-device circuits of a fire alarm system, in order to automatically detect a fire condition, and communicate that information to the building occupants and emergency response personnel, through operation of the Fire Alarm Control Unit.

Automatic fire detection devices are designed to respond to external stimuli that are typically produced by a combustion process. We refer to these stimuli as fire 'signatures' that are generally produced, in varying relative amounts, by all fires.

This chapter discusses the various types of automatic detectors that are commonly used in today's fire alarm systems designs.

## 3.2    Learning Objectives

After studying the contents of this chapter, the reader should be able to do the following:

- Recognize and understand the commonly available automatic detection devices

- Understand how each type of device functions

- Be able to properly select the appropriate detector for a specific application

- Be able to apply the requirements found in the applicable *Building Code*

- Understand the importance of automatic sprinklers to Fire Alarm System design

- Understand the application details contained in the ULC-S524 Installation Standard

- Be able to explain detection coverage beyond the minimum requirements

3: Fire Detectors

## Language defined

Throughout the various codes and standards, certain words and phrases are used to identify specific items, situations, assemblies or processes. Before beginning a study of any of these documents, it is important that the definitions applicable to fire protection are clearly understood. Failure to understand the meaning of a defined term in a code requirement often leads to an incorrect interpretation of that requirement. Special terms that will be found in this chapter are listed below. Also refer to the Main Glossary at the end of this Manual.

| Term | Definition |
| --- | --- |
| **Authority Having Jurisdiction** | The organization, office, or individual responsible for approving equipment, an installation, or a procedure. Most often, the municipal Fire Department |
| **Control Unit** | A device with the necessary circuits or components needed to provide acceptable operating power for a fire alarm system, receive signals from alarm initiating devices, cause audible alarm signals to operate, and electrically monitor the installation wiring and device placement against certain faults and/or removal |
| **Exit** | A facility such as a door, stairs or ramp that leads from the floor area that it serves to an open public thoroughfare, or to a protected exterior open space that has access to an open public thoroughfare. Once in an exit facility, a person should have a continuous path leading to the building exterior |
| **Fire Detector** | A device that detects a fire condition and automatically initiates an electrical signal, and includes heat and smoke detectors |
| **Fire Detector – Heat** | A device for sensing an abnormally high air temperature or an abnormal rate of increase of temperature |
| **Fire Detector – Smoke** | A device for sensing the presence of visible or invisible particles of combustion, the concentration of which exceeds a pre-determined level |
| **Floor Area** | The space on any storey of a building between the exterior walls and required firewalls, including the space occupied by interior walls and partitions, but not including exits and vertical service spaces that pierce the storey |
| **Smoke Alarm** | A combined smoke detector and audible alarm device designed to sound an alarm within a room or suite in which it is located, upon the detection of smoke within that room or suite |

©

## 3.3    Codes and Standards

As previously discussed, when a Fire Alarm System is designed for a building to be constructed, or when a replacement Fire Alarm System is designed, it must comply with the descriptors contained in either the National or a Provincial *Building Code*, dependent upon the jurisdiction.

The *Building Code* establishes the minimum life safety levels that society mandates at that point in time for various occupancies in 'ordinary buildings'. The documents are revised at regular intervals to maintain requirements that reflect current experience or societal values.

The *Building Code* requires that fire detectors must be installed in certain types of rooms. It becomes more specific by requiring that some types of rooms must be fitted with smoke detectors.

Of course, the *Building Code* references the standard *CAN/ULC-S524 Installation of Fire Alarm Systems*. This standard contains descriptors relating to specific requirements of fire detectors. More specifically, the standard requires that fire detectors be installed with regards to occupancies, size of rooms, types and heights of ceilings, spacings of detectors and other parameters.

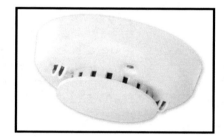

**Smoke Detector**

### 3.3.1    The Building Code

The current minimum life-safety requirements for the occupants of buildings are based upon the following parameters:

- Type of building construction

- Occupancy classification

    - Group A - Assembly (live theatres, stadiums, cinemas etc)

    - Group B - Health care (care and treatment occupancies)

    - Group C - Residential (apartments condos etc)

    - Group D – Business and personal services

    - Group E – Mercantile

    - Group F – Industrial

- Size of the building floor area, and number of occupants

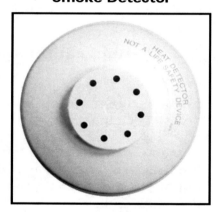

**Heat Detector**

- Building height above grade to highest occupied floor level (additional requirements applicable for buildings classed as high rise).

- Special features such as atriums, floor openings etc

The specific Fire Alarm System design requirements to be used for a particular building are derived from the parameters identified above. The precise design requirements to be used for a particular building are normally defined by the project engineer who is responsible for the creation of a design that meets at least the minimum requirements of the applicable *Building Code*. Often the designer will select devices and/or operational features that exceed the minimum requirements, in order to provide higher levels of life safety, to deal with unique hazards, or as an alternative to offset other building issues.

### 3.3.2    The Installation Standard

When we consider the selection of a particular fire detection technology to be used, and the density and location of the fire detectors, we generally are looking at how long it will take to detect a given fire scenario. Earlier detection allows for control and extinguishment with a minimum of damage to property or risk to life safety. The standard *CAN/ULC-S524 Installation of Fire Alarm Systems* identifies the basic arrangements for detector locations, and basic coverage. Where faster detection is deemed appropriate, detectors with earlier detection capability, closer spacings, mounted closer to the hazard, or even multiple device types may be warranted.

## 3.4    Application Requirements

The *Building Code* contains the application requirements for fire detectors in various areas and/or rooms, and for different types of occupancies.

**Addressable Smoke Detector**

*Fire detector* is a defined term. It means a device that detects a fire condition and automatically causes the fire alarm system to initiate an alert signal or alarm signal, and includes heat detectors and smoke detectors.

In certain situations the *Building Code* requires the installation of *fire detectors*, and therefore allows the choice of either heat or smoke actuated devices. In other situations the *Building Code* specifically requires one or the other.

**Addressable Heat Detector**

### 3.4.1    Fire Detectors

The *Building Code* states that where a fire alarm system is required in a building, then fire detectors are to be installed in the following spaces if they are not sprinklered:

©

- storage rooms not within dwelling units,

- service rooms not within dwelling units,

- janitor's rooms,

- rooms where hazardous products are to be used or stored,

- elevator and dumbwaiter shafts, and

- a laundry room in a building of residential occupancy, but not one within a dwelling unit.

Some jurisdictions also require that fire detectors be installed in hazardous classrooms and change rooms in elementary and secondary schools.

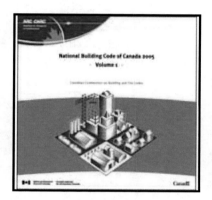

The *Building Code* does not state the type of fire detector to be used. The system designer must select the appropriate detector based upon cost and that best suited to the expected fire scenario. The designer must initially choose between heat detectors and smoke detectors based upon which will provide the best response to the expected fire condition while at the same time guarding against unwanted spurious alarms. If a heat detector is chosen, then the designer must select a fixed temperature or rate-of-rise type heat detector, and its temperature rating. If a smoke detector is selected then one must choose between ionization and photoelectric type of smoke detector. Remember that the listed spacing requirement for the different detectors varies considerably and must be taken into account when establishing the quantity and location of the detectors. Also remember that while the applications designer has the choice of heat or smoke detector (when the *Building Code* calls for a fire detector), so too does The Authority Having Jurisdiction and their choice of detector may differ from that of the designer.

Finally, the *Building Code* specifies only the minimum requirements, and this is not necessarily the best available protection. The application designer has to make the right selections for proper protection. The designer can and should install additional detection capability if conditions warrant.

## 3.4.2  Heat Detectors

Some jurisdictions specifically require that heat detectors be installed:

- in every room in portions of buildings classified as Group A, Division 1,

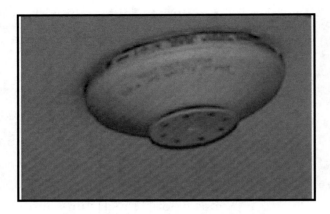

- except in a hotel, in every suite, and every room not located within a suite, in portions of buildings classified as Group C major occupancy and more than three storeys in building height, and

- in a floor area containing a hotel, in every room in a suite and in every room not located in a suite other than washrooms within a suite, saunas, refrigerated areas and swimming pools.

Heat detectors need not be installed where the floor area is sprinklered, and the sprinklers are monitored by the Fire Alarm System.

### 3.4.3    Smoke Detectors

The *Building Code* contains requirements for the installation of smoke detectors. It states that where a fire alarm system is required, smoke detectors must be installed:

- in each sleeping room and each corridor serving as part of a means of egress from sleeping rooms in portions of a building classified as Group B major occupancy,

- in each room in a contained use area and corridors serving those rooms,

- in each corridor in portions of a building classified as Group A, Division 1 major occupancy,

- in each public corridor in portions of a building classified as Group C major occupancy,

- in each exit stair shaft, and

- in the vicinity of draft stops in certain situations.

Some jurisdictions require that smoke detectors be installed in each corridor serving classrooms in elementary and secondary schools.

Smoke detectors required in sleeping rooms of a *care or detention occupancy* shall upon activation provide an audible and visual indication to staff serving those rooms.

In order to fully understand all of the many requirements, various definitions such as Fire, Heat or Smoke Detectors and other general definitions, such as Major Occupancy, Dwelling Units, Suites, Public

©

Corridors, Exit, and Service Rooms, should be reviewed in the *Building Code.*

## 3.5    Fire Signatures and Device Selection

What is important is that the fire will increase at an exponential growth rate until it totally destroys the space, all of the material, all oxygen is consumed, or the fire is extinguished.

We must keep in mind when selecting the detection devices to be used, that none of them actually detect a 'fire', but rather respond to a particular stimulus released during combustion sometimes referred to as a fire signature. Unless the detector senses the appropriate fire signature for which it is designed, then there will be no response

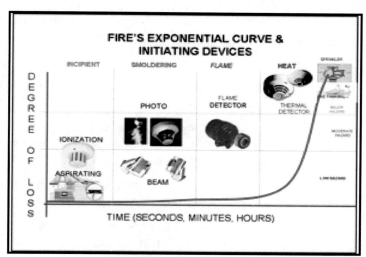

In the first stage of the combustion process (the incipient stage) products of combustion, in the form of aerosols, are released, and these can be detected using an ionization smoke detector. There may be little, if any, heat and/or flames.

If unchecked, the combustion process will continue and will begin to generate visible smoke. At this point, a photoelectric type of smoke detector can sense the fire.

As the combustion process continues, flames appear and material is quickly consumed. The fire growth is becoming faster and will continue to grow at an ever-increasing rate. Flame detectors would be appropriate at this stage.

The fire growth is now rapidly consuming material and is releasing substantial amounts of heat. It is at this stage that heat detection devices (and sprinklers) would detect the fire condition.

### 3.5.1    Smoke Detectors

Smoke detectors break down into two distinct categories based upon their operating principal. Both must pass the same set of test fires in order to obtain a ULC product listing. Ionization type detectors sense products of combustion released in the early stages of fires occurring in most combustible materials. Typically the individual particles have weight and mass. While they are too small to be seen individually, they may be seen as a collective group as a mist or haze. Other small particles which can be suspended in the atmosphere such as dust, vapours from drying paint, various gases such as Freon, FM-200 etc. as well as the small smoke particles may also cause the detector to respond.

Detectors that operate on the photoelectric principal sense the visible smoke either through obscuration (the reduction of intensity of a beam of light because of the presence of particulate such as smoke), or the refraction of light by the light source being redirected (by particulate such as smoke) and being detected by a photosensitive receiver. Particles, other than those created by combustion, which also may affect photo-electric detectors includes dust, burning toast, making popcorn, theatrical smoke or mist.

In addition to the basic smoke detectors designed for ceiling mounting, other detectors designed for specific applications are also available:

- Duct type smoke detectors designed for mounting to air handling ducts to monitor a sampling of the air moving through the duct and shut down fan systems in the event of smoke contamination,

- Beam type smoke detectors consisting of a beam traversing large unobstructed open spaces up to 100 m in length

- Air aspirating smoke detectors withdraw continuous samples of air from a protected space and use a very sensitive laser to check for smoke particles.

### 3.5.2    Heat Detectors

A heat detector detects the presence of a certain predetermined ambient temperature, and in some cases is designed to also see a rapid increase in temperature. When selecting the 'rated temperature' at which we want a detector response to occur and which detectors might be most appropriate, we must take into account the environment in which the detector is to be installed. If the ambient temperature at the ceiling ordinarily reaches a temperature of 45°C then the selected detector must take this into account and a setting of 88°C would be selected and not one rated for 56°C. Similarly, if a detector will be in a warehouse next to an overhead door we need to select a detector not having the 'rate-of-rise' feature. In the winter when the door is opened the temperature falls and then when it closes the temperature recovers rapidly, often from a nearby unit heater.

### 3.5.3    Air Movement

In order for a heat detector to respond to a fire, sufficient heat to satisfy the response characteristic of the detector must reach the detector. Similarly, in order to have a response from a smoke detector, either the products of combustion or visible smoke, in sufficient quantity to satisfy the detectors alarm criteria, must enter the detection chamber.

The various products of combustion are obviously very lightweight and are easily carried away from a fire because of the thermal lift generated by the combustion process.

Air currents may be naturally present in large rooms, and they may be caused by mechanical air-handling systems directing heat and/or smoke away from detector locations.

As a result, fire-detection may be delayed because of air currents that carry heat away from the detector locations and needs to be taken into account when selecting and locating detectors.

**Atrium Smoke Release
Test in Large Area**

### 3.5.4    Detector Locations

When we consider the selection of a fire detection technology to be used and the density and location of the fire detectors, we generally are looking at how long it will take to detect a given fire scenario. Earlier detection allows for control and extinguishment with the minimum damage to property or risk to life safety. The ULC-S524 Installation standard identifies the basic arrangements for detection location, mounting and basic coverage. Where faster detection is deemed to be desirable, detectors with closer spacing, mounted closer to the hazard or multiple device types may be warranted to get faster response with therefore less fire damage.

### 3.5.5    Accessibility

In addition to the criteria detailed in *CAN/ULC S524*, consider detector accessibility for annual testing, repair and replacement in the future. For example:

*   Smoke detectors at the top and intermediate levels in stairwells should be located over the landings wherever possible and not over the open stair where ladders cannot provide access,

*   Detectors located directly over transformers or switchgear may require the presence of the Hydro Authority and/or shutdown of power to the building in order to access for service. Locate the detector to one side and add a second detector on the other side if warranted due to spacing requirements,

- In atrium spaces consider an air aspiration detector with the detector assembly located in an accessible location for service and maintenance,

- In a large high warehouse consider beam detectors mounted on an end wall where easier access is available.

## 3.6　Exemption for Sprinklers

Today, most large buildings are required to be sprinklered. Although we may think of sprinklers as providing only fire suppression by discharging water in the immediate fire area to control and extinguish a fire, sprinklers actually do much more. Each sprinkler head contains a heat-sensing element that 'opens' the sprinkler thereby allowing water discharge when a preset temperature is reached at the sprinkler head. That pre-set temperature rating of sprinklers is, generally speaking, very similar to that of heat detectors.

Where sprinklers are installed, alarm flow switches on the sprinkler system are electrically connected to the Fire Alarm System in order to initiate alarm signals to alert the occupants and initiate fire service response. Also, sprinkler valves and other components are electrically connected to (supervised by) the Fire Alarm System as off-normal or fault conditions.

The presence of a sprinkler system supervised by the Fire Alarm System satisfies the need for heat detectors in most applications, and heat detectors do not therefore have to be installed. It is important to note, however, that even when sprinklers are installed, area and duct-type smoke detectors are still required as and where identified in the *Building Code*.

## 3.7　Optical Flame Detectors

Optical flame detectors are actually able to 'see' a naked flame (one of the fire signatures) and initiate an alarm. Flame detectors are a line-of-site device. Although they may receive some optical energy due to reflection off surrounding surfaces, they generally must be able to see the flame directly. This may mean that more than one detector might be needed in order to fully protect a target or an area.

Because of their optical sensing characteristics, flame detectors are often the best choice of detector for flammable liquid fires. Flammable liquid tank farms, liquids dispensing areas, and truck loading docks are typical examples of dangerous areas. In fact, the most common use of optical detection devices is to trigger the release of special extinguishing systems.

Flame detectors are of two basic types; infrared (IR) detectors are responsive to energy in the infrared range of the light spectrum, while ultraviolet (UV) detectors are responsive to energy in the ultraviolet segment of the light spectrum. Many devices now contain sensing elements for both infrared and ultraviolet segments of the spectrum.

Optical energy travels at the speed of light; therefore the response of flame detectors to a naked flame is usually instantaneous (2-3 seconds). Some care must be taken to ensure that detectors are not 'blinded' by black smoke from a fire before detection occurs.

Fuels such as natural gas, naphtha, butane and propane burn with a blue colour and are best sensed by the UV detector, whereas fuels such as gasoline, jet fuels, diesel fuels, etc burn with a red hue, and the infrared detector is more responsive.

Unfortunately there are many sources of infrared and ultraviolet energy that are not fire related. These would include sunlight, light fixtures, matches, flash bulbs, welding operations torches and jet engines. Therefore it is easy for detectors to quickly detect a fire, it is also easy for the detector to be tricked and to be put into alarm by a non-fire stimulus. To try to distinguish an actual fire from other sources, manufacturers have introduced detectors that discriminate based upon steady signal versus oscillating, selective narrow frequency bands, and multi-sensor detectors with two or three sensors each looking at separate frequency bands present in different intensity ratios when there is a real fire.

Some industrial-grade devices require their own control panel, whereas some Fire Alarm Manufacturers provide optical flame detectors that operate on 24 volts DC and can be connected directly to a Fire Alarm Control Unit. Such devices must be ULC-listed and obviously must be compatible with the Control Unit. Many optical devices are listed for use in areas with hazardous atmospheres. If this is a requirement, check carefully to ensure device acceptability.

It must be noted that there are no requirements (in the *Building Code*) for the use of flame detectors in normally occupied buildings. This is because the storage of flammable liquids is not allowed in normally occupied buildings other than those classified as Group F Industrial. Good design engineering practice however suggests that optical devices be used in an industrial areas such as used for the re-charging of battery-powered forklift trucks.

## 3.8    Detection beyond the Minimum

Up to this point we have been reviewing what we must install to satisfy the 'minimum' requirements of the *Building Code*.

**High Value Asset
Computer Room**

When we wish to provide detection that exceeds the minimum Code requirements, or when dealing with improved protection for the equipment or services for specific hazards such as a plant process or a telecommunications room, there are a number of factors that must be considered:

- Value of the risk – is the risk an irreplaceable object such as art or heritage item, or does it provide a service which is extremely important to a business such as a communications room

- Fire source - We must assess the hazard for the type of material that will likely be the fire source, and how it will ignite and burn. For instance in an electrical room or top of elevator shaft where a fire detector is required, provide a smoke detector rather than a heat detector as being far more able to detect the type of expected combustion at a much earlier point in time.

- Burning characteristics - Obviously fires involving flammable liquids ignite, grow and expand differently and far more rapidly than ones starting in a cable tray.

- Actuate extinguishment system - Pre action sprinkler systems, deluge systems and special hazard extinguishment system require appropriate detection for activation

- Length of time to start suppression – Where automatic suppression is included, extinguishment generally starts almost at the point of detection, while if physical response of building fire services or the remote fire service is required, initiating their response rapidly may, be critical.

- Physical parameters of the space and/or the objects requiring protection - Consider the room or area, possible obstructions, ceiling heights, air movement, presence of other combustibles, potential device locations, etc. If the hazard is an object or open surface where and how can detection be mounted.

As we have learned previously, fire is a chemical process where materials are consumed releasing particulate matter consisting of smoke particles and soot, as well as producing significant heat. The rate at which these items are released is dependent upon the material being consumed and the surrounding environment.

The fastest and most reliable detection method applicable for one situation is unlikely to be the best suited for other situations. Typically, we are concerned with detecting a fire early in its development when it is small, so that action can be

©

taken and the fire extinguished, thus negating the need for evacuation of the building or resulting in significant damage to equipment or its operation. Hopefully, the water sprinklers will not have to discharge, and the fire department will not have to use their hoses.

By assessing the type of fire signature we are dealing with, together with the manner or rate at which it will burn, we can select the fire detection technology most suited to the risk. In all cases, the faster we can detect a fire and begin the response process, the less is the risk to life safety, and damage to the building and its' contents.

3: Fire Detectors

## 3.9    Chapter Summary

1.    The system designer is directed to use automatic fire detectors in various rooms. The *Building Code* is the document that contains those instructions.

2.    The term 'fire detector' includes both heat detectors and smoke detectors.

3.    Smoke detectors are considered to be life-saving early-warning devices because they will respond to a fire scenario before a heat detector or a sprinkler.

4.    Smoke detectors therefore are required by the *Building Code* to be installed in rooms of a residential nature such as bedrooms in hospitals and nursing homes as well as some exit corridors and stairwells.

5.    Heat detectors, on the other hand, are often required in service rooms such as elevator rooms, electrical rooms and boiler rooms.

6.    Heat detectors do not have to be installed if automatic sprinklers are present – as long as the Fire Alarm System monitors the sprinklers.

7.    Fire detectors depend upon the movement of air within any detection area for proper detection of a fire. Careful placement of the detectors on the ceiling is very important. Optical flame detectors, on the other hand, are line-of-site devices. Infrared (IR) and ultra violet (UV) detectors will therefore react almost instantly to a naked flame.

8.    Acceptable detector ceiling locations are determined by referring to *CAN/ULC-S524 Installation of Fire Alarm Systems*.

9.    Different combustibles produce different by-products including heat and various visible and invisible toxic gasses. Proper selection of detection device is critical to the early detection of a fire condition without the nuisance of false alarms.

10.   Remember that the requirements provided in the Code are minimum requirements. The owner/designer may well opt to install a greater degree of fire safety by going beyond the listed minimums.

## 3.10    Review Questions

| # | ? | Question | Section |
|---|---|----------|---------|
| **3-1** | | **Where sprinklers are installed, alarm flow switches on the sprinkler system are _____to the Fire Alarm System in order to initiate alarm signals to alert the occupants and initiate fire service response.** | |
| | A | Mechanically altered | |
| | B | electrically connected | |
| | C | pneumatically supervised | |
| | D | not connected | |
| **3-2** | | **In order for a heat detector to respond to a fire:** | |
| | A | sufficient smoke to satisfy the response characteristic of the detector must reach the detector | |
| | B | sufficient heat to satisfy the response characteristic of the detector must reach the detector | |
| | C | sufficient products of combustion to satisfy the response characteristic of the detector must reach the detector | |
| | D | sufficient time and smoke to satisfy the response characteristic of the detector must reach the detector | |
| **3-3** | | **Smoke detectors at the top and intermediate levels in stairwells should be located:** | |
| | A | over areas where high humidity is in the environment | |
| | B | in locations where large amounts of saw dust can ignite the atmosphere | |
| | C | over the landings wherever possible and not over the open stair where ladders cannot provide access | |
| | D | in areas where the temperature reaches minus thirty degree Celsius | |
| **3-4** | | **Flame detectors are:** | |
| | A | alarm flow switch devices | |
| | B | a type of smoke detector | |
| | C | a line-of-site device | |
| | D | required in all building transformer rooms | |

3: Fire Detectors

| # | ? | Question | Section |
|---|---|---|---|
| 3-5 | | **A combined smoke sensor and audible alarm device designed to sound an alarm within a room or suite in which it is located, upon the detection of smoke within that room or suite is identified as:** | |
| | A | Smoke detector | |
| | B | Heat detector | |
| | C | Smoke Alarm | |
| | D | Air Sampling Type Detector | |
| 3-6 | | **Building Code specifies only the _____ requirements,** | |
| | A | minimum | |
| | B | maximum | |
| | C | local authority | |
| | D | municipal specific | |
| 3-7 | | **Heat detectors need not be installed where the floor area is** | |
| | A | sprinklered, and the sprinklers are monitored by the Fire Alarm System. | |
| | B | heated, and the floor temperature is monitored by the Fire Alarm System. | |
| | C | not occupied, and the presence of occupants are monitored by the Fire Alarm System. | |
| | D | An assembly area and the storage rooms are not sprinklered. | |
| 3-8 | | **Smoke detectors required in sleeping rooms of a care or detention occupancy:** | |
| | A | shall upon activation provide evacuate the entire facility immediately | |
| | B | shall upon activation provide an audible and visual indication to staff serving those rooms. | |
| | C | shall only send for the emergency response team | |
| | D | shall remain silent so not to worry the patients | |
| 3-9 | | **By assessing the type of fire signature we are dealing with, together with the manner or rate at which it will burn, we can select the fire detection technology most suited to the risk.** | |
| | A | True | |
| | B | False | |

| # | ? | Question | Section |
|---|---|----------|---------|
| **3-10** | | **When we consider the selection of a fire detection technology to be used and the density and location of the fire detectors, we generally are looking** | |
| | A | how much does it cost as the primary concern | |
| | B | at how long it will take to detect a given fire scenario | |
| | C | how does it look in the environment as the primary concern | |
| | D | at how long it will last following a fire condition | |

# Chapter 4: Heat-Actuated Fire Detectors

## 4.1    Chapter Overview and Key Concepts

Heat-actuated fire detectors (heat detectors) are designed to respond to the 'heat' signature associated with fire. This signature is characterized by change (increase) of the ambient temperature of the air surrounding the detector, and it is the detection of this change that initiates an alarm.

A Heat Detector is described as a 'spot-type' detector because it is ceiling-mounted and is given a specific area of coverage that is related to the way in which it functions.

This chapter also discusses Linear Heat Detection, another method of detecting heat generated by a fire condition. This system consists of heat sensitive cable that creates a short-circuit condition when heated to a prescribed temperature.

## 4.2    Learning Objectives

After studying the contents of this chapter, the reader should be able to do the following:

- Understand that the design of heat detectors is governed by a ULC Standard
- Understand how detectors are affected by heat
- Identify the different types of heat detection devices
- Understand the advantages of rate-of-rise devices
- Discuss the method of wiring supervision
- Apply heat detectors into appropriate types of rooms
- Discuss the concept of detector spacings
- Understand how differing room sizes, heights and ceiling structures affect detector spacing
- Determine the required number of detectors for a given room
- Discuss the application of heat detectors into a hazardous-atmosphere area
- Know how to test each type of heat detector

## Language defined

Throughout the various codes and standards, certain words and phrases are used to identify specific items, situations, assemblies or processes. Before beginning a study of any of these documents, it is important that the definitions applicable to fire protection are clearly understood. Failure to understand the meaning of a defined term in a code requirement often leads to an incorrect interpretation of that requirement. Special terms that will be found in this chapter are listed below. Also refer to the Main Glossary at the end of this Manual.

| Term | Definition |
|---|---|
| **Fire - Incipient Stage** | The earliest phase in the development of fire in which invisible products of combustion are given off. No visible smoke, flame or appreciable heat is present |
| **Fire - Smouldering Stage** | The stage in the development of fire where combustion products are now visible as smoke. Flames or appreciable heat are still not present |
| **Fire - Flame Stage** | A phase in the development of fire in which flame has occurred. |
| **Fire - Heat Stage** | The most dangerous phase in the development of fire in which uncontrolled heat and rapidly expanding air complete the development of the fire |
| **Fire Detector** | A device that detects a fire condition and automatically initiates an electrical signal, and includes heat and smoke detectors |
| **Fire Detector – Heat** | A device for sensing an abnormally high air temperature or an abnormal rate of increase of temperature |
| **Fire Detector – Smoke** | A device for sensing the presence of visible or invisible particles of combustion, the concentration of which exceeds a pre-determined level |
| **Flame Detector** | A detector that is designed to sense the radiation emanating from a flame. Two common types of flame detectors are 'infrared' and 'ultraviolet' detectors |
| **Heat Transfer – Conduction** | Heat transfer from one object to another of different temperature, by means of direct contact of the two objects |
| **Heat Transfer – Convection** | Heat transfer by the motion of particles within a medium (air, gas, liquid) |
| **Heat Transfer – Radiation** | Heat transfer by means of transmission of invisible heat energy across a space between two objects |

©

| Term | Definition |
| --- | --- |
| **Sprinkler Supervision** | A method of electrically monitoring critical elements of an automatic sprinkler system to detect potentially disabling abnormal conditions, and provide a warning signal |
| **Waterflow Switch** | A device used to detect the flow of water through some portion of the automatic sprinkler system piping, as will occur when one or more sprinkler heads has operated, and will operate a set of electrical contacts for interconnection to a fire alarm system. An adjustable time delay mechanism may be installed between the paddle-operated stem and the contacts of paddle or vane type devices to keep brief water movements from initiating an alarm signal |

## 4.3    Design Standard

The ULC Standard pertaining to the design of heat detectors is *ULC-S530 Standard for Heat Actuated Fire Detectors for Fire Alarm Systems*. This Standard details the mechanical and electrical construction requirements of heat detectors. Some of the more pertinent items are:

- Detectors must be practical to install and maintain,

- Detectors must be reliable and consistent in operation,

- Detectors must not be significantly affected by moisture, dust, insects, or other foreign material,

- Detectors must be resistant to corrosion

- Detectors must operate at the specified temperature range

Automatic heat detectors that have passed the rigorous testing requirements contained in this standard are allowed to carry the appropriate ULC label. This identifies the device as an acceptable product for installation on a fire alarm system in Canada.

Generally speaking, heat detectors, especially the conventional (non electronic) type, are used in any indoor application as well as environments that are inappropriate for smoke detectors. These environments include very high or very low ambient temperatures, airborne dust, gases, vapours and chronic presence of moisture. When enclosed in an explosion-proof housing, the conventional heat detector can be installed in hazardous locations.

Electronic heat detectors are generally relegated to indoor use, in normal corrosion-free, room-temperature environments.

## 4.4    Principles of Operation – Conventional Devices

Heat detectors are designed to monitor the ambient temperature at the ceiling in a room or area being protected. This ambient temperature will change as heat from a fire will, in the form of a heat plume, rise to the ceiling and travel across its surface. Some heat detectors are capable of responding to a rate of ambient temperature increase as well as a fixed temperature threshold. These response capabilities define the type of detector as either "dual-action" or "fixed-temperature only".

### 4.4.1    The Dual-Action Detector

The rate of change of the ceiling temperature is called *'rate-of-rise'*. One of the functions of the dual-action detector is to sense this rate-of-rise and respond by initiating an alarm. In product standard S530, ULC has determined that a rate of temperature increase of 8.4°C (15°F) over one minute, simulates a fire during its growth period, as opposed to any

©

other likely cause that could be considered "normal". For this reason, dual-action or 'rate-of-rise' detectors must operate when the ceiling temperature matches (or exceeds) this prescribed rate.

The design of the conventional heat detector includes an air chamber that is almost airtight. This air chamber contains a moveable diaphragm and a set of electrical contacts. When the heated ceiling air attacks the detector, the air inside the chamber expands, ultimately extending the diaphragm that in turn pushes the contacts together causing the alarm condition. It is important to note that the air chamber is not completely sealed. If it were, than any amount of temperature increase would cause an alarm. Instead, a certain amount of the expanding air is allowed to escape through a calibrated orifice referred to as the 'vent'. The amount of air allowed to escape from the vent is commensurate with a ceiling temperature increase of less than 8.4°C per minute. If the ceiling temperature increase is faster, the expanding air cannot escape fast enough, and starts to push the diaphragm against the contacts.

Every dual-action detector includes a 'fixed-temperature' function. This is basically the fusible link principle, in which a spring-loaded plunger is held in place over the detectors contacts, with a special solder that will melt at a specific temperature. When the solder melts, the plunger is released striking the contacts and holding them closed. This fixed-temperature function provides a back-up for creating an alarm condition, if the ceiling temperature increase is too slow to activate the device on the rate-of-rise function.

**Typical appearance of conventional heat detector characterized by the enclosed air chamber and heat-collecting fin.**

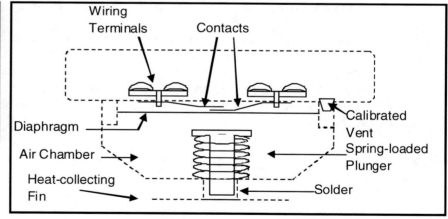

The fixed temperature at which the retaining solder melts and releases the plunger is selectable in order to accommodate rooms or areas that may have a higher than normal ambient temperature. The typical melting or 'fusing temperature is 57°C (135°F). This is well below the standard sprinkler head fusing temperature of 73°C (165°F), and is used in all areas where ceiling temperatures are not expected to exceed normal levels. Higher fusing temperatures are available, namely 73°C (165°F), 93°C (200°F) and 140°C (285°F).

### 4.4.2    Fixed-Temperature Detector – Non-Restorable

**Back of heat detector**

There are many rooms or areas in a building where rapid fluctuations in the ceiling temperature are common. A dual-action type of detector would not be suitable in this case as the rapid increases in temperature would be a source of nuisance alarms. In these areas, detectors that respond only when the fusing temperature is reached are used. Examples of these areas include boiler rooms, industrial kitchens, janitors' closets with hot water sinks, and un-insulated attics. The design engineer is responsible for selecting the correct detector, based on the environmental conditions surrounding that detector.

In many cases, the fixed-temperature only detector is similar in appearance to the dual action device, but on close inspection it is noted that the calibrating vent has been removed, allowing the detector to vent freely thus disabling its ability to respond to a rate-of-temperature increase. It should be noted that a detector whose fixed-temperature function is that of a fusible solder, is referred to as 'non-restorable', which means that upon release of the plunger the unit must be replaced as the plunger cannot be re-attached to the heat-collecting fin.

It is important for technicians to recognize detectors that are fixed-temperature only, so that they will not attempt to test such devices for rate-of-rise operation during a fire alarm system inspection. A black dot approximately ¼" in diameter on the heat-collecting fin can be seen from the floor level and is an indication that the detector is fixed-temperature only.

### 4.4.3    Fixed-Temperature Detector – Restorable

Sometimes referred to as the 'bi-metallic disc' detector, this device uses a temperature sensitive thermostat mechanism that is also found as a temperature controller in coffee pots and similar applications. A dime-sized

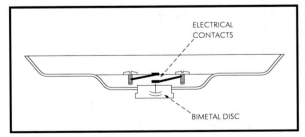

bi-metal disc is positioned in the center of the flat detector housing. As the ceiling temperature rises to the pre-determined alarm temperature setting, the two metals expand at different rates causing the disc to 'warp'. This warping or 'oil can' action causes a set of contacts to close,

©

initiating the alarm. As the temperature begins to decrease the action of the bi-metal disc will reverse and the electrical contact will revert back to its normally open position. Because these detectors automatically restore to normal condition after the actuating heat has dissipated, they are called restorable or resettable detectors, and can therefore be re-used. These detectors are available with alarm temperature set points of 57°C (135°F) and 88°C (190°F).

### 4.4.4  Rate-Compensating Detector (Rate-of-Anticipation)

Rate-compensating is another type of detector designed to sense an abnormally high temperature. The rate-compensating detector consists of a set of metal strips with a normally open electrical contact contained within a metal shell.

The operation of this detector relies on the expansion of its metal components when heat is applied. As with the bi-metallic disc, the volume of any metal will increase when heated and this increase varies from one metal to another. The metal shell and the metal strips are made of different materials. When heat is applied to the outer shell of the detector the shell lengthens (expands), pulling the metal strips containing the electrical contacts closer together. The metal strips within the shell also lengthen, counteracting the expanding outer shell. At a specific temperature level the outer shell has a greater expansion ratio than the inner strips and this expansion of the outer shell will inevitably cause the two strips to make electrical contact.

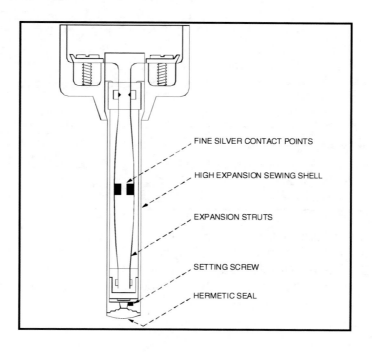

FINE SILVER CONTACT POINTS

HIGH EXPANSION SEWING SHELL

EXPANSION STRUTS

SETTING SCREW

HERMETIC SEAL

The operation of the rate-compensating detector is similar to a fixed-temperature detector, but it is able to respond quicker than a normal fixed-temperature detector because of greatly reduced thermal lag. Thermal lag (or time delay) is the time taken for a detector to heat up to its operating temperature. The detector is so designed that it will always operate at the specific temperature at which the detector is calibrated irrespective of the rate of temperature increase. If there is a rapid temperature increase the outer shell will expand and the inner strips will not have a chance to *compensate* thereby giving the detector the capability of responding quicker and also at a slightly lower temperature than its actual setting. When subjected to a very slow heat rise, the tubular shell and the inner strips lengthen at about the same rate. At the detector's set point, the inner strips are fully extended, the contacts are closed, and the alarm has been initiated.

## 4.5    Multiple Circuit Detectors

In some instances, a heat detector will be required to perform more than one function when it operates. This requires a second set of contacts, set as normally-open (N/O) or normally-closed (N/C). This set of contacts may be used to turn on an indicating light, shut off a machine or fuel supply, shut down a process, open a vent etc., in the area local to the detector. The multiple circuit detector is a conventional-type device, and can be either Dual-action or Fixed Temperature Only, non-restorable.

## 4.6    Electrical Wiring Supervision

A heat detector, as is the case with any fire alarm device, is connected to the control panel in such a way that if it is removed the circuit wiring will be interrupted causing the panel to go into the Trouble mode. On a conventional circuit (as opposed to addressable), a trouble condition will exist as soon as one wire is disconnected from the detector. For this reason, the wiring to each device is said to be 'broken' at each terminal, which means that the wire is not a continuous conductor coming into and leaving the device.

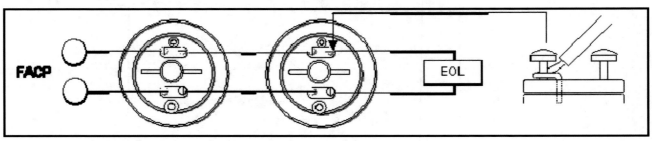

In the case where two terminal screws or two wire fly leads are provided for the connection of one side of the switch to the initiating circuit, the conductor is terminated on one of the terminals or fly leads and then is terminated anew as it leaves the detector. Shown here, the conventional Class B arrangement.

©

Removal of a heat detector from a conventional circuit will result in an open circuit. The panel will respond with a system trouble condition accompanied by an indication of the zone in trouble. If the circuit is Class B in style, then any detectors beyond the open circuit will not be able to initiate an alarm. In a Class A style circuit, all devices will continue to be effective in the event that only one open circuit occurs. In either case, the location and description of the disconnected device or the devices that are missing due to the open, is not available. Class A and B circuits are discussed in Chapter 7.

Removal of a heat detector from an *addressable* circuit can be done in one of two ways. The detector head can be twisted out of the mounting base, or the entire unit can be disconnected from the Data Communication Link (DCL). In either scenario, the device will fail to respond to a poll from the panel and will be therefore noted by its absence. A trouble condition complete with trouble LED and trouble audible will be produced and the detector's location will be displayed on the panel's Liquid Crystal Display (LCD), accompanied by the phrase typically worded "device missing".

## 4.7     Code Requirements

The *Building Code* requires the use of heat detectors:

- in suites and rooms not within suites (i.e. storage, utility) in Group C occupancies,

- throughout buildings described as Group A, Division 1 (theatres)

Good engineering practice would place heat detectors instead of smoke detectors in environments that would be described as hostile with respect to humidity, dust, extreme temperatures etc. These locations would include:

- Kitchens

- Janitor closets

- Change rooms (i.e. swimming pool)

- Elevator shafts

- Boiler/furnace rooms

- Loading docks

- Cold storage

- Utility rooms, transformer vaults, sprinkler rooms

- Hazardous locations (Explosion-proof and dust tight considerations)

In general, *conventional* (non-electronic) heat detectors can tolerate a wide range of ambient temperatures, and are less susceptible to dirt, dust, corrosion and moisture.

## 4.8    Detector Spacing

Each type of heat detector is listed by Underwriters' Laboratories of Canada as to the maximum spacing allowed *between similar* detectors when installed in open areas. This spacing rating also specifies the *maximum* distance from a detector (measured at right angles) to a wall or partition. The ULC *List of Equipment and Materials, Volume 1* lists all the detectors that have been tested and subsequently listed, with the various spacings permitted, by ULC. This information is also available at the Online Directory on the ULC website. It is important to determine the spacing limitations of any detector prior to using it in a system.

Heat detectors are designed to operate when the thermal energy of a fire reaches the detector. This heat rises up through the area by convection, i.e. the thermal column effect of heated air and gases rising above the fire surface. This column is referred to as the plume effect. The ceiling is obviously very important as the reflector of this fire plume energy output, and different ceiling features can affect the convected heat flow across the ceiling surface.

Therefore the ideal location for a detector is on the ceiling, away from obstructions, so that the flow of air across the ceiling will contact the device. Since this flow tends to deflect downward where the ceiling meets the side wall, a detector will be less sensitive in this space and must be set back from the corner by a minimum of 100 mm.

All spacings for detectors assume a flat, smooth ceiling three metres high, with normal air movement, and no physical obstructions such as solid beams between the fire source and the detector. This is generally regarded as the most favorable condition for distribution and spread of heated air currents resulting from a fire, and these conditions are reflected in Underwriters' testing facilities. However, ceiling conditions will vary. Ceilings that are higher than 3 meters, or are sloped or peaked, will have a direct effect (usually a reduction) on the spacing of detectors in order to achieve equivalent performance.

Spacing requirements are described in detail in *CAN/ULC-S524 Installation of Fire Alarm Systems.* In many cases the spacing requirements are the same for both heat detectors and smoke detectors. These include:

- Cannot be located closer than 100mm to a sidewall
- Cannot be closer than 450mm to supply or exhaust air diffusers
- Cannot be closer than 450 mm to shelving
- On a peaked or sloped ceiling, detectors must be at least 900mm down from the peak.

Other requirements relating to galleries, mezzanines and balconies are also described in *S524.*

Specifically relating to heat detectors, *CAN/ULC-S524 Installation of Fire Alarm Systems* addresses the following issues:

- Ceiling Height – on a ceiling that is up to 3 meters high (the 'reference' height) heat detectors are at 100% of their spacing. A graph that is printed in the *S524* standard indicates that the spacing is reduced by slightly more than 10% with each additional meter in height.

- At the reference height (3 meters) a ceiling that is has solid beams dividing the ceiling will automatically reduce the detector spacing to 66%, if the beam(s) depth is more than 100 mm but less than 450mm. An increase in ceiling height will further reduce the spacing.

- Note: If the solid beams are *less than* 100mm in depth, than the ceiling is considered to be 'smooth'.

- If the solid beams exceed 450mm in depth, than the area(s) contained by the beam(s) are to be considered as their own separate area. There would therefore be at least one detector in each of these areas. Again, if this beamed ceiling increases in height, the spacing in each of the separate areas will be reduced.

## 4.8.1   Spacing vs. Detector Type

Unlike smoke detectors that generally have a spacing of 9 meters regardless of type, heat detectors have different spacings depending on their technology.

- Dual-action detectors have a spacing of 15 meters.

- Fixed Temperature Only – Non Restorable have a spacing of 9 meters

- Fixed Temperature Only – Restorable have a spacing of 6 meters.

Note: Maximum distance to the nearest wall in each case is 50% of the rated spacing.

## 4.8.2   Required Number of Detectors in a Space

We can refer to the plan or layout of a space in a building as either symmetrical (typically a square or rectangle), or asymmetrical (curved walls, large indents etc.) In the former, we simply divide the length and the width of the space by the detector's assigned spacing. If the calculation results in a fraction, we round up. In the latter case, we divide the space into circular areas with the detector in the middle of each circle. A circle must exceed the distance to any wall containing the area.

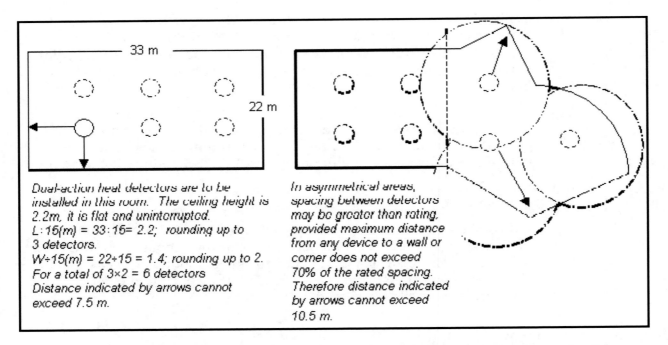

33 m

22 m

Dual-action heat detectors are to be
installed in this room. The ceiling height is
2.2m, it is flat and uninterrupted.
L÷15(m) = 33÷15= 2.2;  rounding up to
3 detectors.
W÷15(m) = 22÷15 = 1.4; rounding up to 2.
For a total of 3×2 = 6 detectors
Distance indicated by arrows cannot
exceed 7.5 m.

In asymmetrical areas,
spacing between detectors
may be greater than rating,
provided maximum distance
from any device to a wall or
corner does not exceed
70% of the rated spacing.
Therefore distance indicated
by arrows cannot exceed
10.5 m.

Once again we are reminded that these drawings assume a standard
ceiling. The rules relating to height above 3 meters, pitch, and solid
obstructions may yet come into play.

## 4.9     Hazardous Areas

Hazardous areas are locations where the potential for fire
or explosion exists due to the presence of flammable
vapours, flammable dust or where there are airborne
particles or fibres that are easily ignited. Obviously fire
alarm devices would be required in these areas however
the very devices installed to detect and warn the
occupants, may actually cause an explosion! This is
because the operation of a device, especially if it is the
closing or opening of a set of contacts, produces a spark.
Even though the spark may be infinitesimally small, it
can ignite surrounding vapours or dusts, resulting in an
explosion.

For this reason, fire alarm detection devices as well as audible devices are designed
to be 'explosion proof' meaning that they cannot cause an explosion if installed in a
hazardous area. In order to make a device explosion-proof, it must be contained in
such a way that the environmental conditions cannot inhabit the same space as
the contact portion of the device.

In the case of the heat detector, a typical explosion-proof unit is characterized by a
cast enclosure, assembled with substantial bolts, complete with sealing O-rings.
The casting will contain information regarding the types of hazards that the
detector can accommodate. For example, there will be a series of 'Classes', namely

©

Class I (presence of flammable gas or vapour), Class II (presence of flammable dust) and Class III (presence of flammable fibres). The next designation is 'Division'. Division 1 indicates that the presence of the explosive material is characteristic of normal operating conditions. Division 2 indicates that the explosive material may be present, but under abnormal conditions such as the rupture of a container or ventilation failure.

Explosion-proof devices also meet the criteria for water-tight and in many cases, weatherproof applications. They are installed using rigid conduit (as opposed to EMT) that is threaded into the device's enclosure. The rigid conduit must also have appropriate seals around any joints and connections.

## 4.10     Testing

### 4.10.1    Rate-of-Rise

In order to test the detector's response to a temperature increase, heat has to be applied to the unit at a rate that exceeds 8.4°C per minute (15°F). This can be accomplished by the use of a hair dryer of approximately 1500 Watts, or by any other device recommended by the manufacturer of the detector. ULC standards S537 (Verification) and S536 (Inspection) make it clear that any heat source produced by open flame is not acceptable as a means to test heat detectors.

Portable, cordless testing devices provide a convenient way to test the rate-of-rise function in both conventional and addressable (electronic) units. In the case of the conventional type, care must be taken to remove the heat source before the fusing temperature of the Fixed Temperature device is reached. If using a hair dryer for example, a conventional detector should respond within a nominal time period of eight to fifteen seconds. If the unit does not respond within this time window, it should be replaced. Rate Compensating detectors can be tested in a similar way.

Electronic detectors will have varying response times depending on the method that is used to communicate temperature change information to the control panel. Again, the manufacturer will supply the specific response information.

### 4.10.2    Fixed Temperature Only

Detectors that are Fixed Temperature Only – Non-restorable, cannot be tested with heat as their activation will render them inoperable. However, their connection to the input circuit must be confirmed during a verification or inspection by placing a momentary short across the detectors terminals to simulate its operation. This will also confirm the correct zone location for the device.

Fixed Temperature Only – Restorable units can be tested with a heat source (again, no open flame), and sufficient time must be allowed for the device to cool and reset. In this case the heat source will have to be able to reach the operating temperature of, for example 57°C (135°F) that may be beyond the capability of some hair dryers. A cloth soaked in very hot water is sometimes used to test this type of unit.

## 4.11 Linear Heat Detection

This method of heat detection relies on the shorting of two conductors within a cable, to create the alarm condition. Typically, the conductors are solid wires, approximately AWG 20 in size with a high ferrous content making them less pliable than standard electrical wiring of the same gauge. The two conductors are individually coated with a thin wax-like material that keeps them insulated from each other. They are then gently twisted together and then inserted into a common sheath. When heat from a fire attacks the cable, the coating melts, allowing the conductors to touch together and produce a short-circuit.

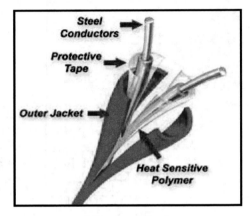

**Linear Heat**

**Linear Heat Cables**

This type of detection is a system unto itself in that the cable is connected to a proprietary control panel especially designed to monitor the current levels flowing through the circuit. The control is designed to recognize a specific distance along the cable where a short has occurred, and translate this information as a zone location. A linear detection system may be used as a component of a building's fire alarm system, monitoring a specific area or hazard such as a cold storage vault, or protecting high-voltage electrical conductors on a cable tray. The control panel would then be interconnected to the Fire Alarm Control Unit to initiate an alarm and to annunciate the device/location. This would be done using a normally-open alarm-operated non-powered contact connected on a Class B circuit back to the FACU.

**Linear Cable Tray Application**

©

## 4.12    Chapter Summary

1.    The *Building Code* requires that some form of automatic fire detection be installed in many types of rooms in buildings where a Fire Alarm System is required.

2.    In some cases, the *Building Code* requires smoke detectors, whereas in other rooms/areas it allows the designer to choose the type of detectors to use.

3.    Where automatic sprinklers are installed, and where the sprinklers are monitored by the Fire Alarm System, then heat detectors are not also required. This is referred to as heat detector exemption for sprinklers.

4.    Rate-of-rise heat detectors are perhaps the most sensitive, and therefore the quickest responding, type of spot detector.

5.    When a fixed-temperature non-restorable detector responds to a high-heat condition, it must then be replaced.

6.    Heat detectors must generally be installed at the highest point in the protected room.

7.    Each detector must be installed in accordance with the listed spacing of that particular device.

8.    An open flame (or any other very high heat method) must never be used to test a heat detector, because such high heat would probably damage the device and render it inoperative.

9.    Linear detectors are well suited for fire detection in confined areas or inside control equipment cabinets.

10.   All detectors must be tested in accordance with the manufacturers recommendations.

4: Heat-Actuated Fire Detectors

## 4.13    Review Questions

| # | ? | Question | Section |
|---|---|----------|---------|
| **4-1** | | **Which of the following is true?** | |
| | A | Heat-actuated fire detectors are designed to respond to the 'heat' signature associated with fire | |
| | B | Heat detectors signature is characterized by change (increase) of the ambient temperature of the air surrounding the detector | |
| | C | The detection of an increase of the ambient temperature of the air surrounding the heat detector that initiates an alarm | |
| | D | All of the above | |
| **4-2** | | **Which of the following is false?** | |
| | A | heat detectors, especially the conventional (non electronic) type, are used in any outdoor application as well as environments that are perfect for smoke detectors | |
| | B | Heat-actuated fire detectors are designed to respond to the 'heat' signature associated with fire | |
| | C | The detection of an increase of the ambient temperature of the air surrounding the heat detector that initiates an alarm | |
| | D | Heat detectors, especially the conventional (non electronic) type, are used in any indoor application as well as environments that are inappropriate for smoke detectors. | |
| **4-3** | | **The conventional heat detector is allowed to be installed:** | |
| | A | without a secured electrical back box | |
| | B | With the electrical connections twisted together and placed under one terminal | |
| | C | In hazardous locations, provided that it is listed for the hazardous environment | |
| | D | In all outdoor applications under minus 30 Celsius | |
| **4-4** | | **Every conventional dual-action detector includes:** | |
| | A | a 'fixed-temperature' function. | |
| | B | a spring-loaded plunger held in place over the detectors contacts | |
| | C | a special solder that will melt at a specific temperature | |
| | D | All of the above | |

| # | ? | Question | Section |
|---|---|---|---|
| **4-5** | | **The typical melting or 'fusing temperature is _____ This is well below the standard sprinkler head fusing temperature of _____** | |
| | A | 57°C (135°F)    73°C (165°F) | |
| | B | 45°C (135°F)    71°C (165°F) | |
| | C | 73°C (135°F)    57°C (165°F) | |
| | D | 33°C (135°F)    105°C (165°F) | |
| **4-6** | | **The following statement describes: "the 'bi-metallic disc' detector, this device uses a temperature sensitive thermostat mechanism that is also found as a temperature controller in coffee pots and similar applications"** | |
| | A | Rate of rise detector | |
| | B | Fixed-Temperature Detector – Restorable | |
| | C | Smoke detector | |
| | D | Rate-compensating detector | |
| **4-7** | | **The _____ detector consists of a set of metal strips with a normally open electrical contact contained within a metal shell.** | |
| | A | Fixed-Temperature Detector – Restorable | |
| | B | Rate-compensating | |
| | C | Rate of rise detector | |
| | D | Smoke detector | |
| **4-8** | | **A heat detector, as is the case with any fire alarm device, is connected to the control panel in such a way that if it is removed the circuit wiring will be**  **interrupted causing the panel to go into the** | |
| | A | Alarm mode | |
| | B | Trouble mode | |
| | C | Supervisory mode | |
| | D | All of the above | |

4: Heat-Actuated Fire Detectors

| # | ? | Question | Section |
|---|---|----------|---------|
| **4-9** | | **Building Code requires the use of heat detectors:** | |
| | A | In parking garages that are sprinklered | |
| | B | in suites and rooms not within suites (i.e. storage, utility) in Group C occupancies, | |
| | C | In storage rooms that are sprinklered | |
| | D | In all stair shafts serving high rise buildings | |
| **4-10** | | **Heat Detectors and smoke detectors:** | |
| | A | Cannot be located closer than 100mm to a sidewall | |
| | B | Cannot be closer than 450mm to supply or exhaust air diffusers | |
| | C | Cannot be closer than 450 mm to shelving | |
| | D | All of the above | |

©

# Chapter 5: **Smoke-Actuated Fire Detectors**

## 5.1    **Chapter Overview and Key Concepts**

A smoke detector (typically an ionization or photoelectric type) consists of an assembly of electrical/electronic components arranged to detect one or more of the fire signatures (by-products of the combustion process). These by-products may consist of gases, and water vapour as well as both visible and invisible smoke particles.

The detector includes provision for connection to a source of power, alarm indication and signalling, and optional remote indicator circuits.

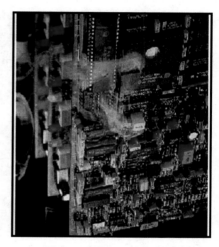

**Electronics Smoke**

Numerous refinements have been made over the last 50 years in the development of smoke detection devices, in order to reliably detect a fire condition as early as possible in the developmental stages and before the presence of the heat levels necessary to trigger heat actuated devices such as heat detectors and sprinkler heads.

This chapter describes the different detection methods currently used by detector manufacturers. Advantages and disadvantages are discussed, so the reader can make proper choices for detection in differing environments.

## 5.2    **Learning Objectives**

After reading this chapter, the reader should be able to:

- Understand the different by-products created by the combustion process

- Understand the term 'fire signatures' and its importance in the detection process

- Differentiate between the various stimuli that affect smoke detectors

- Discuss the reasons for the application of smoke detectors

- Determine the better choice of ionization or photoelectric detector

- Select the detector least apt to 'false-alarm' in any particular ambient situation

- Understand the importance of continuing maintenance of smoke detectors

## Language defined - Chapter Glossary (Also see Main Glossary)

Throughout the various codes and standards, certain words and phrases are used to identify specific items, situations, assemblies or processes. Before beginning a study of any of these documents, it is important that the definitions applicable to fire protection are clearly understood. Failure to understand the meaning of a defined term in a code requirement often leads to an incorrect interpretation of that requirement. Special terms that will be found in this chapter are listed below. Also refer to the Main Glossary at the end of this Manual.

| Term | Definition |
| --- | --- |
| **Active Field Device** | A device that can be uniquely identified by the control unit to determine its presence and operating status, and which may be commanded to operate or to change its operating parameters independently of other field devices that share a common circuit |
| **Addressable Device** | A device that can be individually and uniquely identified by a control unit. The address is set using binary/hexadecimal/decimal methods using dipswitches, rotary switches or solid-state memory |
| **Fire Compartment** | An enclosed space, separated from all other parts of the building by fire separations having the required fire-resistance rating |
| **Fire Detector - Smoke** | A device for sensing the presence of visible or invisible particles of combustion, the concentration of which exceeds a pre-determined level |
| **Flame Detector** | A detector that is designed to sense the radiation emanating from a flame. Two common types of flame detectors are 'infrared' and 'ultraviolet' detectors |
| **Interconnected Floor Spaces** | Superimposed floor areas or parts of floor areas in which floor assemblies that are required to be fire separations are penetrated by openings that are not provided with closures |
| **Plenum** | A chamber forming part of an air-duct system |
| **Return Duct** | A duct for conveying air from a space being heated, ventilated or air-conditioned back to the heating, ventilating or air-conditioning appliance |
| **Self-Closing** | An approved device which will ensure closing after having been opened |
| **Smoke Alarm** | A combined smoke detector and audible alarm device designed to sound an alarm within a room or suite in which it is located, upon the detection of smoke within that room or suite |

©

| Term | Definition |
|------|------------|
| **Smoke Barrier** | A continuous membrane, either vertical or horizontal, such as a wall, floor, or ceiling assembly that is designed and constructed to restrict the movement of smoke. A smoke barrier may or may not have a fire resistance rating. Such barriers may have protected openings |
| **Smoke Compartment** | A space within a building enclosed by smoke or fire barriers on all sides, including the top and bottom |
| **Supply Duct** | A duct for conveying air from a heating, ventilating or air-conditioning appliance to a space to be heated, ventilated or air-conditioned |
| **Vertical Service Space** | A shaft oriented vertically that is provided in a building to facilitate the installation of building services including mechanical, electrical and plumbing installations and facilities such as elevators, refuse chutes and linen chutes |

## 5.3      Detector Design Standard

The Underwriters Laboratories of Canada standard pertaining to the design of smoke detectors is *CAN/ULC-S529 Standard for Smoke Detectors for Fire Alarm Systems*. This *ULC Standard* contains the design parameters to which all system smoke detectors are tested and listed. Detector design varies from manufacturer to manufacturer, and so the following tabling of design specifications contains both ULC requirements and typical or average industry parameters:

- Operating voltage: Nominal 22V. DC (16V - 30V)

- Current Draw (standby): 20 microamps,

- Current Draw (alarm): 25 milliamps

- Temperature Range: O° C to 38° C

- Humidity Range: O% to 93% Relative Humidity (non-condensing)

- Air Velocity: O-300 Metres Per Minute

- Altitude: Sea level to 2,000 metres

- Sensitivity: Variable from 0.5% to 4.0% per-foot obscuration.

To re-state, the foregoing parameters are `typical' and are for general information. It is of great importance that a system designer carefully selects the appropriate detector for the particular hazard description, paying close attention to operating principles and application guidelines.

## 5.4      Principles of Operation

The two most common types of smoke detectors are ionization (or products of-combustion) detectors, which generally respond more quickly to invisible smoke particles in the incipient stage of a fire, and photoelectric detectors which generally respond more quickly to visible smoke in the smouldering stage of a fire. Beam type detectors, which are also discussed in this chapter, operate under the photoelectric principle.

### 5.4.1      Ionization Smoke Detectors

### Sensing Chambers

The ionization-sensing chamber, with a so-called bi-polar design, consists of one negative and one positive electrically charged plate, separated by an air gap, which is open to the atmosphere. A very small amount of radioactive material ionizes the air between the plates and creates molecules containing both positive and negative ions. These are attracted to their oppositely charged plates thus creating a small ionization current. When particles of combustion (in the .01 to 0.4 micron range, and not detectable by the human eye) enter the chamber, there is a corresponding decrease in the ionization current, which in turn is sensed by electronic circuitry monitoring the chamber. When the current is reduced by a predetermined amount, a threshold is crossed, and an alarm condition is established.

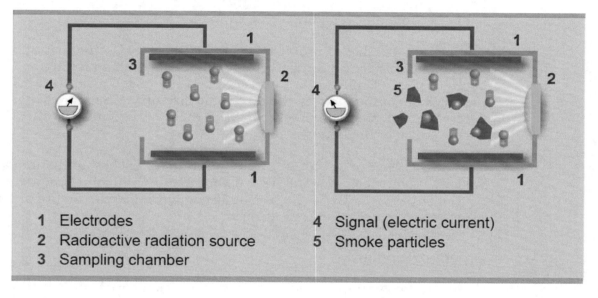

1  Electrodes
2  Radioactive radiation source
3  Sampling chamber
4  Signal (electric current)
5  Smoke particles

Dual-chamber detectors were first used in the 1950's and have proven themselves to be reliable. This design utilizes two ionization chambers. The first is a sensing chamber that is open to the outside air as described above. Many things such as particulate matter, humidity and atmospheric pressure affect this sensing chamber. The second, or reference, chamber is partially closed, and is not affected by particulate matter such as smoke, because its tiny openings effectively block their entry. It is, however, affected by atmospheric changes. In this manner the dual-chamber design automatically compensates for normal atmospheric changes and considerably reduces, or even eliminates, resultant nuisance alarms.

In a dual-chamber ionization detector, electronic circuitry monitors both chambers and compares their outputs. If the humidity or the atmospheric pressure changes, both chambers are affected equally and cancel each other. If combustion particles enter the sensing chamber, its current flow will decrease while the current flow in the reference chamber remains unchanged. The resulting imbalance is detected by the electronic circuitry.

With present technology, within certain limitations, it has been possible to eliminate one of the ionization chambers and replace it with an electronic reference and compensating circuit. The use of dual or single chambers does not directly affect the sensitivity of the detector. It does however, affect the ability to compensate for environmental changes. The dual chamber design is still regarded as having a greater ability to compensate for environmental changes with respect to humidity and atmospheric pressure. For many years, these problems were not a primary concern of designers, because the sensor did not have to be set that sensitively. Approval agencies have added a slow, smouldering fire test to their test series, and conventional dual chamber sensors had to be set more sensitively (closer to their alarm threshold) to pass this test. Dust, humidity, air currents and their effect on chamber performance again became an overriding concern to chamber designers.

There are a number of problems that can affect dual-chamber and single-chamber ionization detectors. Dust, excessive humidity or condensation, significant air currents and tiny insects can be misread as particles of combustion by the electronic circuitry. The more sensitive a detector is set, the more likely it is that these conditions will affect the performance of the detector.

This design cannot successfully compensate for excess ambient air velocity. Some detectors will have a very minor change in sensitivity as air velocity varies, while others may become dramatically more or less sensitive, depending on their design.

## Unipolar/Bipolar

There are two variations of ionization chambers: Bipolar and Unipolar.

The important difference is that the unipolar design reduces the area within the chamber, where ionization occurs, making it approximately three times more sensitive to products-of-combustion than a comparable bipolar chamber. The difference between the unipolar and the bipolar chamber detector does not necessarily make the unipolar detector (as a unit) more sensitive to smoke. All ionization detectors are threshold alarm devices and are capable of a much higher sensitivity than what is practical for a fire detector. However, for a given detector's sensitivity, a much more positive signal is produced by the unipolar detector than by the bipolar detector. There is a greater signal-to-noise ratio, and therefore greater stability is obtained.

## Particle Size

The current in an ionization chamber also depends upon the molecular structure or composition of the gas between the electrodes. Depending upon the type, number and size of gas molecules, a larger or smaller quantity of ions will be produced. The rate and drift of the ions is also dependent upon their size. The ionization detectors become more sensitive with gases that are heavier than air and less sensitive with gases that are lighter than air.

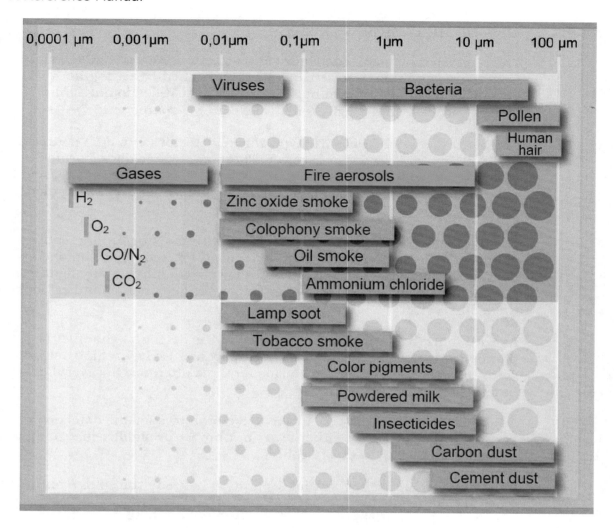

However, current flow is quite different. When products of combustion enter an ionization chamber such gases cause a sharp current drop. During the combustion process a large number of particles are produced. These particles are considerably larger and heavier than normal gas molecules.

One effect of these large particles is an increased absorption of the radioactive alpha particles, which reduces ionization in the chamber. The main influences, however, are the heavy particles that are less mobile than normal air ions. The heavy ions require a much longer time to travel to the electrodes in the ionization chamber. The probability of them colliding with another particle of opposite charge and thus recombining to form a neutral particle is therefore much greater than in the case of normal air ions. This increase in recombination results in a lowering of the ionization current.

### 5.4.2    Photoelectric Smoke Detectors

The photoelectric smoke detector senses the presence of visible smoke from a fire condition. The sensing is accomplished either by the obscuration of a light beam by smoke, or by the reflection of light off smoke particles onto a light sensitive electronic component.

The heart of any photoelectric type smoke detector is its light source and its light-sensitive sensor or receiver. These are physically separated within the detector chamber housing. Over the years, the incandescent lamp has been replaced by high-intensity infrared light-emitting diodes (LEDs).

The light source and sensor are enclosed within a surrounding labyrinth or shroud. Constructed of a maze-like, multi-layered, black-finished, light-absorbing material, the labyrinth effectively inhibits any light from outside the detector from penetrating into the detection chamber housing the light receiver.

As with Ionization detectors, the design of the detection chamber of photoelectric detectors is also very complex and early warning detection with freedom from unwanted alarms requires attention to several design parameters.

A high-intensity light source in the detector allows for the detection of smoke particles that are either fewer in number or smaller in size than when using a lower intensity source.

In a similar manner, the spatial separation between the source and receiver affect detector sensitivity. It is critical that the type of light source, light-sensor and the spatial separation be considered at the same time when designing the chamber.

The use of a pulsating light source allows the detector to require the presence of repetitive alarm pulses prior to triggering an alarm response, as well as reducing the average power requirement of the detector.

## Obscuration Type

This detector relies on the ability of certain types of smoke to block or absorb light, and consists simply of a light source and a light-sensing element.

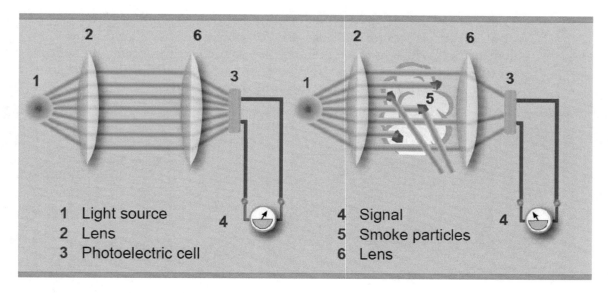

| | | |
|---|---|---|
| 1 Light source | 4 Signal | |
| 2 Lens | 5 Smoke particles | |
| 3 Photoelectric cell | 6 Lens | |

The light-receiving cell will be some type of photovoltaic or photo-resistive cell. Photovoltaic cells are normally selenium or silicon cells that produce a voltage when light strikes the cell. Photo-resistive cells are normally cadmium or cadmium selenide sulphide cells that change their electrical resistance characteristics when light strikes the cell. The light source and the light receiving cell must be compatible with respect to the light levels and spectral composition of the light.

## Reflected-Light Type

This type of photoelectric detector is commonly referred to as either 'reflected-beam' or 'light-scattering'. There are many variations of this type of detector. The main operating characteristics of this detector are completely the opposite to the obscuration type of detector. Under normal conditions, light from the light source does not reach the light sensitive cell. This is accomplished by housing the light source and light sensitive cell in a labyrinth, which is a dark chamber, so that the sensor cell does not see either the light source or any extraneous light from outside the detector.

Some detectors are designed to be sensitive to a specific light wavelength that is only generated by the light source located in the detector. In the design of this type of detector it is only essential that the light from the light source does not reach the light-receiving cell. Extraneous light entering the detector will have no effect.

Reflected-light photoelectric smoke detectors operate on the principle of light reflection off visible smoke. Light from the internal source is scattered by smoke particles in its path, and a portion of this light is reflected toward the sensor. Because black smoke will absorb light, this type of detector is most responsive to grey or light-coloured smoke.

There are presently two types of construction used in spot-type photoelectric detectors. These are 'forward scattering' and 'side scattering'. When light strikes smoke particles, it is basically scattered in all directions although particle size and wavelength of the light source influence the degree and direction of the scattering.

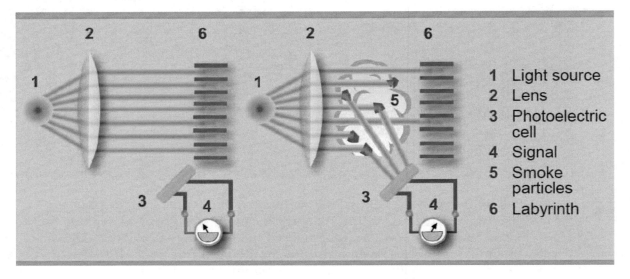

| | 1 | Light source |
|---|---|---|
| | 2 | Lens |
| | 3 | Photoelectric cell |
| | 4 | Signal |
| | 5 | Smoke particles |
| | 6 | Labyrinth |

In the forward scattering detector, the light source and sensor are 'in line' and the light from the light source is blocked from reaching the sensor by a physical barrier. When light is scattered by smoke particles, the scattered light will bypass the barrier to reach the sensor.

Current technology utilizes highly dependable, infrared, light-emitting diodes as the light source. If smoke entering the detection chamber exceeds approximately 1.5% obscuration-per-foot, sufficient light is reflected onto the sensor to trigger the detector into alarm. Laser diodes can achieve sensitivities of below 1% obscuration per foot.

In some models, the light source is pulsed, and a second pulse of reflected light is required before the detector will alarm.

## 5.5 Detector Selection Considerations

Buildings contain a variety of combustibles, making it very difficult to predict what size of particulate matter will be produced by a developing fire. The fact that different ignition sources have different effects on a combustible will further complicate the choice. A lighted cigarette will produce a slow smouldering fire if dropped onto a bed or a chesterfield, however if it falls on a newspaper or in a waste basket, the resulting fire may be more of a fast flaming fire than a slow smouldering one. Given all the numerous variables, with fire load and ignition sources, it is imperative to carefully consider the type of detector best suited for a particular application.

The selection process firstly involves a thorough understanding of fire phenomena and the types of fires that may be encountered. Secondly, the types of combustible materials and the corresponding by-products of combustion produced, must be taken into consideration.

## 5.5.1    Fire Phenomena

Fire phenomena (e.g. temperature increase, light obscuration or flames), are physical values that are subject to measurable change during the development of a fire.

The combustion process can be principally viewed from the perspective of a conversion of both energy and substance. Energy conversion releases energy into the environment. Substance conversion produces many by-products ranging from non-toxic to highly toxic, depending on the substances present at the seat of the fire.

Energy conversion releases energy through both radiation and convection. The frequencies of radiated energy released during a fire are to be found across a broad spectrum in the ultraviolet frequency (UV) band, the visible light band, and the infrared (IR) band.

**High-rise Fire Aftermath**

Energy release by convection essentially takes place through the ambient air. First, the kinetic energy of the air molecules is increased, resulting in a temperature increase. The associated expansion leads to an upward air flow. Due to this flow, cooler air and thus oxygen flows to the seat of the fire.

The conversion of substances taking place during a combustion process is characterized by the various chemical reactions that can occur at the seat of the fire, depending on the substances present. The substance conversion of a fire is determined by the different chemical reactions that may occur at the seat of the fire. The resultant substances either remain at the fire seat (e.g. ashes) or are distributed into the environment surrounding the fire. In the latter case, they in the form of very fine, and evenly distributed, solid or liquid matters mixing with the ambient air. These gaseous conversion by-products are referred to as aerosols, and are always spread through the air.

©

### 5.5.2    Types Of Fires

The fire phenomena occurring with a smouldering or open fire differ both in terms and intensity.

The main property of the combustion process is that it does not go on independently but requires a continuous supply of new energy. The fire can be extinguished by stopping the energy supply. The propagation of that fire type is thus restricted to the size of the heat source, which is why we can speak of overheating accompanied by chemical decomposition. As soon as the ignition temperature is reached, the fire develops to a glowing or even open fire.

The glowing fire is an independent process. The glowing temperatures are high and the particles produced are thus relatively small. The visible particles are only a small part of the particle spectrum generated. Typical for a glowing fire are incipient fires in hay or cotton bales.

Characteristic of open fires is the production of soot, i.e. black smoke. Although here too, the major part of the particles generated is in the non-visible range. Studies have shown that in almost all cases, including the early stage and smouldering phase, more invisible particles than visible ones are generated.

Summarizing, we can state that large volumes of volatile fire aerosols are produced with almost all hostile fires. Smoke has thus become the most important fire phenomenon for early detection of fire. Depending on the size and concentration of the fire aerosols, they may be visible or invisible.

### 5.5.3    Test Fires

Both ionization and photoelectric smoke detectors are required to respond to the same test fires established by Underwriters Laboratories of Canada. The allowable sensitivity ranges are verified by their performance in these test fires, to ensure that they have sufficient sensitivity to certain fire phenomena, albeit some faster than others depending on the type of fire.

Manufacturers produce smoke detectors for the global marketplace, therefore, they must meet country or region specific test fire requirements, in order to gain proper approvals.

**Airport Smoke Test**

©

From an international perspective, the following data from the *European EN-54 Test Fire protocols*, should provide invaluable information. The tests are set up in such a way that each fire produces a different, typical aerosol spectrum. Such fires are mandatory to achieve approval, as well as being used for testing the response behaviour of existing fire detection systems.

| EN Test fire | TF1 | TF2 | TF3 | TF4 | TF5 | TF6 |
|---|---|---|---|---|---|---|
| Fire type | Open cellulose fire (wood) | Pyrolytic smoldering fire (wood) | Glowing / smoldering fire (cotton) | Open synthetic fire (polyurethane) | Liquid fire (n-heptane) | Liquid fire (ethyl alcohol) |
| Heat development | Strong | Negligible | Negligible | Strong | Strong | Strong |
| Upward air flow | Strong | Weak | Very weak | Strong | Strong | Strong |
| Smoke generation | Yes | Yes | Yes | Yes | Yes | No |
| Aerosol spectrum | Predominantly invisible | Predominantly visible | Predominantly invisible | Partly invisible | Predominantly invisible | None |
| Visible property | Dark | Light, strongly scattering | Light, strongly scattering | Very dark | Very dark | None |

EN-54 test fires are artificially induced, ideal fires that rarely occur in practice, as real fires usually produce a mix of smoke types. The advantage of the EN-54 test fires is that they produce reproducible fire phenomena and thus enable exact comparisons between the response behaviour of different detectors or sensors.

The figure above shows the qualitative, basic capability of the various detectors to respond to EN-54 test fires. A heat detector cannot respond when a fire does not produce heat (TF2 and TF3). The sensor design has an additional impact on the quantitative response behaviour of the sensor. The response of optical smoke detectors to TF1, for example, depends on the scattering angle.

Ionization detectors are generally superior in detecting fast-flaming fires that are characterized by combustion particles in the .01 to 0.4 micron size range and are thus more sensitive to dark or black smoke. Photoelectric detectors, on the other hand, may be slow in responding to dark or black smoke. Neither detector is particularly sensitive to the type of thick black smoke generated by a oil-filled transformer fire.

**Ionization Smoke Detector**

Ionization detectors are preferable when complex and sophisticated machinery is to be protected, because of the superior detection of invisible products of combustion. As nearly all plastics (such as polyurethane and polystyrene) or combustible liquids (gasoline, naphtha) produce black smoke when they burn, an ionization detector will provide quicker response.

**Opened Photo Smoke Detector**

Photoelectric detectors are superior in detecting slow smouldering fires that are characterized by particulates in the 0.4 to 10.0 micron size range and are thus more sensitive to light grey smoke.

Photoelectric detectors are better utilized, when combustion particles are present from combustion producing machines, such as fork lifts, welders etc., and near kitchens. Any areas containing materials that might produce lighter-coloured smoke from a slow smouldering fire will be better protected with photoelectric detectors.

To be able to reliably detect all expected incipient fires, where fires can be expected to produce different products of combustion, a mixture of two detectors may be of benefit. These areas may include electrical risks such as computer rooms, switching installations and telephone exchanges.

Selecting the best-suited detector type requires both profound technical knowledge and a grasp for the application itself, its risk, the combustible load, the possible fire progression and the probable and achievable fire size.

## 5.6    *Building Code* Requirements

As is the case with all fire alarm devices, it is the *Building Code* that contains the application requirements for smoke detectors.

Where a fire alarm system is required, smoke detectors must be installed:

- in each sleeping room and each corridor serving as part of a means of egress from sleeping rooms in portions of a building classified as Group B major occupancy,

- in each room in a contained use area and corridors serving those rooms,

- in each corridor in portions of a building classified as Group A, Division 1 major occupancy,

- in each public corridor in portions of a building classified as Group C major occupancy,

- in each exit stair shaft, and

- in the vicinity of certain draft stops.

Some jurisdictions require that smoke detection be provided in each corridor serving classrooms in elementary and secondary schools.

The *Building Code* makes no reference to the type of detector that is required - the designer therefore can choose either a photoelectric detector or an ionization type of detector for each application requirement. This selection process should take into account the detection capability of each type, as well as the affect that the anticipated environment might have on either of the two types.

Indeed, because a beam type detector is considered to be a smoke detector, it is entirely permissible to utilize beam type smoke detectors instead of area type detectors in any application. In this case, the designer would also have to consider the cost factors in addition to the detection capability and the environmental aspects.

## 5.7    Installation Requirements

### 5.7.1    Maximum Spacing and Area Coverage

The installation of smoke detectors must be in accordance with the recommendations of the manufacturer and the current *CAN/ULC S524 Installation of Fire Alarm Systems*. Each smoke detector carries a maximum area rating of 81 square metres and a spacing of 9.1 metres.

Smoke detectors installed on the ceiling must be not less than 100 mm from the wall, measured to the edge of the detector. Detectors may also be installed on the wall 100 to 300 mm from the ceiling, measured to the edge of the detector.

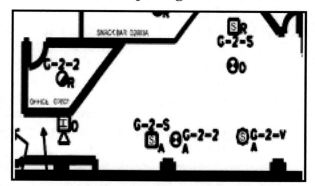

**Smoke, Heat and Speaker Layout**

The maximum distance from a smoke detector to the furthest point of a side wall or corner within its zone of protection cannot exceed 70% of the detector spacing. This would apply to rectangular areas as well as corridors.

For irregularly shaped areas, the distance between smoke detectors may be greater than the specified spacing, provided the maximum distance from a detector to the furthest point of a side wall or corner within its zone of protection is not greater than 70% of the detector spacing.

The above ratings are maximum ratings for areas that may have solid beams up to 100 mm in depth. Careful consideration should be given to all features which would have a bearing on detector location, such as ceiling heights, peaked or sloped roofs, air handling system diffusers, air stratification currents, partial partitions, uninsulated roofs, thermal barriers, smoke, air pollution, vapours, dampness, danger of explosions, high stock piling and type of fire load, burn characteristics and value of contents in any given room.

Ideally, smoke tests should be performed, where feasible, to investigate prevailing conditions prior to installation, to obtain the best detector placement and spacing. One should also take into account the visibility of the detector, especially the alarm indicator, or additional remote indicators used and especially accessibility of the detector for cleaning and maintenance.

## 5.7.2    Ceiling Heights

Smoke detector spacing is not required to be reduced for higher ceiling height but may be affected by ceiling beam construction. On ceilings above 3600 mm in room height, detector spacing should be based on fire type, growth rate, engineering judgment and manufacturer's recommendations.

As smoke and heat rise from a fire, they tend to spread or disperse in the general form of an inverted cone. Therefore, the concentration within the cone varies inversely as an exponential function of the distance from the source while a reduction in thermal lift results from the horizontal dilution of the combustion products (normal inverted cone effect), and a simultaneous cooling of the products. This effect is significant in the early stages of a fire, and as it progresses in intensity, the cone angle narrows and the significance of the height effect is lessened. As smoke detectors are 'early warning' devices, the room height becomes of prime importance.

## 5.7.3    Beam Construction

Beam-type ceilings are allowed to be treated as a smooth ceiling if the beams project no more than 100 mm below the ceiling, and smoke detectors are installed in accordance with the spacing requirements of Subsection 5.7.3 of *CAN/ULC-S524 Installation of Fire Alarm Systems*

Where the beams project more than 100 mm and less than 300 mm below the ceiling, and the ceiling height is less than 3600 mm, the detector spacing of smoke detectors at right angles to the direction of beam travel must be a maximum of 50% of the smooth ceiling detector spacing allowance.

©

Where the beams project more than 300 mm below the ceiling, or the ceiling height is more than 3600 mm, each bay or area formed by the beams must be treated as a separate area.

### 5.7.4    Exit Stair Shafts

A smoke detector must be installed at the highest point of the exit stair shaft. In exit stair shafts exceeding 18 m, smoke detectors must be installed at every third floor.

Interior horizontal exit passageways forming exit stair shafts exceeding 18 m in height must also be provided with spot type smoke detectors in accordance with Clause 5.7.1.1 and Subsection 5.7.3.7, Corridors.

When spot type smoke detectors cannot be used due to abnormally low ambient temperature, below 0° C, appropriate fixed temperature spot type heat detectors may be installed as an alternative.

**Exit Stair Entrance**

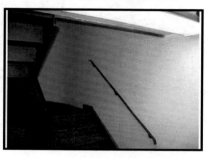

**Exit Stair Shaft**

### 5.7.5    High Air Movements And Humidity

Smoke detector spacing must be reduced proportionately in areas with high air movements and cannot be installed directly in the stream of the air supply.

Smoke detectors in areas above a relative humidity of 93% or an air velocity greater than 1.5 m/s must be of a type compatible for such applications.

**High Humidity Water
Treatment Room**

### 5.7.6    Thermal Layers

Because the temperature differential between the air at the floor and the air at the ceiling is accentuated on high ceilings, peaked or steeply gabled ceilings, as well as uninsulated roofs and skylights, a thermal barrier may exist which inhibits combustion products from reaching the ceiling. In such areas it becomes necessary to install the detectors some distance below the ceiling. There are also occasions where thermal barriers may not be present at all times:

- In a building with an uninsulated roof, a thermal barrier may develop during the day, yet at night the phenomena may not occur because of the cool night air. It is required to locate two detectors per detector area, one on the ceiling for night detection, the other a 10% distance below the ceiling for day detection.

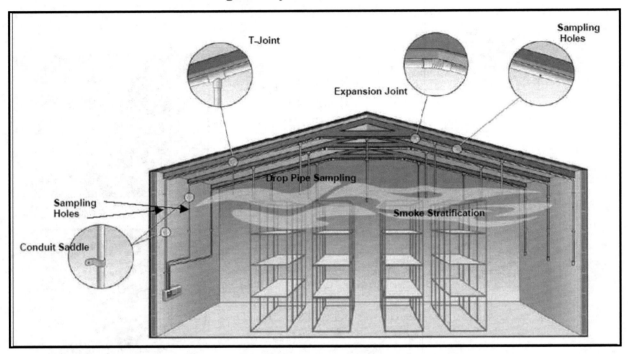

**Stratification**

- In a skylight which constitutes a surface area of more than 10% of the area assigned to one detector, and with a depth exceeding 300 mm, additional detectors are required to be installed at a distance of 50% the depth of the skylight. Where such skylights are open at times and even equipped with fans, careful attention should be given regarding air currents and their effect on smoke movement.

- With large exposed glass areas, where the ceiling height exceeds 6000 mm and the area of the exposed glass is greater than 50% of the exposed exterior wall, a second identical layer of detectors is required, projecting 10% below the ceiling height.

## 5.7.7    Air Movements, Changes And Air Velocity Factors

Airflow patterns must also be considered, and a general rule is to keep detectors away from air supply points. Detectors should be installed near air return points so that products of combustion are drawn towards the smoke detector. *CAN/ULC-S524* (5.7.2.4) states that spot type fire detectors shall not be located in a direct airflow or closer than 450 mm from an air supply outlet or from an air exhaust outlet measured to the edge of the detector.

Porous ceilings or ceilings containing perforations which are used to supply air into the room must also receive special consideration. If this type of ceiling is encountered then a baffle must be mounted above the detector to prevent air blowing down past the detector that would prevent products of combustion from reaching the detector.

Again, for critical applications, the air velocities or the number of air changes in a given area should be considered. Higher air velocities or air changes are encountered mainly in computer or electronic equipment rooms, and good engineering practice calls for a reduction in the designed area coverage of detectors. This factor must be considered from two separate aspects. The first being that with higher air velocities or air changes, smoke is either diluted or quickly vented from the protected area and therefore detection becomes difficult. This requires additional detectors for proper protection. The second factor is that the sensitivity of ionization detectors is affected by air moving across the sampling chamber. As mentioned earlier, some detectors become more sensitive, some less sensitive and with some the influence is negligible. If detectors become less sensitive then even more detectors should be considered.

If the HVAC system is shut down due to repairs or energy savings measures, the placing of smoke detectors is affected as they may no longer protect adequately and such has to be taken into consideration. The following general rules apply:

- In areas having moderate air conditioning or ventilation, such as offices, the detector coverage should be slightly reduced, about 15% to compensate for this movement.

- In areas with high air movements, e.g. computer rooms, detector spacing should be reduced substantially to about 20 m$^2$.

- An asymmetrical layout is generally the most important tool for applying detectors in air-conditioned areas.

## 5.7.8   Extraneous Environmental Influences

Atmospheric pressure changes, humidity and temperature variations, as well as air velocities can influence smoke detector sensitivity as mentioned earlier.

Minor changes of atmospheric pressure are compensated for within the detector and do not materially affect sensitivity. However, lower air pressure at higher altitudes, will decrease ionization type detector sensitivity, while higher air pressure will increase sensitivity.

An increase in relative humidity can increase the detectors sensitivity. While some particular detectors may operate above 93% humidity, with increased sensitivity, such operation is not advisable because of condensation in the detector chamber or on the photoelectric LED. Generally, most detectors will operate normally at temperatures between 0°C and 38°C. However, the lower the temperature, the more sensitive the detector will be in the majority of cases, but gradual changes are usually within the compensation range. Detectors must be protected against the danger of water condensation.

Air velocity affects detectors, although effective performance can be expected from a well-designed detector up to 300m per minute. Detectors should be carefully placed so that they are not subject to air blasts. Under the influence of air currents, in an ionization detector, part of the ions generated will be blown out of the detecting chamber, reducing the current, which increases the sensitivity. Possible nuisance alarms by moving air, which does not contain fire aerosols, can be expected. On the other hand, this effect may be advantageous under some circumstances, because, with a quick spreading fire, the increased sensitivity will signal a fire incident faster.

Tests have proven that negative and positive air pressures above or below the neutral plane within a building can have an effect on the smoke detector sensitivity to the point of non-operation or too high sensitivity. Such pressures can invade the electrical raceways connecting the various devices, and could be released through the back box into the detector, either driving smoke or smoke particles away, or drawing in dirt or dust. To avoid smoke detector false alarms, raceways leading to the detectors are required by the *ULC Installation Standard* to be sealed with a sealing compound or fitted with a special seal plate if the detectors will be subject to pressure differentials.

Each of the above environmental items alone, generally do not signal a false alarm, since the compensation circuit or chamber can make the necessary adjustments. However, when a combination of changes in humidity, temperature and air currents occur, the chances of a false alarm are suddenly magnified. If the temperature increases, together with an increase of humidity, then the sensitivity will also increase, and if exposed to air currents, as well as some dust particles carried by the air current, then a detector will most likely initiate an alarm.

In conclusion, special consideration is required when placing detectors in such environmental problem areas and will require not only special detectors, designed for industrial application, but also special placement selection, possibly using a test fire and instrumentation to determine the best position.

## 5.7.9    Application Do's and Don'ts

Smoke detectors offer the earliest warning of a fire at a reasonable cost. They have saved thousands of lives in the past and will save more in the future. Nevertheless they do have limitations.

As seen above, the perfectly engineered application using the correct type of detector is the most important factor in fire detection system design, as it is also the only way to avoid unnecessary nuisance alarms. The problem most often encountered when using smoke detectors is the

©

incorrect application, not only by the engineer, who produces the system design, but also by the installer, who may not be generally familiar with these units and their operation.

The best way to avoid unwanted alarms is not to install detectors in environments that can cause them to malfunction, or to install detectors specially designed for those environments. Examples follow:

- Excessively Dusty or Dirty Areas: Consider using specialty detectors. Applications would include textile mills, dusty manufacturing facilities, paper mills, recycling centres and animal holding areas.

- Outdoors: Avoid using detectors outdoors, in open storage sheds, or other open structures affected by dust, air currents, or excessive humidity and temperature extremes.

- Wet or Excessively Humid Areas: Avoid damp, wet or excessively humid areas, or next to bathrooms with showers.

- Extreme Cold or Hot Environments: Avoid very cold or very hot environments, or unheated buildings or rooms where the temperature can fall below or exceed the operating temperature range of the detector. At temperatures above or below the operating range of the detector, its internal components may not function properly.

- Areas with Combustion Particles: Avoid areas where particles of combustion are normally present, such as in kitchens, or other areas with ovens and burners, or in garages where particles of combustion are present in vehicle exhausts. When a detector must be located in or adjacent to such an area, a heat detector may be more appropriate.

- Manufacturing Areas: Avoid manufacturing areas, battery rooms, or other areas where substantial quantities of vapours, gases, or fumes may be present. Strong vapors can make detectors overly sensitive or less sensitive than normal. In very large concentrations, gases heavier than air, such as carbon dioxide, may make detectors more sensitive, while gases lighter than air, such as helium, may make them less sensitive. Aerosol particles may collect on detector chamber surfaces and cause nuisance alarms.

- Fluorescent Light Fixtures: Avoid placement near fluorescent light fixtures. Electrical noise generated by fluorescent light fixtures may cause unwanted alarms. Install detectors at least 0.3m away from such light fixtures.

## 5.8    Beam-Type Smoke Detectors

### 5.8.1    General

Beam Detectors are normally referred to by two slightly different names and the two names are synonymous: Projected (or reflected) Beam Detector, and Linear Beam Detector.

Beam type smoke detectors are used in areas where smoke-generating incipient fires are to be expected and where spot type detectors cannot be used. Typical application areas are:

- very high rooms (atriums, hangars)

- large rooms or spaces where maintenance of spot type detectors would be more difficult or more expensive (libraries, galleries)

- areas with strong operational danger of contamination of spot type detectors (sawmills, corrosive atmospheres, high air turbulence)

- historical buildings in which spot type detectors are unwanted for aesthetic reasons

### 5.8.2   Design Standard

At present, there is no *ULC Standard* pertaining to this type of detector, but is considered as an individual unit, using the smoke detector *Standard S529* as the operational guide with additional design parameters.

### 5.8.3   Mode Of Operation

The detector operates on the principle of light obscuration, whereby they measure the light attenuation caused by smoke. In systems without a reflector, they consist of separate transmitter and receiver units usually mounted at the opposite ends of the area to be protected. Some systems accommodating the transmitter and receiver in the same housing, use a remote reflector, and have the advantage that they need to be connected to the detection circuit at one point only and therefore maintenance is easier.  Both systems work according to the same measuring principle - reduction in light intensity due to smoke.

The transmitter emits a parallel light bundle in an invisible infrared beam through the lens. In the absence of smoke, virtually all light reaches the light-sensitive receiver and produces a specific electrical signal. As a smoke field develops, the detector senses the cumulative obscuration – the percentage of light blockage created by a combination of smoke density and the linear distance of the smoke field across the projected beam, and therefore a weaker electrical signal is received.

Some of the light beams are absorbed by contact with smoke particles, while others are reflected or scattered by the particles, and may simply change direction. However, the particular contribution of these two effects is unimportant to the operation of the receiver, because black particles result in a greater amount of absorption, while white particles produce more scattering, resulting in a similar response characteristic.

©

If the above-mentioned weaker signal falls below the receiver's field programmed sensitivity, the receiver will actuate an alarm condition. Very small, slow changes in the quality of the light source are not typical of a smoke signature. These changes may occur because of environmental conditions such as dust and dirt accumulation on the reflective surface and are therefore offset by the receiver's compensation circuit. If the beam is totally obstructed by a solid object or if the housing cover of any of the units is removed, then the incoming signal falls below the trouble reference voltage and a trouble signal is initiated. The detector provides both alarm and trouble relays and these can be used to interconnect into a building Fire Alarm System or off-site monitoring system.

### 5.8.4  Response Characteristics

The beam detector measures the total smoke accumulation between the transmitter and the receiver. The smoke density reading that triggers the alarm is dependent upon the distance between the two units. If the smoke is evenly distributed in the room or area, the response sensitivity will decrease over an increased distance between the two units. The main reason for this is that the beam emitted by the transmitter is not strictly a parallel bundle of rays. It exhibits a certain degree of scattering that makes it conical in shape. As the radiation energy decreases towards the outside, the beam can be divided into three regions:

- the effective region corresponding to the line of sight to the receiver with the diameter of the beam approximately 35 mm,

- the second or core region contains sufficient radiation to operate the receiver. Some deviation is permitted, which is mainly due to cold or heat effecting structural building changes, and

- the last is the scattered region; the energy within this area can influence the receiver but is not sufficient to trigger an alarm

Therefore the alignment of the detector is very important, as the beam can only be adjusted by about 10% in all directions. Solid mounting is imperative, so that the beam direction is guaranteed within the limits allowed.

Electrically, each unit (transmitter and receiver) requires a filtered and regulated 24 Volts D.C. supply.

The photocell light source is generally a gallium arsenide LED, a source that is highly reliable and has a long life. The reduction in efficiency during the life of the LED is very low, giving the beam a stable sensitivity over time. It is normal for the LED to be pulsed, helping to produce a high intensity beam.

The receiver is comprised of an optical assembly, a phototransistor and an amplifier. The silicon phototransistor produces an electrical output that is proportional to the intensity of the received beam. In addition to the expected beam focusing function, the lens discriminates against light sources that are situated away from the beam axis and therefore not focused onto the phototransistor. Thus, the detector does not respond to extraneous light.

The output pulses from the phototransistor are fed to comparator circuits which delay any alarm response until there has been sufficient obscuration of the beam intensity to warrant an alarm condition. Usually, a further delay is designed into the circuit to ensure that the reduction in beam intensity was not caused by transient conditions.

Some beam detectors will also produce an alarm condition when quantities of heat pass through the beam, causing turbulence. In this situation, the beam is deflected by refraction as it passes through the turbulent air and this causes fluctuations in the intensity of the received beam. The frequency of fluctuation is dependent upon the size of the fire but typically ranges from about 1 Hz for large fires to 30 Hz for small fires.

Beam intensity fluctuations due to heaters tend to be outside this frequency band. Fans typically produce higher frequencies and radiators produce lower frequencies. The detector usually discriminates against this cause of false alarm. It is interesting to note that in some units the heat-sensing portion can be de-activated in the event of false alarm problems and subsequently the units function as smoke detectors only.

## 5.8.5    Location and Spacing

To adequately protect a room, several beams may be required, the distance between the beams being dependent upon the room height. *CAN/ULC-S524 Installation of Fire Alarm Systems* states that location and detector spacing shall be in accordance with the manufacturer's documented installation instructions. It is also recommended that the detector be installed near the ceiling free of obstructions, such that smoke and other fire-related gases will pass through the beam as they rise to the ceiling. A minimum distance requirement is given by *CAN/ULC-S524 Installation of Fire Alarm Systems* to prevent cross-interference, and this distance is dependent on the distance between transmitter and receiver.

Location and spacing parameters are recommended by manufacturers. For example, on smooth ceilings, a space of not more than 18.3 m between projected beams, and one-half of the maximum spacing between a projected beam and a sidewall (wall parallel to the beam travel) may be used as a guideline. Some manufacturer's recommendations may limit this criterion.

The noted spacing applies to rooms or areas with flat ceilings. Generally, the length of the beam can be, as mentioned earlier, up to a maximum of

100m. Beam detectors can monitor up to 20 m high rooms. In higher rooms such as a very high atrium of a hotel, its suitability may need to be ascertained by test fires and then be supplemented by additional beam detectors at a second, and possibly a third, level.

Thermal barriers below the ceiling can prevent ascending smoke from reaching the ceiling. Therefore beam type smoke detectors must be installed below the thermal barrier to be expected based upon the ceiling height. One manufacturer recommends 3-30 cm below the ceiling on a 6 metre room height, and up to 20-80 cm on a 12 m room height.

In applications where reduced spacing is required, care should be given to keep two parallel beams at a minimum distance so that the receiver from one detector cannot see the light source from another detector

There are other spacing guidelines for areas with beams, sloped ceilings or rooms divided by glass partitions, etc. For these spacing guidelines the detailed manufacturer's instruction must be consulted and strictly followed.

## 5.8.6    Installation Guidelines

The transmitter, receiver and/or reflector units may themselves be mounted in any orientation (horizontally, vertically or at any angle) as long as the two units face each other so that the beam can be properly aligned.

There must be a permanent line of sight between the transmitter and receiver. Care should be taken that the beam is not constantly interrupted by moving objects such as overhead cranes.

The detector must be secured in a way that it is fixed and inflexible. The mounting surface should be free from vibration. Concrete and brick walls are acceptable, whereas wood or steel construction is mostly unsuitable, as they may be affected by temperature or moisture changes, wind or snow pressure. The location should not experience direct sunlight or high intensity halogen or fluorescent lighting that could shine directly into the receiver.

High levels of dust, smoke or vapours may cause nuisance alarms or high maintenance costs. In general, the beam detector is not affected by normal changes in ambient environmental conditions.

As with every type of smoke detector great care must be taken as to the accessibility of both parts of the beam detector.

## 5.9     Air Sampling/Aspiration Type Detectors

### 5.9.1     General

**ASD Pipes**

Air sampling detectors are also known as aspiration smoke detection (ASD). Generally speaking, air sampling type systems can be used in any application where a conventional smoke detector might be used. It also might be used where environmental conditions such as high air currents make the use of conventional detectors problematical.

These systems are most often used in special detection situations such as room monitoring (storage rooms, cooling facilities, computer rooms, art galleries, aircraft hangars) and for object monitoring (control panels, IT and telephone facilities, radio stations)

### 5.9.2     Mode of Operation

Air is continuously drawn (by a pump) from the protected space through an air sampling tube network. The typical sampling network has a maximum area coverage of 1,858 m². This sampling of air is fed through a detector chamber. In a manner similar to a light scattering photoelectric ceiling detector, the air sample is monitored for smoke content.

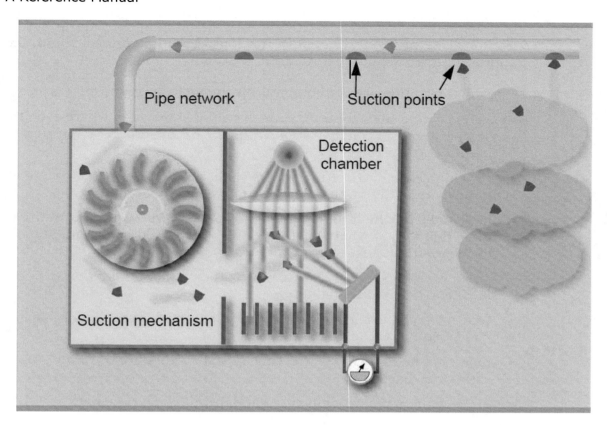

The pump, air filtering, and smoke detection features are all quite highly specialized, to the extent that the control unit is able to quite accurately measure varying levels of smoke content. The ASD triggers an alarm as soon as the average smoke concentration of all sampling openings exceeds the alarm threshold level. It does not matter whether this value is caused by very high smoke concentration at one sampling opening or by a slighter higher smoke concentration at several sampling openings.

As a general rule, ASD systems are classified in the following sensitivity categories:

- normal sensitivity with a range of 1.0 to 0.1%/m
- high/highest sensitivity with a range of 0.1 to 0.005%/m

If a fire is to be detected as early as possible, the ASD system must trigger an alarm as soon as there is smoke at one sampling point. Such systems usually require a very high ASD sensitivity.

### 5.9.3    Application

Current technology requires that these systems be designed and installed as separate stand-alone systems.

Interconnections from the controller into the building Fire Alarm System would utilize auxiliary contacts of the controller interconnected into the appropriate zone(s) of the Fire Alarm System.

Typical application areas for aspirating smoke detectors are:

- rooms with a high concentration of valuable property where even the smallest aerosol concentrations must be detected (EDP rooms, chip production facilities)
- very high rooms where the smoke concentration below the ceiling is strongly diluted due to the large volume (atriums, hangars)
- large halls in which the maintenance of spot-type detectors would be more difficult, or where spot-type detectors would be essentially more expensive than air sampling detectors
- areas where spot-type detectors are prone to contamination (recycling facilities, heavy-duty industry)
- rooms where strong deceptive phenomena such as moisture condensation are to be expected
- historical buildings in which spot-type detectors are unwanted for esthetical reasons
- areas with increased danger of vandalism (e.g. in prisons)

### 5.9.4    Installation Guidelines

*CAN/ULC-S524 Installation of Fire Alarm Systems*, Section 5.10 states that location and detector spacing of air sampling type detectors shall be in accordance with the manufacturer's documented installation instructions. Networks shall be designed on the basis of and be supported by sound dynamic fluid principles to ensure proper performance. Network design details shall include calculations showing the flow characteristics of the piping network and for each sampling point. Inlet ports must be not less than 100 mm from the wall or ceiling.

With normal room monitoring, the pipe system and the suction points are selected in a way that each sampling point has a coverage area of 40 to 80 m$^2$, which is comparable to spot-type smoke detectors. The pipe system is mounted below the ceiling. In false floors and suspended ceilings with a corresponding combustible load, the pipe system is mounted in such a way that the sampling points are at the highest possible point.

Due to the large air volume, strong smoke dilution can be observed in large high rooms such as storage rooms, atriums or hangars. If a fire in such a room is to be detected at an early stage, a correspondingly sensitive system must be chosen. In addition, in high rooms, thermal barriers often occur below ceilings, caused by strong solar radiation or by air warming due to fire. Such thermal barriers partially or completely

©

prevent the smoke from reaching the ceiling. This must be taken into account in placing the ASD sampling tubes.

When planning ASD systems in special areas, additional points mentioned below must be taken into consideration.

<u>Installation in Dirty Environments</u>: In addition to maintaining a reliable detection, ASD systems must also be resistant to contamination in rough environments. The smallest of particles are deceptive elements for optical systems, leading to false alarms or, in the worst case, impairing the system in such a way that it can no longer work reliably. For this reason, filters are built in the pipe system in rough environments, filtering dirt particles before they can penetrate the measuring system. In certain environments, the suction pipes are additionally purged periodically to clean them from dirt or deposits. This assures a reliable transport of the aspirated air to the measuring system.

<u>Installation in Areas with High Air Circulation</u>: Air conditioning equipment or air recycling systems can cause high air circulation, which in turn sometimes produces essential smoke dilution, as the smoke is mixed with fresh air before it reaches the detectors. In such conditions, it makes sense to use ASD systems with increased or very high sensitivity. It also makes sense to feed a sample of exhaust air to the ASD, in addition to the "pure" ambient air. The exhaust air is monitored directly before reaching the room ventilation system's outlet opening.

<u>Installation in Humid Environments</u>: In humid environments, water traps with sluice valves are installed in the suction pipe.

<u>Installation in Refrigeration Warehouses</u>: Due to the very dry air and the highly combustible isolating and packaging material, refrigeration warehouses constitute a high fire risk. A fire in such a facility may propagate quickly and cause a lot of damage, therefore early detection of a spreading fire is of utmost importance in this case. In refrigeration warehouses, ASD with high sensitivity are normally used. To prevent frost formation on the suction openings, the pipe systems are provided with a blow-out mechanism. This is of special importance in the entrance area where high relative air humidity prevails due to the air circulation, resulting in a high tendency of frost formation.

<u>Installation in Areas Prone to Vandalism</u>: In areas prone to vandalism, the suction pipe is mounted in the ceiling. Only very small, almost invisible holes are present in the monitoring area. This type of installation can often be found in penal institutions.

<u>Installation in Culturally Significant Buildings</u>: In culturally significant buildings, for example with historic ceilings, spot-type fire detectors are often not wanted for aesthetic reasons. In buildings such as churches, cathedrals, museums, libraries or other historical buildings, ASD systems are increasingly applied, systems in which the pipe system is

integrated in the ceiling and is thus invisible. The same applies to sophisticated modern buildings, such as concert halls, hotels and office buildings.

Object Monitoring: IT systems, server racks, telephone systems, radio stations and other electronic or electrical facilities are potential fire risks due to their relatively high power consumption. A typical electrical fire is usually preceded by a rather long smouldering phase, with the normally low smoke volume being additionally diluted by ventilation. If this low smoke volume can be detected early enough, it usually suffices to disconnect the endangered equipment from the power supply. This is exactly where ASD systems in object monitoring come into effect: An incipient electrical fire must be detected as early as possible so that appropriate countermeasures can be initiated and possible damage can be minimized. ASD systems for object monitoring are designed in such a way that at least one suction opening is provided in each object, for example in a server rack or control panel.

## 5.10    Air-Duct-Mounted Detectors

The purpose of an air-duct-mounted smoke detector is to respond to a build-up of smoke within the duct and to then shut down the air handling system so as to stop the spread of smoke from the fire area to other parts of the building. It is designed to protect people from the resulting negative effects that may result if smoke were re-circulated, will protect building contents from smoke damage, and protect the HVAC system itself from fire, since many fires start within the HVAC motor controls themselves.

It is not meant to be an area fire detector and must never be considered as a replacement for ceiling mounted area detectors for the following reasons:

- Smoke may not be drawn from open areas when the HVAC system is shut down due to power failure, energy savings measures or during repairs,

- Dilution of smoke laden air by clean air from other parts of the building, or by dilution of outside air intakes, may allow high density of smoke in a room or area without sufficient density of smoke in the duct system necessary to alarm the detector in the duct, and

- If the air filters in the duct become clogged through dust or dirt accumulation, air quantities may be reduced causing less air circulation, thus reducing detection opportunities.

### 5.10.1   Code Requirements

The *Building Code* requires that every circulating HVAC system be equipped with a duct type smoke detector to prevent the circulation of smoke where the air handling system:

- Serves more than one storey, or more than one suite in a storey, or

©

- Serves more than one area in a Group B 2 Division 2 occupancy, which requires two zones or fire compartments, each not more than 1000 square metres in area, or

- Is not provided with fire dampers as permitted in a Group B Division 3 occupancy

### 5.10.2   Operating Principles

Essentially, an air-duct-mounted type smoke detector is a smoke detector head mounted within a box-like, aerodynamically designed enclosure for mounting on the outside wall of the air-handling duct. Two air-sampling tubes complete the assembly. One tube with a row of holes along its length, which extends the width of the duct, carries a sampling of the air from the duct into the enclosure. The air is forced through the detector head and then is pushed out through a short exhaust tube back into the air duct. In this manner a constant sampling of the air in the duct is tested by the smoke detector.

Most manufacturers provide technology enabling duct smoke detection throughout a broad range of airflow environments. Many difficult to solve HVAC problems occur in low airflow duct applications where reliable smoke detection is critical. These technologies allow for smoke detection at air speed velocities of 30 metres per minute or greater, while continuing the same reliable performance up to 1200 metres per minute. The manufacturer's installation guidelines should be consulted for specific air velocity restrictions.

### 5.10.3   Installation Guidelines

*CAN/ULC-S524 Installation of Fire Alarm Systems* sets the following additional requirements for location and quantity of detectors to be installed in an air duct system:

- Air duct type smoke detectors are to be installed in the main supply duct, downstream of the mixing box, filters, and fan. Where this cannot be done, detectors shall be installed in each of the branch lines as close as practical to the supply fan downstream of the mixing box, filters and fan.

- Where air velocities are greater than 1.5 metres per second, one air duct type smoke detector shall be installed for every 1.5 square metre of cross-sectional duct area.

- Where air velocities are less than 1.5 metres per second, one air duct type smoke detector shall be installed for every 0.5 square metres of cross-sectional duct area.

- Air duct type smoke detectors shall be securely installed in such a way as to obtain a representative sample of the air stream from the central area of the duct by:

- Rigidly mounted to the wall of the duct with the sensing element protruding into the duct; or

- Outside the duct with rigidly mounted sampling tubes protruding across the width of the duct.

- Air duct type smoke detectors mounted outside of a duct employing utilizing sampling tubes, shall permit access for verification of airflow from the duct to the smoke detector.

- Smoke detector locations shall be selected to permit access to the entire assembly.

- Smoke detectors shall be installed in a straight section of duct,

From a practical point of view the following considerations should also be taken into account when installing duct smoke detectors:

- Avoid locations where, within a short distance, warm heated air meets cold outside air which could result in water condensation on the detector.

- Also, locate the detector upstream of any humidifier in the system.

A recommended practice is to use remote alarm indicators in conjunction with duct detectors, as it will help to identify the detector in alarm. Many manufacturers also offer a remote reset unit, so that one does not necessarily have to reset at the detector unit, often located in the ceiling. Consideration must still be made for access to the detector for maintenance purposes.

## 5.11    Smoke Alarms

### 5.11.1   General

Smoke alarms are self-contained units (containing both fire detection and signalling components) that provide local warning only to occupants in the immediate area, typically being a dwelling unit or suite. In new construction, these devices are usually connected to a 120 VAC power source. In cases of residential retrofit, the *Fire Code* allows for the installation of battery-operated smoke alarms to satisfy code requirements for occupant safety. As with smoke detectors installed in a Fire Alarm System, these smoke alarms are available as either ionization or photoelectric models. Some utilize both sensing principles. Combination ionization smoke alarms and carbon monoxide detectors

provide convenient protection for a multitude of hazards where required
by various codes and by-laws.

## 5.11.2 Building Code Requirements

The *Building Code* provides the following
detailed requirements for the installation
of smoke alarms;

- Smoke alarms conforming to
  *CAN/ULC-S531, Smoke Alarms*, shall
  be installed in each dwelling unit
  and, except for care or detention
  occupancies required to have a Fire
  Alarm System, in each sleeping room
  not within a dwelling unit.

- At least one smoke alarm shall be
  installed on each storey and mezzanine of a dwelling unit.

- On any storey of a dwelling unit containing sleeping rooms, a smoke
  alarm shall be installed in a location between the sleeping rooms and
  the remainder of the storey, and if the sleeping rooms are served by a
  hallway, the smoke alarm shall be located in the hallway.

- A smoke alarm shall be installed on or near the ceiling.

- A smoke alarm shall be installed with permanent connections to an
  electrical circuit and shall have no disconnect switches between the
  overcurrent device and the smoke alarm.

- If more than one smoke alarm is required in a dwelling unit, the
  smoke alarms shall be wired so that the actuation of one smoke
  alarm will cause all smoke alarms within the dwelling unit to sound.

- Smoke alarms shall be installed in conformance with *CAN/ULC-S553,
  Installation of Smoke Alarms.*

- A manually operated device
  is permitted to be
  incorporated within the
  circuitry of a smoke alarm
  installed in a dwelling unit
  so that it will silence the
  signal emitted by the
  smoke alarm for a period of
  not more than 10 minutes,
  after which the smoke
  alarm will reset and again
  sound the alarm if the level
  of smoke in the vicinity is
  sufficient to reactivate the
  smoke alarm.

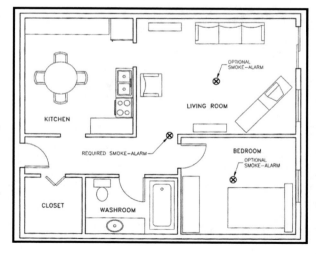

## 5.11.3   Testing And Maintenance

The *Fire Code* mandates that smoke alarms in dwelling units, guest suites and in each sleeping room not within a dwelling unit must be maintained in operating condition by the owner. In the case of a rental unit, the landlord is deemed to be the owner. Fire alarm technicians may also perform required testing and maintenance as part of their regular Fire Alarm System inspections.

*The (Ontario) Fire Code* requires that where an interconnected smoke alarm system has been installed in residential occupancies, that may also incorporate manual stations and heat detectors, these systems must be tested and maintained by qualified persons. These interconnected systems operate as a fire detection and alarm signalling system, except they only operate on 120 VAC power and therefore have no control panel providing standby battery power in the event of a power failure.

The *(Ontario) Fire Code* states the following;

> *Any person who performs work on an interconnected smoke alarm system shall have successfully completed a programme or course acceptable to the Fire Marshall, and must perform the test and maintenance in accordance with the requirements of Part 6, whereby reference is made to CAN/ULC-S552, Standard for the Maintenance and Testing of Smoke Alarms.*

The Canadian Fire Alarm Association's educational programme satisfies these qualification requirements, in order to allow fire alarm technicians to legally comply with the interconnected smoke alarm system test and maintenance requirements.

©

## 5.12    Chapter Summary

1.    The design standard covering all smoke detectors is *CAN/ULC-S529 Standard for Smoke Detectors for Fire Alarm Systems.*

2.    There are two common types of smoke detectors in use in Canada: ionization and photoelectric. The former are considered to be quicker at detecting fast flaming fires, whereas the latter are better at detecting slow smouldering fires.

3.    Ionization devices are sensitive to several different types of common non-fire aerosols including steam. Photoelectric detectors are responsive to non-fire dusts. Therefore care must be taken to ensure that smoke detectors are properly applied and installed in correct locations. Further, the *Building Code* requires only that smoke detectors be installed – the choice of detector type is left up to the system designer.

4.    The *Building Code* tells the designer where, in a building, smoke detectors must be installed. Generally speaking they must be used where people sleep, or where they are confined because of mental or physical restraints.

5.    *CAN/ULC-S524 Installation of Fire Alarm Systems* is the document that we refer to, to learn precisely where in a room, and how, smoke detectors are to be installed.

6.    As was true of heat detectors, smoke detectors have a definite maximum area of allowable coverage. It is referred to as the maximum allowable spacing between similar devices in a large room.

7.    Air must enter the inner detecting chamber of all smoke detectors. Because of this, smoke detectors can quickly become dusty or dirty. They therefore must be cleaned and tested on a regular basis.

8.    Aspiration detectors are highly accurate smoke detection devices. Because they are a stand-alone system, and still rather expensive compared to standard ion and photo devices, aspiration systems find use as special detection systems for computer rooms, electrical control rooms, libraries etc.

9.    Air-duct-mounted smoke detectors are an important detection method, to ensure that smoke from the fire area of a building is not spread through the HVAC system to other parts of the building. They are not a replacement for required ceiling-mounted devices.

10.    All smoke detectors must be provided with specific needs such as filtered and regulated DC power. Smoke detectors must be 'compatible' with the control unit with which it is intended to work.

## 5.13    Review Questions

| # | ? | Question | Section |
|---|---|----------|---------|
| 5-1 | | **The Fire Code mandates that smoke alarms in dwelling units, guest suites and in each sleeping room not within a dwelling unit must be maintained in operating condition by the** | |
| | A | Owner | |
| | B | Technician | |
| | C | Electrician | |
| | D | Fire Official | |
| 5-2 | | **A smoke alarm shall be installed with permanent connections to an electrical circuit and shall have no disconnect switches between the overcurrent device and the smoke alarm.** | |
| | A | True | |
| | B | False | |
| 5-3 | | **Air duct type smoke detectors are to be installed:** | |
| | A | in the main supply duct, downstream of the mixing box, filters, and fan. | |
| | B | in the main return duct | |
| | C | on roof top units serving just one compartment | |
| | D | On both supply and return fans serving just one compartment | |
| 5-4 | | **In culturally significant building, for example with historic ceilings that have painted frescos, what is the best detector to utilize for aesthetic reasons?** | |
| | A | Spot-type fire detectors | |
| | B | Air Sampling Detection | |
| | C | No detection institute a permanent fire watch | |
| | D | Heat detectors | |

| 5-5 | | **Thermal barriers below the ceiling can prevent ascending smoke from reaching the ceiling. Therefore _____ may be installed below the thermal barrier to be expected based upon the ceiling height.** | |
|---|---|---|---|
| | A | Beam type smoke detectors | |
| | B | Flame detectors | |
| | C | Sprinkler heads | |
| | D | None of the above | |
| 5-6 | | **Smoke detectors should not be located too close to a supply-air diffuser because** | |
| | A | It causes the detector to get dirtier quicker. | |
| | B | If placed directly in the stream of the air supply it will not be able to detect the smoke since the air stream will push the smoke away from the detector. | |
| | C | CAN/ULC-S524 does not allow smoke detectors to be installed within 450 mm of the air diffuser. | |
| | D | All of the above | |
| 5-7 | | **Atmospheric pressure changes, humidity and temperature variations, as well as air velocities can influence** | |
| | A | smoke detector power capacity | |
| | B | smoke detector addressability | |
| | C | smoke detector ascetics | |
| | D | smoke detector sensitivity | |
| 5-8 | | **This detector operates on the principle of light obscuration, whereby they measure the light attenuation caused by smoke. What classification of detector?** | |
| | A | Thermal | |
| | B | Ionization | |
| | C | Photo | |
| | D | All of the above | |

5: Smoke-Actuated Fire Detectors

| 5-9 | | **Due to the large air volume, strong smoke dilution can be observed in large high rooms such as storage rooms, atriums or hangars. If a fire in such a room is to be detected at an early stage, a correspondingly sensitive system must be chosen. The most recommended system for this type of application is?** | |
|---|---|---|---|
| | A | Thermal Detector | |
| | B | Linear Thermal Detector | |
| | C | Air Sampling Detection (ASD) | |
| | D | Rate of Rise Heat Detector | |
| **5-10** | | **The purpose of an air-duct-mounted smoke detector is to:** | |
| | A | Respond to a build-up of smoke within the duct and to then shut down the air handling system so as to stop the spread of smoke from the fire area to other parts of the building. | |
| | B | Respond to a build-up of heat within the duct and to then shut down the air handling system so as to stop the spread of smoke from the fire area to other parts of the building. | |
| | C | Respond to a build-up of smoke within the floor area and to then shut down the air handling system so as to stop the spread of smoke from the fire area to other parts of the building. | |
| | D | Respond to a build-up of heat within the floor area and to then shut down the air handling system so as to stop the spread of smoke from the fire area to other parts of the building. | |

©

# Chapter 6: Audible And Visible Signalling Devices

## 6.1 Chapter Overview and Key Concepts

This chapter discusses the physics of sound. This is the very basis of the development of a thorough understanding of all aspects of the audible requirements of the various codes and standards.

From the physics, the reader will move to the practical aspects of designing signalling device layouts in order to achieve conformity with the code requirements.

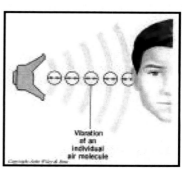

Measurements are required when conducting verification testing under *CAN/ULC S537 Verification of Fire Alarm Systems*, and when resolving audibility problems. Therefore this chapter discusses how to make accurate and meaningful sound level measurements.

This chapter describes how various audible devices operate and their particular applications.

Lastly, this chapter describes visible signal devices and their application.

## 6.2 Learning Objectives

Upon successful completion of this chapter, the reader should be able to:

- Understand how sound is developed and transmitted,
- Apply the Inverse Square Law to sound transmission,
- Know the difference between the A-Scale and the C-Scale of measurement,
- Understand how different structural assemblies affect sound transmission,
- Know how signalling devices are physically constructed,
- Know how devices are connected to signalling circuits, and how electrical placement supervision is achieved,
- Learn when and how to apply visible signalling devices, and
- Understand why code requirements are structured as they are, and how to apply them.

## Language defined - Chapter Glossary (Also see Main Glossary)

Throughout the various codes and standards, certain words and phrases are used to identify specific items, situations, assemblies or processes. Before beginning a study of any of these documents, it is important that the definitions applicable to fire protection are clearly understood. Failure to understand the meaning of a defined term in a code requirement often leads to an incorrect interpretation of that requirement. Special terms that will be found in this chapter are listed below. Also refer to the Main Glossary at the end of this Manual.

| Term | Definition |
| --- | --- |
| **Alarm Signal** | An audible signal transmitted throughout a zone or zones to advise occupants that a fire emergency exists; also called an EVACUATION signal |
| **Alert Signal** | An audible signal intended to advise designated persons of a fire emergency |
| **Authority Having Jurisdiction** | The organization, office, or individual responsible for approving equipment, an installation, or a procedure. Most often, it is the municipal Fire Department |
| **Candela** | The SI or metric unit of measure for luminous intensity or candlepower of a light or strobe |
| **Control Unit** | A device with the necessary circuits or components needed to provide acceptable operating power for a fire alarm system, receive signals from alarm initiating devices, cause audible alarm signals to operate, and electrically monitor the installation wiring and device placement against certain faults and/or removal |
| **Decibel** | A unit of measurement for comparing levels of sound power, based on a logarithmic scale. Generally expressed in deciBels (dB) |
| **Dwelling Unit** | A suite operated as a housekeeping unit, used or intended to be used, as a domicile by one or more persons and usually containing cooking, eating, living, sleeping and sanitary facilities |
| **Floor Area** | The space on any storey of a building between the exterior walls and required firewalls, including the space occupied by interior walls and partitions, but not including exits and vertical service spaces that pierce the storey |
| **Means Of Egress** | A continuous path of travel provided for the escape of persons from any point in a building or contained open space to a separate building, an open public thoroughfare, or an exterior open space protected from fire exposure from the building and having access to an open public thoroughfare. Means of egress includes exits and access to exits |

©

| Term | Definition |
|---|---|
| **Occupant Load** | The number of people for which a building or part of a building is designed, on a square-metre basis for each person. This figure is set by the authorities, is different for different occupancies, and is quite likely different than the actual occupant load the building may eventually experience |
| **Public Corridor** | A corridor that provides access to exit from more than one suite |
| **Suite** | A single room or series of rooms of complementary use, operated under a single tenancy, and includes: |

(a)   dwelling units,

(b)   individual guest rooms in motels, hotels, boarding houses, rooming houses and dormitories, and

(c)   individual stores and individual or complementary rooms for business and personal services occupancies.

## 6.3    Principles of Sound

### 6.3.1    Sound Generation

Fire alarm signals must be heard in order to be effective. Understanding the principles of sound is one factor in determining if the fire alarm system is capable of meeting its' objective of effectively warning people of a possible fire danger.

When an object (such as the gong of a bell, or the diaphragm of a speaker) vibrates, it causes the surrounding air to vibrate. Sound is the result of rapid vibration of air pressure. The compression waves radiate away from the source. Sound waves travel at about 1,238 km/hr or 335 m/s (1129 ft/s).

The human ear responds to these compression waves in the air as recognizable sounds. The normal human ear can hear sounds from a low of about 20 vibrations per second, up to about 18,000 vibrations per second. The term 'hertz' (Hz) meaning 'cycles per second' is generally used when referring to sound vibrations-per-second. Therefore human hearing is generally said to be in a range of from 20 Hz up to about 18,000 Hz.

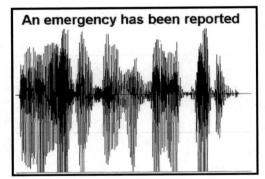

An emergency has been reported

The sounds that we hear are not usually just one frequency or one tone, but a complex mixture of many different frequencies and different intensities.

### 6.3.2    Sound Level Intensity

A particular sound level cannot be assigned a specific, finite value. Rather, one sound level is always compared to another sound as being louder or quieter, and by a particular amount.

The intensity or strength of sound is usually measured and stated using the decibel (dB) scale. The dB scale is a ratio of two or more sound level

| Intensity Ratio | Level Difference |
|---|---|
| 1.0 | 0 dB |
| 1.3 | 1 dB |
| 1.6 | 2 dB |
| 2.0 | 3 dB |
| 2.5 | 4 dB |
| 3.2 | 5 dB |
| 4.0 | 6 dB |
| 5.0 | 7 dB |
| 6.3 | 8 dB |
| 7.9 | 9 dB |
| 10.0 | 10 dB |
| 100 | 20 dB |
| 1000 | 30 dB |
| ... | ..... |
| ... | ..... |
| $10^n$ | 10n dB |

©

intensities, and it is a logarithmic ratio. Based on this logarithmic scale, a change of 3 dB is a change of power of 100%. In other words, a sound that is +3 dB greater than another sound actually has twice the sound power as the other sound.

To compare two sounds of different levels, use the following formula:

SPL = 10 log P2/P1 where P1 is the original power in watts and P2 is the new or changed power in watts.

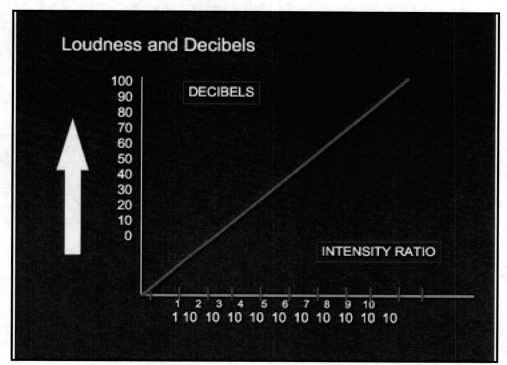

The dB change is 10 times the logarithm of the power ratio. For example if the power is changed from 5 to 10 watts, the ratio of the change is 10/5 or 2/1. As a dB measurement, this is 10 x the log of 2/1 which is 10 x the log of 2. The log of 2 is 0.3. Therefore the power change is 10 x 0.3 or 3 dB.

The rule of thumb for power measurements is:

Double the power equals a +3dB change

Half the power equals a -3dB change.

When considering the intensity of sound it must be remembered that there is always a background sound level present, and it is comprised of sounds from various sources such as traffic or air conditioners. This background sound is referred to as the ambient sound level. For an alarm sound to be heard, it must be significantly louder than the ambient levels.

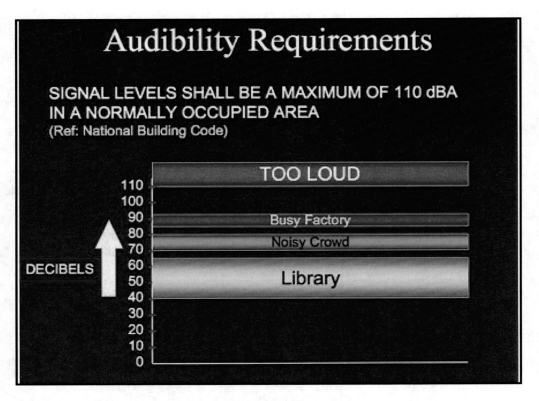

The intensity of the ambient sounds will significantly affect the ability of building occupants to hear the alarm sounds and voice announcements. This ambient sound level is always present, and is present both before and after the period when alarm signals are sounding. Whether or not the alarm sounds are heard, depends (among other things) upon the power differential between the alarm sound levels and the ambient sound levels. With any fire alarm signalling system sound measurement, the ambient sound level must therefore be recorded.

Prior to designing audible signal coverage for a building, the Fire Alarm System designer should anticipate typical ambient noise levels in the different rooms or areas of the building.

For alarm signals to be heard, they must generate a sound intensity that is greater than the ambient sound level. To be heard consistently and clearly, the desired sound levels must usually be at least +10 dB above the ambient sound level.

©

## Table 1: Typical Ambient Sound Levels (*CAN/ULC-S524*)

| AREA | CONDITIONS | dB LEVEL |
|---|---|---|
| **Very Noisy** | | |
| Printing Dept | Difficult or impossible to be heard | 80 – 90 |
| Machine Shop | | 80 to 95 |
| Factory (Noisy) | | 90 to 100 |
| **Noisy** | | |
| Noisy Restaurant | Voice must be raised to be understood | 70 – 80 |
| Busy Office | | 70 to 75 |
| Auditorium | | 70 to 75 |
| Supermarket, Accounting Dept, Average Factory | | 65 to 80 |
| Average Assembly Line | | 70 to 75 |
| **Normal** | | |
| Hotel Lobby | Conversation is easily understood | 40 – 65 |
| Private Office, Quiet Office, Hospital | | 45 to 55 |
| Average Office | | 50 to 65 |
| Restaurant | | 50 to 65 |
| Bank | | 40 to 55 |
| Department Store | | 55 to 65 |
| **Quiet room** | | 20-30 |

### 6.3.3    Measuring Sound Levels

The unit of measurement is the decibel or dB, and sound measurements are usually made with a hand held sound level meter.

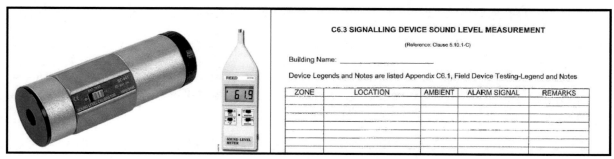

An important (and very interesting) factor of human hearing is that humans do not hear all frequencies equally. Both the low and high frequencies are more difficult for humans to hear, than are the mid-range frequencies. This means that humans will think that a high frequency sound is not as strong as a mid-range sound, whereas in reality both sounds may be of the same intensity if measured by a meter. Handheld meters therefore are capable of measuring sound intensities using two different scales. These two scales provide quite different results. The two scales are the 'A-weighted' scale and the 'C-weighted' scale.

The meter's 'A' scale reflects the reality of human hearing. It reacts to the different frequencies in much the same way as human hearing that does not perceive low frequencies (below about 20 Hz) or high frequencies (above about 16,000 Hz) frequencies to be as loud as those frequencies in between. This is the scale that should always be used in the fire alarm industry. The letter A should be used with the meter readings (i.e. 65 dBA) to indicate that the received sound pressure level has been measured on the 'A' scale of the meter.

The C-weighted scale reflects the true machine response to received sound levels, but is never used in our industry, because it does not reflect the reality of human hearing.

## Measurement Method

The handheld decibel (dB) meter should be held approximately 1.5 m above the floor and at least 0.5 m away from hard reflecting surfaces. The meter should also be held as far away as is comfortably practical from the body of the person taking the measurement. These precautions are to minimize the effects of reflected and absorbed sound waves.

The meter should be set to the A-weighted measurement scale. If the meter also has a fast/slow response selector switch, the switch should be on the fast response setting.

Sound-level meters must be used per the manufacturer's instructions. The types of measurements taken, may vary, and are dependant on the type of meter. Two common methods are described as follows:

Integrating Type Meter: An integrating type sound-level meter provides calculated Equivalent Sound Level (Leq) readings. The meter takes sample measurements once per second and over a 20-second sample period. If using this type of meter it is important that intermittent noises do not occur during the sample period; and

Non-Integrating Type Meter: This is the more common type of instrument. A non-integrating type sound level meter requires a series of separate measurements to be taken. It is recommended that four measurements be obtained. The average of the three closest readings should be recorded. Visual averaging of meter readings can be performed in lieu of the above.

The measurement should be made with a high quality sound level meter that is calibrated before any measurements are taken, in order to minimize dB measurement errors

## Selecting Locations for Sound-Level Readings

Readings should be taken near the centre of the occupied area where it would appear to be the most difficult for the alarm signals or voice messages to reach the occupants (the listeners). In the case of sound-level measurements in bedrooms, the suite selected for the sound measurements should be representative of the lowest anticipated fire alarm system audibility. This will generally be the suite with the greatest number of bedrooms, the one located at the far end of a corridor, the one located in the far corner of the building, or the one behind/beside the elevator.

Ambient sound level measurements should always be made at the same location as the measurement of the alarm signal and/or voice messages.

**LS devices in suite**

Wall-to-wall carpeting may also significantly reduce fire alarm audibility. It may be necessary to conduct exploratory measurements to identify the suite or suites that represent the lowest audibility levels in the building. The selected suite or suites should be fully furnished at the time of the tests. The sound level measurement should be made in the approximate centre of the most acoustically remote bedroom of the residential suite.

**Speaker in suite**

The suite door, bedroom door and any intervening doors must be closed. The measurements in the bedroom should be made within a 1 m radius of the centre of the room, although it must be noted that many AHJs hold the meter above the pillow

## Ambient Noise Level Measurements

When providing the sound level measurements for alarm signals, it is necessary to have corresponding ambient sound level measurements. Meaningful ambient sound level measurements are at times difficult to make. Precautions are necessary to achieve consistent ambient noise level measurements. Temporary or intermittent sound sources such as a flushing toilet, running shower, stereo, television, traffic or exterior construction noise may cause peaks in sound levels. The bedroom windows should be closed in order to minimize the affect of outdoor noise. Ambient noise level measurements should be recorded when these sounds are absent or are at their lowest level. The building heating, ventilating, and air conditioning (HVAC) system should be running during the test with the fan speed set on high. Portable air conditioners installed within the suite should be in the 'off' position during the tests. Occupants of the suite under test should refrain from talking or from other activities that may affect the readings. Measurements should be taken during a normal workday period.

### Loudness of Alarm Signals

To be effective, the fire alarm audible signals must be clearly heard by the building occupants. The general requirement found in the *Building Code* is that the alarm signal level must be at least 10 dBA above the ambient sound level, and must not be less than 65 dBA.

For example, if the ambient sound level is 58 dBA and the sound level with the alarms sounding is 70 dBA the requirement is met. If the ambient sound level is 40 dBA and the alarm signal sound level measured is 62 dBA the criteria is not met.

The *Building Code* requires that higher sound levels be produced in sleeping areas. The higher sound level is necessary to waken the occupants. The sound level in bedrooms (or other sleeping areas) must be at least 75 dBA with the bedroom door and any intervening doors closed. This higher decibel requirement, and the distance from the sound source, and the closed doors all significantly complicate the challenge of providing adequate fire alarm sound levels.

### 6.3.4    Sound Transmission Factors

Many factors affect the transmission or 'carry' of sound from the sound source to the occupants:

- The distance between the signal source and the listener.

- Barriers and obstructions to the travel of sound pressure waves such as walls and closed doors.

- The intensity of the background ambient sound levels

- The paths that the sound waves take between the source and the listener especially through doorways and around corners.

- Sound absorbing surfaces such as carpeting and drapes that can affect (reduce) the sound level by three to six decibels

Remember that the effect of these factors is cumulative!

©

## Sound Attenuation over Distance

A number of factors affect how the intensity of the received sound is reduced. The reduction of received sound is referred to as sound 'attenuation'. The distance between the source of the sound and the occupant is one of the major factors. The amount of attenuation due to distance is determined by a very common law of physics: the Inverse Square Law.

This law states that as the distance from the sound source increases, the received sound intensity is inversely proportional to the square of the distance. This means that as the distance from a sound source doubles, the received sound intensity is reduced to just one-quarter of that which was received at the original distance from the source.

The Resulting Rule of Thumb:

Double the Distance (further) produces One Quarter the Power   - 6dB

Half the Distance (closer)        produces Four times the power     + 6dB

As a result, the received sound level measured at 10 m from a signalling device will be 6 dB less (-6 dB) than that measured at 5 m from the device. It follows that the received sound level measured at 20 m from a signalling device will be 6 dB less (-6 dB) than that measured at 10 m from the device. Cumulatively, therefore, the received sound level at 20 m will be 12 dB less (-12 dB) than that measured at 5 m. Doubling the distance again, the received sound level at 40 m will be 18 dB less (-18 dB) than that measured at 5 m.

Here is how it works mathematically (remember that 'inversely' means '1' over = $1/x$):

At 3 m from the device, the received sound pressure level is 88 dBA. At 6 m from the device, the distance is doubled! The received sound level will be reduced by a factor of $1/D^2$ (where D is the relative distance from the sound source; in this case D = 2) = $1/2^2 = 1/4$, i.e. one quarter of the sound level received at the original location = -6 dB.

Therefore the received sound pressure level would be 88 less 6 dB = 82 dB.

The starting point for the system designer or installer is the audible signalling device itself. The manufacturer describes the sound pressure levels that are generated by a particular device. The industry standard distance from a signalling device, for measuring the rated output level, is 3 m (or 10 ft) from the device. A particular bell for example, might produce (and therefore be rated at) 88 dB measured at 3m. The manufacturer of each particular device provides this information. A speaker might produce an output level of 87 dB using a 1,000-Hz tone, on the one-watt tap, and measured at 3m. Given similar information for any audible device, the application designer can produce a device floor layout plan.

Instead of using the Inverse Square Law 'rule-of-thumb' discussed above, the designer can use a mathematical formula. This mathematical formula allows us to calculate the theoretical sound pressure level at any distance from the source of a sound, given that we know a reference sound pressure level at some other known distance from the same sound. The formula provides a greater degree of accuracy than does the 'rule-of-thumb' method.

The formula is $S2 = S1 + 20 \times \log (D1/D2)$ where:

- $S1$ (in dB) = Known reference sound pressure level, at distance $D1$ from a source of sound (Usually this is the dB sound level of the alarm signal at 3 meters, taken from the manufacturer's specification data sheet for the device.)

- $S2$ (in dB) = Unknown sound pressure level at a new distance $D2$ from the same source of sound

- $D1$ (in any units) = Measured distance between source of sound and known reference sound pressure level $S1$ (Usually this is 3 meters from the device, as derived from the specification data sheet for the device.)

- $D2$ (in same units as $D1$) = Distance between source of sound and unknown sound pressure level $S2$

Example: A bell produces 88dB measured at 3m. What would be the theoretical sound level received at a distance of 15m?

Therefore:  $S1 = 88dB$  $S2 = ?$
$D1 = 3m$  $D2 = 15m$

Solution:  $S2 = S1 + 20 \times \log (D1/D2)$
$S2 = 88 + 20 \times \log (D1/D2)$
$S2 = 88 + 20 \times \log (3/15)$
$S2 = 88 + 20 \times \log 0.6$
$S2 = 88 + 20 \times (-0.699)$
$S2 = 88 - 13.98$
$S2 = 74.02$
$S2 = 74$ dB (rounded to the closest whole unit)

Generally speaking, the inverse square law (-6dB) rule-of-thumb method is sufficiently accurate for our purposes. When distances are not exact multiples, the formula can be used.

©

## Sound Attenuation – Absorption

The barriers and obstructions, such as walls and closed doors, is another major factor in determining whether or not alarm sounds will be heard. Sound penetration from one area to another (from corridors to rooms as an example) depends very much on the construction of the building.

Modern buildings are purposely constructed with improved sound isolation between corridors and occupied areas. This results in significant attenuation from the location of the alarm signals located in corridors to the occupants in rooms or offices.

Close the door between the sound source and the listener, and the received sound level drops dramatically.

**Table 2: Intervening Material/structure**

|  | Average dBA Loss | Typical Range (dBA) |
|---|---|---|
| Open Door | 8 | 4 - 12 |
| Closed Hollow-core Door (typical bedroom door) | 17 | 10 - 24 |
| Closed Solid-core Door (typical residential suite entry door) | 28 | 22 - 34 |
| Single stud wall with gypsum board on both sides | 39 | 32 - 46 |
| 2 rows of studs staggered complete with gypsum board on both sides | 40 | 36 - 47 |
| 200 mm concrete, gypsum board on one side | 45 | 43 - 51 |
| 200 mm hollow concrete block, gypsum board on both sides | 40 | 39 - 47 |
| 300 mm masonry wall with gypsum board on both sides | 50 | 46 - 56 |

The transmission of sound as discussed here is the theoretical aspect. Actual conditions within different rooms or areas of a building can dramatically alter the received sound levels from those that were anticipated.

### 6.3.5    Achieving Audibility Requirements

The *Building Code* states the requirement that a minimum sound level for alert or alarm signals must be 10 dB above the ambient sound level. It also is required that the sound level must not be less than 65 dB. The *Building Code* also sets an upper limit or maximum sound level to which occupants can be exposed. The actual level will vary slightly depending on the shape and acoustical qualities of the area in which the signalling device is installed. In narrow areas (hallways) with reflective surfaces, the absorption loss will be minimal, whereas in rooms containing sound absorbing materials (e.g. carpets and furniture) the absorption loss will be greater.

Some types of ceiling construction allow high percentages of the sound to be absorbed by, or pass through, the ceiling material. Other ceiling materials reflect sound. The end-result is that sound levels in the corridors and/or associated rooms may vary widely, and may make the difference between acceptable or non-acceptable alarm sound levels.

Floor and wall assemblies and coverings greatly affect sound intensities. Marble or ceramic tile floors will reflect most sound whereas wood flooring will absorb some sound, and cushion-tile floors will absorb more. Carpeting will be even more absorptive, and bedroom thick-pile carpets will absorb the most sound. In a similar manner, different wall coverings will have an impact on sound absorption.

Lastly, the furniture in a suite or floor area will also have an affect on sound transmission. Comfortable leather or cloth materials will absorb far greater amounts of sound power than will wood or metal office furniture.

The result of the environmental impact on sound transmission is quite difficult to predict, and it varies from room to room. In addition to the distance losses, one might expect to lose a further 2 to 10 dB because of absorption in a firm environment, and as much as 10 to 20 dB in an absorptive environment. Besides, the absorption characteristics of a floor area can change as furniture or floor coverings are changed. The applications designer is wise to be conservative when designing the audible signal coverage, and should assume a worse case scenario.

In residential occupancies where people are sleeping, the sound level must be higher, and this presents greater challenges to the designer/installer. The sound level must be 75 decibels at the pillow in order to ensure that sleeping people are wakened.

To raise the sound output level of corridor appliances enough to penetrate into occupied areas would result in corridor sound pressure levels that could cause discomfort to people in the corridor. Building codes state that the maximum sound levels allowed in normally occupied areas is 100 dBA or 110 dBA depending on the jurisdiction.

©

A practical solution is to install signals (normal power) in all parts of the floor area (corridors and suites). Acceptable sound levels for separate bedrooms in a residential suite, would most readily be provided by in-suite signalling appliances.

Private offices off a general office will probably not receive acceptable sound levels, from corridor signals, with all doors closed. In this case, an audible device in the General Office would solve the problem.

## 6.4  Types Of Signals

There are several types of audible alarm signals. Audible signalling devices used in fire alarm system designs during the past many years have included Vibrating Bells, Single Stroke Bells, Horns, Chimes, Sirens and Speakers.

### 6.4.1  Comparative Sound Intensities of Different Devices

| Signalling Device | Typical Output at 3 Metres |
|---|---|
| Horn – Mechanical | 92 |
| Horn - Electronic | 96 |
| Bell – Solenoid | 85 |
| Bell – Motor | 92 |
| Chime - Electronic | 83 |
| Multiple tone - Electronic | 100 |
| Mini-Horn – Piezo | 90 |

A vibrating bell sounds continuously as long as electrical power is applied. It is the fire alarm system device most commonly used over the past several years. It is available in six-inch and ten-inch diameter sizes, with selection determined by sound level output requirements.

A single-stroke bell is identical in appearance to the vibrating bell but produces sound only once each time electrical power is applied. The power must be applied in pulses to provide the alarm signal.

A horn or klaxon is an electro-mechanical signal that produces a harsh vibrating sound as long as electrical power is applied. Usually, horns produce a louder sound than bells.

A chime is a quieter signal that in operation is similar to a single stroke bell. Being quieter, it has found usage most often in health-care facilities.

A siren is an extremely loud signal used to overcome high ambient noise conditions or for outdoor use. Actual motor driven sirens now are seldom used, although a siren tone is often used with speaker-type signals

A speaker is an electro-mechanical device designed to reproduce voice or tones. These may be cone-type speakers or horn-type speakers.

## 6.4.2   How They Work

### Vibrating Bell

A bell is a sounding device comprising an electro-mechanical or electro-magnetically operated plunger that strikes a sound-producing component called a 'gong'. When struck, the gong vibrates, thereby producing a ringing sound. The design, construction and application are further described because of some unique fire alarm considerations.

The design of a bell is best understood as a three-part assembly: the mechanism, the housing and the gong. The mechanism is the active electro-mechanical part and is electrically connected to the Fire Alarm System Control Unit. It comprises a coil, or pair of coils controlling a metallic plunger, and an interrupting electrical contact.

The normal operating power for fire alarm systems is 24 Volts D.C. When it is applied to the bell, the coil becomes energized and this causes the plunger to be driven against 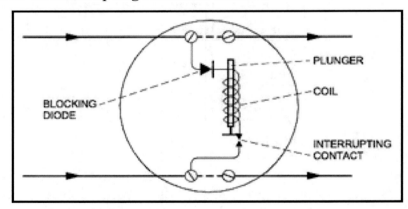 the gong, producing a single sharp sound. The interrupting contact operates at the same time as the plunger and disconnects the applied power from the coil. The coil then de-energizes, allowing the plunger to return to its rest position, and the interrupter contact to close. This allows the entire process to repeat as long as power remains applied to the bell. The repetitive action causes a continuous ringing. Because of the moving plunger, bells may be sensitive to mounting orientation.

A diode is installed in series with the coil and it operates as a current gate for purposes of electrical supervision. It blocks the supervisory current when the power supply is connected in one direction but allows alarm power to flow and operate the bell when the power supply is connected in the opposite polarity.

The housing for the bell is the rigid foundation for the complete bell. The housing is sufficiently large to contain the mechanism and the plunger. It includes provision for mounting the gong and also for fastening the entire assembly to the electrical outlet wall box. The housing is usually located behind the gong.

The gong is generally made of a special steel alloy, which produces a loud resonant sound when struck by the plunger. It is the vibration of the circular edge of the gong that generates the sound.

## Single Stroke Bells

Single stroke bells are constructed similarly to vibrating bells but without the electrical interrupting contact. Each time power of the correct polarity is applied, the solenoid plunger moves to strike the gong. In order to provide an alarm signal, power must be applied as a series of pulses.

## Mechanical Chimes

Mechanical chimes (sometimes used as an Alert Signal but not as an Alarm Signal) are constructed similarly to single-stroke bells except that a chime bar is used instead of a gong. Each time power of the correct polarity is applied, the solenoid plunger moves to strike the chime bar. In order to provide an audible signal, power must be applied as a series of pulses.

## Mechanical Horns (Klaxons)

Mechanical horns are somewhat similar to vibrating bells. In this case when power of the correct polarity is applied, the electrical coil magnetizes and distorts a metal diaphragm. The movement of the diaphragm opens the electrical contact and disconnects the applied power from the coil. It de-energizes, allowing the metal diaphragm to return to its rest position and the interrupter contact to close. This causes the entire process to repeat as long as the power remains applied to the mechanical horn. The repetitive action causes a continuous noise.

## Motorized Bells

Motorized bells have a small motor rather than a plunger, coil and contact mechanism. When power of the correct polarity is applied, the motor shaft spins and causes small metal strikers to repetitively hit the gong.

## Electronic Horn Sirens

Electronic horn sirens use a speaker as the sounding element but have an internal circuit board that generates the siren tone. When dc power of the correct polarity is applied the devices sound. The audible sound may be the temporal pattern of alarm sound. Because the unit provides the tone circuits internally and is dc powered the device is equipped with a series diode to achieve placement supervision.

## Piezo electric signal

When power is applied to a piezo crystal it distorts and produces a high pitched sound pulse. An electronic oscillator circuit in the signalling device causes the crystal to continuously sound when dc power of the correct polarity is connected. These devices are equipped with a series diode to achieve placement supervision.

## Cone Speakers

Cone speakers are most commonly used for fire alarm systems. An amplifier in the fire alarm control unit provides the signal that drives the speaker. Cone speakers use a firm paper or other flexible phenolic-impregnated material for the diaphragm, which is supported on a metallic frame. The permanent magnet and the voice coil are also fastened to the frame.

An impedance matching transformer is mounted on the frame and this transformer is used to match the impedance of the speaker (typically eight ohms) to the fire alarm signal amplifier output circuit to ensure that operating voltages, currents and speaker loading are efficiently balanced. This allows for speakers to be added in the future without affecting the circuit impedance seen by the amplifier.

The entire assembly is then mounted onto a metal or plastic baffle, which is perforated to allow sound penetration. It is then fastened to a wall or ceiling back-box. The baffle must allow sound penetration while at the same time preventing foreign objects such as pens or sticks from damaging the internals of the speaker.

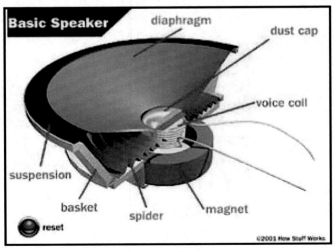

©

The electrical output of an amplifier passes through the transformer to the voice coil of the speaker and produces varying magnetic forces in the coil. These magnetic forces alternately drive the coil forward and backward in rapid vibrations. The diaphragm, which is connected to the voice coil, vibrates with it. The vibrations of the diaphragm produce vibrations in the air. The ear hears these air vibrations as sound.

Unlike other fire alarm signals, speakers have a matching transformer that provides various output sound levels depending on the tap setting used. The tap setting will also determine the amount of amplifier power required to achieve that sound level. Such transformers typically provide taps with the following ratings: ¼ watt, ½ watt, 1 watt, 2 watt, 4 watt, and 8 watt. These taps allow the sound level output to be increased or decreased as needed to suit the ambient noise level of the protected room or area. Note that because the tap settings are in multiples of 2 (getting larger) or ½ (getting smaller) then the output sound will differ by +3dB (getting louder) or –3dB (getting quieter.)

Since speakers are driven by AC signals from the amplifier, speakers cannot be placement supervised by using diodes. Instead, a

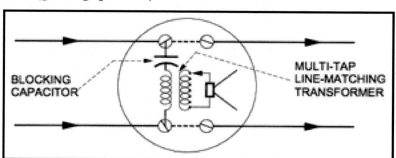

capacitor blocks the DC supervisory current flowing from the Control Unit. However, the capacitor allows the AC tones (ALERT/ALARM) and voice messages to pass through to the coil of the speaker.

A broad frequency response is not desirable for voice-only applications such as Fire Alarm Systems. The speaker (and the associated amplifiers) should operate over only the voice range of frequencies with a minimum of distortion. Distortion is a measure of the fidelity of reproduction - that is, how closely the output sound matches the input sound. Any distortion reduces the intelligibility of the voice message. Amplifiers and speakers for Fire Alarm Systems should have a reasonably flat frequently response of approximately 400 Hz to 4,000 Hz.

### Re-entrant Horn Speakers

Horn speakers operate and are placement-supervised in a similar manner to cone speakers. The difference is that the large paper cone diaphragm is replaced with a smaller flexible metal diaphragm. The sound from the diaphragm is coupled to a horn shaped chamber that has a larger opening at the opposite end. This type of speaker mechanism is capable of providing much higher output sound levels, and usually operates at higher efficiencies The horn speaker is also more directional. Usual power ratings for this type of speaker are 1 watt, 2 watt, 4 watt, 8 watt, and 16 watt, using line-matching transformers. These speakers are designed with stronger materials, enabling the use of higher wattages, and they are normally used in larger open areas or high-noise confined areas.

**Typical Speaker Sound Intensity Levels at Different Tap Settings**

| Tap Setting | Intensity Level at 3 Metres |
|:---:|:---:|
| 8w | 96dB |
| 4w | 93dB |
| 2w | 90dB |
| 1w | 87dB |
| 1/2w | 84dB |
| 1/4w | 81dB |
| 1/8w | 78dB |

The foregoing figures should not be surprising because we have already learned that doubling the power of a sound increases it by only + 3 dB. Doubling from a ½ watt tap to a 1 watt tap shows a + 3 dB increase.

### 6.4.3    General Requirements for Signals

Each audible signal device must be provided with suitable terminals or integral leads for connection to the signal circuit wiring. In either case, four termination points must be provided so that the installer uses two for the connection of incoming conductors and two for outgoing conductors. In this manner, the signalling device is said to be 'placement supervised'. Placement supervision means that it must not be possible for a device to be removed from the circuit wiring without the action causing a trouble condition on the Control Unit. Each of the mechanical devices is equipped with a series diode to achieve placement supervision.

©

Speaker signalling devices utilize a capacitor to achieve placement supervision.

Any audible signal appliance must be capable of operating properly when the voltage of the supply circuit is either ten percent more or twenty percent less than the normal rated voltage of the appliance. Any audible signal appliance must be able to operate continuously at its rated voltage without malfunctioning or without any manifestation of a hazardous condition.

Additional details relate to signal appliances intended for outdoor application and include such requirements as the need for anti-corrosion protection and weatherproofing.

Audible signal devices for use in hazardous locations are judged on the basis of their compliance with appropriate examinations and tests to determine that they are suitable for the intended purpose. If so, they are identified accordingly.

Each signal appliance must be plainly and permanently marked in a location readily visible and this marking must include:

- the manufacturer's name or trademark,

- the catalogue or model number,

- the electrical rating including voltage, frequency, and current,

- the position in which the appliance should be installed (usually only vertically), and

- further information as applicable, indicating its suitability for outdoor mounting.

The sound output levels are included in the manufacturers device specification sheet.

## 6.5    Temporal Pattern of Sound

The *Building Code* has established that new Fire Alarm Systems have a standard recognizable sound pattern for the evacuation alarm signal. It is called the Temporal Alarm Signal. The phrase 'temporal pattern' refers to a timing sequence that can apply to any sound. For example, vibrating bells can be pulsed in a temporal pattern. The 1,000-Hz alarm tone being generated by system speakers can be pulsed in a temporal pattern. Similarly, the temporal pattern can apply to the 'whoop' sounds produced by speakers

The use of the temporal pattern of alarm sound is an attempt to standardize on an audible signal that building occupants will

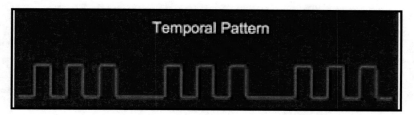

Temporal Pattern

recognize no matter where they might be. Because the actual sounds will be different from building to building, the pattern of the sound is the only available means at our disposal to produce some type of consistency.

The temporal pattern of an alarm signal relates to the time intervals between the individual signal pulses. The characteristic of the pattern is a three-pulse phase followed by an 'off/silent' phase followed by another three-pulse phase, and etc. The three-pulse phases each consist of three half-second 'on' pulses separated by half-second 'off' periods. The three-pulse phase is followed by an 'off' phase lasting for 1.5 seconds. The entire cycle is then repeated. The precise duration of the pulses is not critical - the important part of this is the general pattern of three pulses followed by silence followed by three pulses, and continuing.

## 6.6    Application Notes for Signalling Devices

When a Fire Alarm System is required in any portion of a building, it must be installed so that the sound from the audible signal appliances will be heard throughout all floors of the building. This means that a sufficient quantity of audible signal appliances must be installed in all corridors, rooms and in such other locations as may be required, and that they should be sufficiently loud so as to be clearly audible and recognized by all occupants within the floor area served by the appliances.

The audible signalling appliances should be used only for the purpose of signalling an emergency condition, and the alert and alarm signals must be readily distinguishable from each other, and from other signals, which may be in the building. The same sound should be used throughout the building to avoid confusion that would result if different signals were used in different parts of the building.

Sound pressure levels in a sleeping room from a fire alarm audible signalling device must be not less than 75dB in a building of residential occupancy when any intervening doors between the device and the sleeping room are closed.

In floor areas used for other than residential occupancies, the sound shall be not less than 10dB above the ambient noise level, but with a minimum value not less than 65dB.

Usually, better sound distribution can be achieved by carefully positioning a greater quantity of lower-power appliances than a lesser quantity of higher-power appliances. When speakers are used for voice communication the system should be capable of providing clear undistorted messages. Good intelligibility of the system requires more speakers with closer spacing.

Even though no industry figures are available, mounting signal appliances inside flush wall boxes with grilles, or mounting them above drop ceilings will dramatically reduce the resultant sound levels in the occupied areas, and a greater concentration of signal appliances will be required to produce the necessary sound levels.

©

The systems design engineer must carefully calculate the loss of sound level strength caused by the inverse square law. Doubling the distance from a signal will theoretically cause a 6dB reduction in the received sound pressure level.

The actual level will vary slightly depending on the shape and acoustical qualities of the area. In narrow areas (hallways) with reflective surfaces, the reduction will be less than the theoretical loss, whereas in open areas or areas with many sound absorbing materials (carpets/rugs/soft furniture) the reduction will be greater.

Sound penetration from one area to another, corridors to rooms as an example, depends very much on the construction of the building. Modern buildings are constructed with much improved sound isolation between corridors and occupied areas and this results in poor sound penetration from corridor-mounted alarm signalling devices. Any solid door will reduce the level of sound penetrating into a room by 22 to 34 dB. To raise the sound output level of corridor appliances enough to penetrate into occupied areas would result in corridor sound pressure levels that could exceed allowable maximums, and cause discomfort to people in the corridor.

The cone type speaker generally has a broader frequency range and higher fidelity (less distortion) than horn type speakers. The cone type speaker however cannot handle as much power (practical limit of about 4 to 8 watts) without introducing too much distortion. The horn speaker can handle much higher dB output and is more useful for high-ambient-noise areas such as industrial plants, garages and large open or outdoor areas.

The quantity of speakers needed for a particular area, corridor or room will depend upon many important factors including the area dimensions, ceiling height, the type of ceiling tiles, wall and floor coverings, furniture, doors and etc. The designer/installer should be aware that system sound levels in an empty vacant area would be between 5 and 10dB higher than the sound levels in the same room or area after it is furnished.

Audible signal appliances must be mounted so that the top of the device will be not less than 2300 mm above the floor level.

An interesting note relating to sound coverage and device location is the difference in sound directivity. The majority of sound produced by a bell radiates outwards from the circumference of the bell. (This is because the bell gong is fastened to the bell mechanism by a centre mounted gong bolt, which inhibits that center part of the gong from vibrating). On the other hand, a speaker projects most of its sound output power towards the front of the device. Therefore, speakers might best be installed at the end of a room or corridor, whereas a bell might best be installed on a sidewall.

## 6.7    Residential Occupancies

This problem of off-corridor audibility is far more serious in buildings of residential occupancy, where greater sound levels are necessary to awaken residents. This is because the main suite entry door is a fire-rated closure that will absorb perhaps 22 to 34 dB of alarm sound, and the bedroom door will absorb perhaps 10 to 24 dB. Current building codes require a minimum of 75 dB in the bedroom with all intervening doors closed. It is very difficult to achieve this level with only corridor signals.

In addition to this attenuation of sound, suites are furnished and carpeted, and have wall coverings - all of which absorb sound.

The *Building Code* further requires that an audible signalling device within a dwelling unit must have a switch to silence the sound for a period not to exceed 10 minutes, after which the device must revert to normal (make sound again if the Fire Alarm System remains in alarm condition). Alternatively, the *Building Code* requires the audible signalling devices within a dwelling unit be wired on a separate circuit from the corridor and common area signals on the floor and the 10 minute silencing timer for the in-suite signals to be controlled by the fire alarm control unit. In this case the in suite switch is not required.

Where silencing switches are separately installed or incorporated in the audible signalling device, the silencing means must be clearly identified and located not less than 1200 mm and not more than 1400 mm above the finished floor level measured from the centre of the silencing switch.

In addition, such a device must be connected into the fire alarm system in such a manner that disconnection of, or damage to, the device will not interfere with the ability of devices to sound an alarm on the same circuit that serves other dwelling units, public corridors or suites.

If signal circuit fault isolators are used to isolate faults within the suite so that they do not affect other suite signals or audible signals in the corridor, the signal circuit fault isolators must be installed in the corridor outside of the suite. Signal circuit fault isolators must be installed so that they are visible for testing during verification and annual testing.

## 6.8 Visual Signalling Devices

Visual signals are required where there are hearing-impaired occupants, and in high-noise areas. The *Building Code* requires

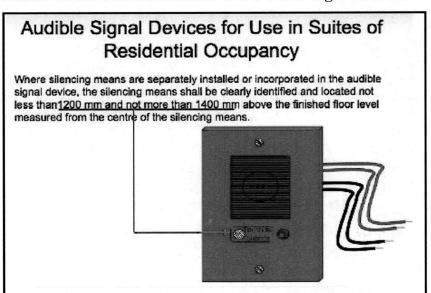

**Audible Signal Devices for Use in Suites of Residential Occupancy**

Where silencing means are separately installed or incorporated in the audible signal device, the silencing means shall be clearly identified and located not less than 1200 mm and not more than 1400 mm above the finished floor level measured from the centre of the silencing means.

©

that visual signal devices must supplement the audible signal appliances in areas where the ambient sound levels exceed 87 dB, or where the occupants of the floor area use hearing protective devices, are located within an audiometric booth, or are located within sound insulated enclosures. This requirement also applies if, in assembly occupancy, music or other sounds related to a performance could exceed 100 dB.

Building codes are moving towards having more visual alarm devices, and some provincial jurisdictions have imposed additional requirements for inclusion of strobes in various occupancies. It is important to confirm the local requirements for these devices.

## 6.8.1 Types of Visual Signals

Visual signals for occupant evacuation must always be in addition to a full complement of audible signalling devices.

The visible signals used in fire alarm system designs include strobe lights, rotating beacons and FIRE-DO NOT ENTER signs

- Strobe lights produce a brilliant flash of high candlepower. Strobes have no moving parts and therefore, most models on the market are reliable solid-state devices requiring little maintenance. Strobes are often used today because of their small size, ease of installation, DC power capability and reliability.

- Rotating reflecting lights tend to be more readily seen because of the sweeping affect. Rotating reflecting lights are usually motor driven, sealed-beam, 360° revolving lights ranging from 50 to 150 candle-power. The dome is made of red plastic or glass.

- The FIRE - DO NOT ENTER sign is usually constructed similarly to an exit light fixture with the words illuminated in either a flashing or a steady mode. This device is normally used to keep people from entering a building or portion of a building complex that is in a fire situation.

## 6.8.2 Application

It is naturally quite difficult to follow any set rules concerning visual signals. Each situation should be treated individually in order to design the best possible system for the particular requirement. In all buildings a careful study should be made to determine which type of visual signal is best for the areas to be protected.

The light output power of strobes is measured in Candela. Effective Candela rating is based on both the peak intensity of the light and the duration of the flash. This measurement should not be confused with the terms peak candela or peak candlepower.

The measurement terms "foot-candles" and "lumens" consider both Candela and the distance from the strobe to the location of interest.

Illumination = Candela (intensity)/distance.

The light output of strobes is not equal in all directions. This is referred to as the dispersion angle. The intensity reduces as one moves off the main centre axis.

The colour of the lens on a strobe also affects the light output. If a strobe is fitted with a white lens with a relative light output of 100 percent, an amber lens on the same strobe would provide only 70 to 100%, a blue lens 35 to 70% and a red lens 25 to 40%. This is why most fire alarm strobes are white.

When visual signal appliances are required, they should be installed in such a manner that at least one visual signal appliance is visible to every person in the room or area. They should be installed such that they can be seen either directly or indirectly by reflection.

Strobes have very significant power requirements and care should be used to ensure the fire alarm control equipment provides sufficient power capacity. Most fire alarm panels have two output circuits one for audible signals and one for strobes.

Visual signal devices also have mounting height requirements that dramatically differ from audible signal devices. *CAN/ULC S524 Installation of Fire Alarm Systems* details the mounting height for strobes. The entire lens of the strobe must be between 2000 and 2400 mm above the floor. The standard also identifies the mounting height when the signalling device is a combination audible and visual signal.

Visual signals each have a defined area of coverage and cannot be less than 15 Candela.

Strobes can be wall or ceiling mounted. The number of strobes needed for any given area, is based upon candela rating, ceiling height and the area to be covered.

©

All areas of a room must receive sufficient light output. *CAN/ULC S524* has a table for wall-mounted strobes that lists various room sizes and the required candela for one strobe or alternatively multiple strobes. Where one visual signal is not sufficient the correct mounting locations are based on the premise that the room space is sub-divided into multiple squares.

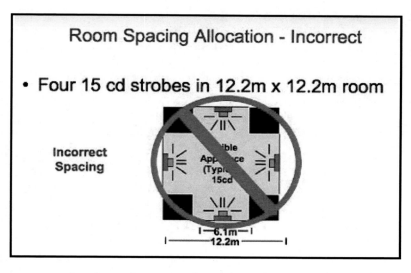

*CAN/ULC S524* also has a table for ceiling mounted strobes that lists the area of coverage and the required candela.

Corridor installations require strobes to be located no more than 4.6 m from the end of a corridor with additional strobes installed no more than 30 m apart. If a door interrupts the viewing path, or if there is a jog in the corridor consider each section of the corridor as a separate corridor with additional strobes. Wall mounted strobes can be mounted on either the end wall or the sidewall of the corridor.

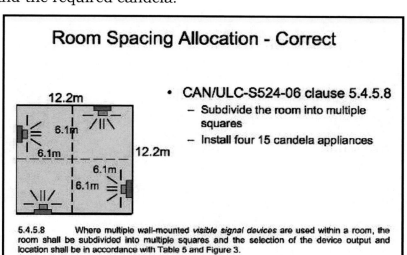

Where two or more visual signals are installed in corridors or rooms, and are located in the same field of view, the flashing of the devices must be synchronized. There are two methods of 'syncing' visual devices: using an external sync module connected onto the signalling circuit, or the sync protocol is built into the Control Unit so that an external module is not required. Sync methods are designed to operate strobes only, or combination audible and visual signalling devices. Not all strobes and strobe sync modules or circuits are compatible. Care must be taken to ensure compatibility.

©

## 6.9    Chapter Summary

1.    Over the years, many Fire Alarm System installations failed to achieve acceptable levels of audibility. Most often this is because signalling devices have been installed only in corridors and the sound does not penetrate into the bedrooms of the residential suite, or inner offices.

2.    The *Building Code* is the document that stipulates the level of audibility that must be achieved by the system.

3.    The deciBel or dB is the standard unit of measurement of sound pressure levels that is based on the logarithmic scale. It is a comparison of two sound levels. For example, a sound that is twice as loud as another, is +3dB greater than the other.

4.    The inverse-square law applies to the transmission of sound. Using this tool, we are able to accurately estimate the received sound levels at various distances from the source.

5.    Various structural elements (such as walls, doors, carpeting) will have a great negative effect on the value of received sound.

6.    Signalling devices must contain a method of connection to the two-wire circuit such that the device can be placement-supervised as well as receive alarm power.

7.    The placement of visible signalling devices is often much different than the layout of audibles.

8.    Audible devices in residential occupancies are allowed to have a silencing method the causes them to resound after a 10-minute period of silence.

9.    The majority of the sound produced by a bell radiates outwardly to the sides away from the vibrating gong. On the other hand, most speaker sound comes directly from the front.

10.    Measuring and recording the received sound levels during an Annual Inspection is critically important.

## 6.10    Review Questions

| # | ? | Question | Section |
|---|---|----------|---------|
| 6-1 | | **Where two or more visual signals are installed in corridors or rooms, and are located in the same field of view, the flashing of the devices must be _____** | |
| | A | Non-Synchronized | |
| | B | Flashing at different rates to alert the occupants | |
| | C | Flashing alternately to alert the occupants | |
| | D | Synchronized | |
| 6-2 | | **This device is normally used to keep people from entering a building or portion of a building complex that is in a fire situation.** | |
| | A | Fire Alarm Annunciator | |
| | B | Graphic User Interface | |
| | C | FIRE - DO NOT ENTER sign | |
| | D | Printer | |
| 6-3 | | **The Building Code requires that visual signal devices must supplement the audible signal appliances in areas where the ambient sound levels exceed _____** | |
| | A | 107 dBA | |
| | B | 87 dBA | |
| | C | 75 dBA | |
| | D | 65 dBA | |
| 6-4 | | **Where silencing switches are separately installed or incorporated in the audible signaling device, the silencing means must be clearly identified and located not less than _____ and not more than _____ above the finished floor (AFF) level measured from the centre of the silencing switch.** | |
| | A | 1200 mm and not more than 1400 mm AFF | |
| | B | 1100 mm and not more than 1500 mm AFF | |
| | C | 1000 mm and not more than 1600 mm AFF | |
| | D | 900 mm and not more than 1700 mm AFF | |

©

| 6-5 | | In floor areas used for other than residential occupancies, the sound shall be not less than ____dBA above the ambient noise level, but with a minimum value not less than ____dBA. | |
|------|---|---|---|
| | A | 10dBA   65dBA | |
| | B | 15dBA   60dBA | |
| | C | 10dBA   75dBA | |
| | D | 15dBA   55dBA | |
| 6-6 | | Each audible signal device must be provided with suitable terminals or integral leads for connection to the signal circuit wiring. In either case, how many termination points must be provided? | |
| | A | One | |
| | B | Two | |
| | C | Three | |
| | D | Four | |
| 6-7 | | The electrical output of an amplifier passes through the transformer to the voice coil of the device and produces varying magnetic forces in the coil. This sentence describes a: | |
| | A | Piezo electronic buzzer | |
| | B | Bell | |
| | C | Speaker | |
| | D | All of the above | |
| 6-8 | | Single stroke bells are constructed similarly to vibrating bells but with one key exception. | |
| | A | no electrical interrupting contact are provided | |
| | B | They are not red | |
| | C | They have a plastic bell shell | |
| | D | They only work on AC supply voltage | |
| 6-9 | | On a Vibrating bell the diode is installed in _____ with the coil and it operates as a current gate for purposes of electrical supervision. | |
| | A | An open position | |
| | B | Series-parallel | |
| | C | parallel | |
| | D | Series | |

| 6-10 | | The industry standard distance from a signaling device, for measuring the rated output level, is at what distance from the device. | |
|------|---|---|---|
| | A | 0 meters | |
| | B | 3 meters | |
| | C | 6 meters | |
| | D | 9 meters | |

©

# Chapter 7: Control Equipment

## 7.1 Chapter Overview and Key Concepts

The main purpose of a Fire Alarm System is to warn people of a fire condition; the overall design criteria are to ensure continuing reliability.

The use of approved/listed devices, with the proper installation methods and materials helps to ensure continuing reliability.

Class B wiring helps to ensure that if any connected field device is disconnected, or any field wiring fault (ground, open, short) develops, the Control Unit will automatically respond with an appropriate message.

The provision of back-up power is of the utmost importance. Such back-up power usually comes from a rechargeable battery, however it may instead come from a generator and battery combination.

Many systems today are based upon addressable-device technology, and serial data communications. The advantages include reduced system wiring costs, yet greater flexibility in the monitoring and control of field devices and ancillary systems.

**Dust on battery**

**Factory test**

## 7.2 Learning Objectives

Upon successful completion of this chapter, the reader should be able to:

- Draw a block diagram of a complete Fire Alarm System

- Describe how a Class B circuit achieves device-placement supervision

- Discuss the three levels of current flow in a Class B circuit

- Describe the role of Supervisory device circuits

- Understand how to size the back-up power capability

- Explain how processor-based communications can help to reduce installation costs

- Describe the possible negatives of a processor-based system

## Language defined - Chapter Glossary (Also see Main Glossary)

Terms that are important to the understanding of this chapter are included below. For a complete listing of such words, expressions and terms, refer to the Main Glossary near the end of this manual. This glossary is not intended to replace or supercede any officially published glossary. It is simply our intent that these be used as a training aid in understanding the contents of this manual. Always refer to the specific code or standard, and to the Authority Having Jurisdiction for the applicable official interpretation.

| Term | Definition |
|------|------------|
| **Active Field Device** | A device that can be uniquely identified by the control unit to determine its presence and operating status, and which may be commanded to operate or to change its operating parameters independently of other field devices that share a common circuit |
| **Addressable Device** | A device that can be individually and uniquely identified by a control unit. The address is set using binary/hexadecimal/decimal methods using dipswitches, rotary switches or solid-state memory |
| **Alarm Signal** | An audible signal transmitted throughout a zone or zones to advise occupants that a fire emergency exists; also called an EVACUATION signal |
| **Alert Signal** | An audible signal intended to advise designated persons of a fire emergency |
| **Ancillary Device** | A device that performs a life safety related function, but that is not part of the fire alarm system |
| **Control Unit** | A device with the necessary circuits or components needed to provide acceptable operating power for a fire alarm system, receive signals from alarm initiating devices, cause audible alarm signals to operate, and electrically monitor the installation wiring and device placement against certain faults and/or removal |
| **Conventional Field Device** | A field device that is usually connected to a control unit and/or transponder on a common wiring circuit with other devices so that all devices on the circuit provide a common status change information (e.g. fire alarm detection or signalling). Such devices cannot be uniquely identified by a control unit and/or transponder unless there is only one device on the circuit. (Refer to active field device) |
| **Electromagnetic Door Release** | A device used to hold doors in the open position, and to release the doors to close automatically when signaled to do so by a fire alarm system or other means |

| Term | Definition |
| --- | --- |
| **Exit** | A facility such as a door, stairs or ramp that leads from the floor area that it serves to an open public thoroughfare, or to a protected exterior open space that has access to an open public thoroughfare. Once in an exit facility, a person should have a continuous path leading to the building exterior |
| **Fire Alarm System** | A system comprising both manually operated devices and automatic fire detectors, alarm signaling devices and a control unit, all electrically interconnected in order to detect fire conditions and to warn the occupants of the building |
| **Floor Area** | The space on any storey of a building between the exterior walls and required firewalls, including the space occupied by interior walls and partitions, but not including exits and vertical service spaces that pierce the storey |
| **Ground Fault** | A circuit impedance to ground sufficient to prevent normal operation |
| **Open-Circuit Fault** | Means a circuit series resistance increase of 10 kOhm or more, unless otherwise stated, resulting from an abnormal condition |
| **Short-Circuit Fault** | A resistance shunt of 0.1 Ohm or less across a circuit, unless otherwise stated, resulting from an abnormal condition |
| **Sprinkler Supervision** | A method of electrically monitoring critical elements of an automatic sprinkler system to detect potentially disabling abnormal conditions, and provide a warning signal |
| **Supporting Field Device** | An active field device that monitors other field devices on a separate circuit and reports the status of that separate circuit to the control unit |
| **Trouble Signal** | A signal (usually a buzzer and an amber lamp) indicating a fault or an off-normal condition in a fire alarm system |

## 7.3  General

The basic purpose of a Fire Alarm System is to receive information or a command from an alarm-initiating device, and then translate that command into a recognizable, understandable signal (using audible, as well as visible devices), thus warning building occupants of the fire condition.

The alarm system may be designed to indicate the exact location within the building from which the alarm was initiated. It may be designed to indicate a preliminary alarm condition or a serious fire requiring evacuation of the building. It may be desirable to have the alarm system shut down the building air-handling systems, or automatically send an alarm report to the nearby fire department or other recognized monitoring centre. Smoke dampers may be operated, and fire doors closed in order to inhibit the movement of smoke-laden air from the fire zone to other sections of the building. Quite commonly, air-pressurization fans are used to maintain tenable conditions within stairwell shafts and elevator shafts.

Fire Alarm Systems comprise many varied components such as manual stations, automatic heat detectors, sprinkler alarm and supervisory switches, smoke detectors, extinguishing system alarm and supervisory contacts, audible signal devices, electro-magnetic door-hold-open devices, annunciators, indicating lights, and a control unit. These items must always work together to perform the primary function of a Fire Alarm System – warn the occupants.

Fire Alarm Systems are electrical systems, and therefore all components are connected together with electrical conductors. They are powered by building electrical power and have, as a standby or secondary source, either a battery, or both a battery and a generator.

A solid understanding of a Fire Alarm System Control Unit is best developed by considering the many operational features as belonging to five distinct groupings:

**Common control**

- Input section (initiating device circuits)
- Output section (signaling device circuits)
- Control section (ancillary functions)
- Common Features section
- Power Supply section

### 7.3.1    Electrical Supervision Of Field Wiring – Conventional Circuits

We have already stated that the primary operational function of a fire alarm system is to sound the alarm. At the same time the primary product design criteria is reliability. Individual components may be properly designed and manufactured, but will perform their functions only as long as they are properly installed and suitably maintained. In a conventional system, electrical supervision of conductors is used to ensure that the components remain properly connected to the circuit conductors, and that all wiring remains intact and properly connected to the Control Unit. All field devices must be connected to the field wiring in such a way that devices cannot be disconnected from the wiring without causing a 'trouble' condition to be initiated on the Control Unit. This feature is referred to as 'placement supervision' of the field devices.

The purpose of electrical supervision is also to detect any abnormal condition in the Fire Alarm System field wiring that could compromise the integrity of the system.  This includes detection of open-circuit faults, short-circuit faults and ground faults. Any such abnormal condition must initiate a 'trouble' condition so that it will be brought to the attention of building maintenance and/or supervisory personnel. This result is known as a trouble condition on the Control Unit. It is also characterized by an audible and visual 'system trouble' indication at the annunciator (at the main entrance or designated fire department response point).  The Control Unit usually also has a trouble output to transmit a signal to a Fire Signal Receiving Centre.

## Class 'B' Circuits - Conventional

The vast majority of Fire Alarm Systems utilize 'Class B', two-wire circuits, terminating at an end-of-line device. 'Class B' circuits are two-wire circuits that electrically connect field devices to the Control Unit. The two-wire circuit leaves the Control Unit and connects to the first field device. Two wires leave that device and connect to the next device that is to be part of the same circuit. When there are no more devices to be connected to that circuit, two wires leave the last initiating or signaling device and connect to the end-of-line device.

Control Unit circuitry (and the associated end-of-line device) is designed to ensure that a relatively small amount of electrical current flows through the two conductors of the continuous two-wire circuit connecting the field initiating devices to the Control Unit. The current flows out over one conductor, through the end-of-line device, then back to the Control Unit over the second conductor. Under normal conditions this current flows continuously, and it is called the 'circuit supervisory' current. This is a typical 'Class B' circuit.

All field devices are either 'open-contact' devices (such as manual stations and heat detectors), or they present a high impedance to supervisory current flow (such as smoke detectors), or they contain a supervisory-current blocking device such as in bells (diodes) and speakers (capacitors). The supervisory current therefore cannot easily pass through the individual field device, and the circuit supervisory current is therefore forced to flow to the end of the circuit, pass through the end-of-line device and return via the second conductor to the Control Unit.

In the event of an open-circuit condition on a Class 'B' circuit, the Control Unit will sense that the supervisory current is too low (in the case of an open-circuit the current is zero) and it must initiate a trouble condition.

In the event of a short-circuit condition on a signal circuit, the Control Unit will detect that the supervisory circuit current is too high and it must initiate a trouble condition.

Initiating-device circuits not only monitor for the presence of current but they also measure the relative value of current in order to make the following assessment:

- Alarm Condition - a high level of current that exceeds the upper or maximum level of normal current.

- Normal Condition - a nominal current level. This is not a specific finite value but a range of current from a definite minimum to a definite maximum, defined as within normal operating parameters for that particular Control Unit.

- Trouble Condition - a low level of current that is less than the lower or minimum level of normal current.

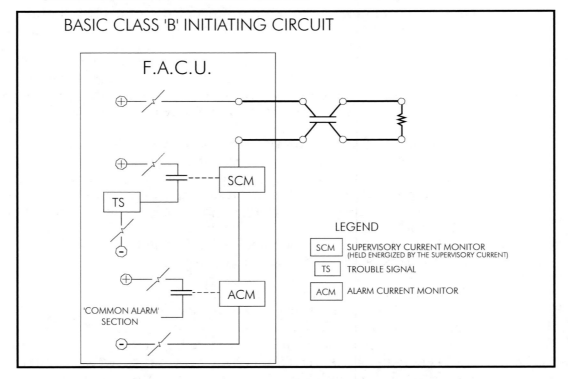

BASIC CLASS 'B' INITIATING CIRCUIT

F.A.C.U.

LEGEND

SCM  SUPERVISORY CURRENT MONITOR
(HELD ENERGIZED BY THE SUPERVISORY CURRENT)

TS  TROUBLE SIGNAL

ACM  ALARM CURRENT MONITOR

'COMMON ALARM' SECTION

©

From the foregoing, we can see that an alarm condition will be initiated in the control unit module if the current flowing in the detection circuit increases beyond the upper level of the supervisory current.

Because the equivalent circuit of a manual station, thermal detector or a sprinkler alarm or supervisory switch is a normally-open contact (usually referred to as a 'shorting' device), when one of these devices goes into alarm condition, it shorts across the circuit pair and the Control Unit recognizes the condition as the operation of a device.

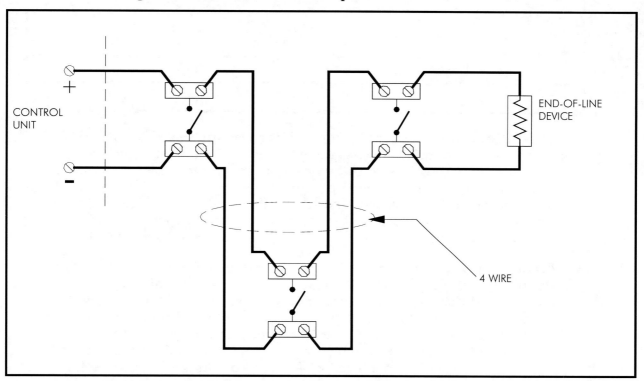

Obviously, this type of detection circuit cannot differentiate between the actual operation of a field device and an inadvertent electrical short-circuit condition across the pair. On the other hand, signaling circuits do not have shorting devices connected to them, and they are able to detect a short-circuit condition as a trouble condition.

## Class 'A' Circuits

The other classification of circuit is called a 'Class A' circuit and is available from most manufacturers as an option. In some Control Units, both types of circuits are available.

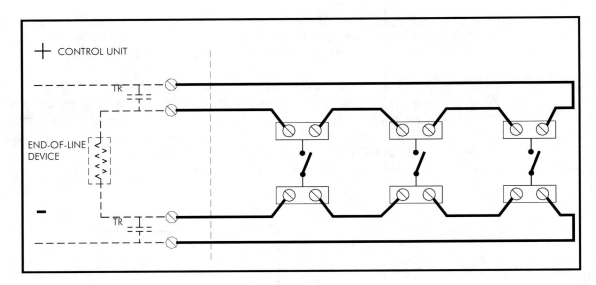

There is one important installation difference between a Class A circuit and a Class B circuit. There is no external end-of-line supervisory device on a Class A circuit, because it is part of the Control Unit. From the last connected device on a Class A circuit, two wires must be brought back, and connected to the designated terminals in the Control Unit. The return loop or pair of conductors must be run in a separate raceway, which must be mounted at least 300 mm from the outgoing raceway.

From an operational point of view there is one major difference between the two types of circuits. In the traditional Class B circuit, an open-circuit condition in the field wiring may cause some, all or none of the connected devices to be non-operational, depending upon the location of the fault. However a Class A circuit guarantees that even with a single open-circuit condition in the field wiring, all connected devices will still be operational. This is achieved by feeding operating power from the Control Unit out to the Class A circuit from all four circuit terminals.

### 7.3.2  Initiating-Device Circuits (Conventional) - Alarm, Supervisory and Monitoring

#### Alarm-Initiating-Device Circuits

Commonly referred to as 'box' circuits or 'zones' or 'detection circuits', initiating-device circuits are used to convey information, via electrical wiring, from the alarm-initiating device to the system Control Unit.

These following components would be classified as alarm initiating devices:

- automatic heat detectors
- manual stations

- sprinkler system alarm switches

- ionization products-of-combustion detectors

- photoelectric smoke detectors

- air-duct-mounted smoke detectors

- flame detectors

- beam detectors

- alarm contacts on special extinguishing systems

These alarm-initiating devices, electrically interconnected on two-wire or four-wire circuits, are connected to the Control Unit. The Control Units have historically provided two types of detection circuits: shorting-device circuits and smoke detector circuits. It is important to note that any alarm initiation from a field device, must cause the Control Unit to electronically latch into alarm condition until such time as the Control Unit is reset.

**Four types of Raceway to FCP**

## 'Shorting Device' Alarm Initiating Circuits

This type of circuit is designed with limited power conditioning but contains all design features of electrical supervision. It electrically locks into alarm condition from even a momentary operation of a field device. It can power an unlimited number of shorting devices. The maximum length of the circuit (to the end-of-line device) varies with the manufacturer, but in general should not exceed 1,000 metres. This circuit is intended for the connection of any initiating device that contains a normally-open initiating contact that reverses when the device goes into alarm condition. Smoke and flame detectors cannot properly function on this type of module.

## 'Smoke Detector' Alarm Initiating Circuits

This type of circuit is similar to the above except for one major design difference. It has the much greater power filtering and voltage-regulation that are needed by smoke detectors. Shorting devices will properly operate on this type of module.

Smoke detectors require a low constant operating current (20 to 160 micro-amps) at all times in order that they can perform their detection capabilities. There is therefore a limit to the quantity of smoke detectors that can be connected to a circuit. Since each smoke detector requires a small amount of power in its normal quiescent condition, the connection of 25 - 50 devices on one circuit draws an amount of current that approaches the upper limit of the supervisory current range. If, for example, 65 detectors were to be connected onto one circuit, the resultant total of supervisory and standby current would probably exceed the lower limit of the alarm threshold, and an alarm condition would be initiated.

## Supervisory Initiating-Device Circuits

Supervisory circuits are used to convey off-normal condition information, via electrical wiring, from the supervisory initiating device to the system Control Unit. These following components are examples of supervisory initiating devices:

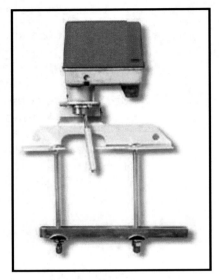

- sprinkler low pressure switches

- sprinkler control valve switches

- electrical power monitor relays on fire pumps

- low water levels in water storage tanks

- other off-normal conditions in fire protective systems or devices

**Supervisory Valve Switch**

Supervisory devices are electrical contact devices similar to the alarm initiating devices discussed above. In the event, for example, that a control valve is operated in order to shut off the water pressure from a sprinkler system (or portion thereof), that operation must be identified at the control unit. Obviously this is not an alarm function, but rather it is an off-normal condition, and therefore must cause a supervisory (trouble) signal within the fire alarm control unit, and as well must indicate the zone or location of the particular control valve.

Sprinkler Supervisory circuits are very similar to alarm-device circuits except that the output to the common control portion of the Control Unit initiates a 'supervisory' or trouble condition rather than an alarm condition. The control valve switch must be a normally open electrical contact to connect into a Class B circuit. These circuits must also latch.

## Monitoring Circuits

Monitoring circuits are also based on the shorting circuit. The operation of one of these circuits, however, does not initiate an alarm or a trouble condition, but provides just a visual status indication. These circuits might monitor (and therefore confirm) the position of dampers

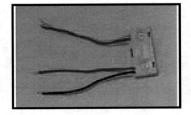

or the actual operation of fans.

## Annunciation

The *Building Code* contains the
requirements for annunciation of the
various zones in the system. Annunciation
of zones is provided to assist the responding
Fire Service in quickly determining the
location of the fire. The *Code* requires that
annunciation be provided at the designated
Fire Service entry point to the building –
which is usually the main front lobby area.

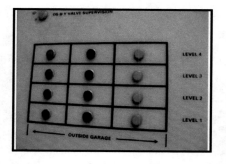

(Generally, annunciation is also provided in the Control Unit). Typically,
all alarm indications are red, supervisory indications are yellow, and
monitor indications are blue. All of the initiating (alarm and supervisory)
and monitoring circuits in the Control Unit provide the outputs for
connection to the annunciator visual indications.

## 7.4 Alarm Signaling Circuits

Alarm signaling circuits, commonly called 'signal circuits', are used to cause the
audible and or visible alarm signals within the protected premises to operate. The
associated circuitry electrically supervises the remote field wiring to all signaling
devices, and provides the necessary operating power to cause the devices to
operate. Audible and visual signaling devices generally are on separate circuits

The Control Unit sends a low supervisory current out over one of the two signal
circuit wires. The current cannot pass through the individual signaling device
because of the supervisory current 'blocking' component in the device, such as a
diode. The circuit supervisory current is therefore forced to flow to the end of the
circuit, pass through the end-of-line device, and return via the second conductor to
the Control Unit. Note that the supervisory voltage may be much less that 24 volts.

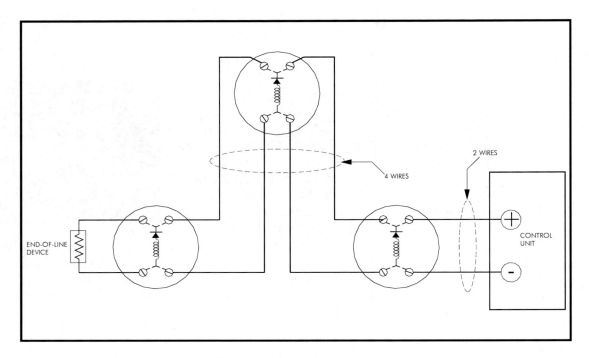

In alarm condition, the Control Unit reverses the polarity of the power applied to the signaling circuit. The blocking device now passes the alarm current flowing in the opposite direction and the signaling devices operate.

## 7.4.1   Signaling Circuit Wiring

The operating voltage used in almost all fire alarm systems is 24 volts D.C. It follows that the power available for use by the signal circuits is also 24 volts D.C. At the same time, most manufacturers of Control Units fuse (or otherwise protect) their signal circuits at anywhere from 1.0 amp to 3.0 amps.

Because electrical signaling devices require operating power, there is a limit to the quantity of signals that can be installed on any given circuit. This quantity is dependent upon three factors:

- the current required by the particular type of device

- the physical size of the electrical conductors

- the actual length of the circuit conductors

The operating power required by a signaling device depends upon the type (bell, horn, chime) and its operating voltage. A 24-Volt DC bell might be expected to draw only 0.075 Amps whereas a chime might draw 0.5 Amps.  The total current required of a circuit is determined by multiplying the signaling-device current by the quantity of devices to be installed.

Conductor Size: Most installations use from # 18 AWG wire up to #14 AWG wire. The lower the number, the larger the wire, the less the electrical resistance to current flow, and therefore the less the amount of voltage loss in the wires.

For example: The resistance of #18 wire is 6.51 ohms per thousand feet whereas the resistance of #14 wire is only 2.53 ohms per thousand feet - a factor of approximately 4:1.

As described in Chapter 6 Audible and Visual Signaling Devices, the potential problem of two or more visual devices flashing at different speeds or at different times can greatly bother some people and even bring on a severe nervous reaction. In such cases, visual devices must be synchronized. Such control of the flashing rates can be accomplished either in the Control Unit or at the device level. Refer to Chapter 11 Installation for a discussion of device level synchronization.

## 7.5 Emergency Voice Communications (EVC)

EVC systems comprise two separate but associated components.

Firstly, a one-way voice communications system provides a means to manually issue voice instructions to the building occupants during emergency conditions. The basic premise behind the use of this method is that if the occupants receive a spoken message concerning a fire condition, they will follow the verbal instructions and be much less likely to become over-excited or apprehensive. This not only reduces the likelihood of death or injury from fire or other accidents but it also frees the fire fighting personnel to perform their duties unencumbered by building occupants.

The use of voice paging speaker systems is now widespread. These speaker circuits are used for the transmission of first-stage alert tones, second-stage evacuation tones, live messages of instruction by fire fighting or building security personnel, and digitally-recorded voice messages. The control equipment provides an array of selector switches allowing ALERT or ALARM tones, as well as voice  messages to be selectively transmitted over the speakers throughout the building. Obviously, there is no need to also install bells or other audible alarm signaling devices.

In addition to the speaker system, an emergency telephone system is used to provide instantaneous private, automatic two-way communication between a fire fighter and the person in charge of the emergency response team. The emergency telephone system is designed to be very similar in operation and appearance to the business telephone, but of course there is no provision for dialing.

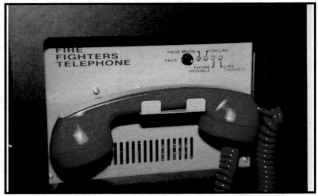

Through the use of call-in tones and visual indications, and an array of circuit selector pushbuttons, the person in charge is able to selectively answer any call from a remote handset and carry on a private automatic two-way conversation with one or more remote handsets.

### 7.5.1    Speaker Circuits

Emergency voice speaker circuits are a special type of signaling circuit utilizing speakers as audible signaling devices. Speakers are connected to the Class B field speaker circuit wiring in such a manner that they are placement supervised. Each speaker contains a supervisory current blocking capacitor in much the same way that bells contain a blocking diode.

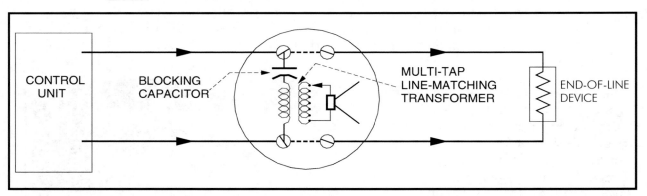

Speaker circuits use a DC current to electrically supervise the two-wire circuit. The capacitor effectively blocks this DC current from passing through the speaker. Of course, all tones and voice messages are AC and therefore are not blocked by the capacitor.

### 7.5.2    Amplifier Sizing - One Bank

The power amplifier section of the Control Unit provides amplification for the ALERT and ALARM tones, as well as for the voice messages.

The amplifier section is designed per project to power a specific maximum load. A certain amount of amplification will be required, depending upon the anticipated speaker loading.

Amplifiers are designed for either 25 volts or 70 volts AC balanced-line operation. (This means that speakers must be properly fitted with an impedance line-matching transformer before connection into the system.) These amplifiers are designed to give proper amplification with minimum distortion over the range of about 400 hertz to 4,000 hertz.

As stated earlier, the total required wattage of amplifiers depends upon both the quantity of speakers and the wattage of each speaker. Typically, speakers used in residential suites or small offices or rooms are tapped at ¼ watt or ½ watt.

Speakers in large rooms or public corridors are generally tapped at ½ watt or 1 watt. In noisy areas two-watt or four-watt horn-type speakers might be used because of their higher decibel output as well as their greater directivity.

Calculations for amplifier sizing might be as follows:

| 172 Suite Speakers | @ ½ watt | = 86 watts |
|---|---|---|
| 24 Corridor Speakers | @ 1 watt | = 24 watts |
| 18 Stairwell Speakers | @ 1 watt | = 18 watts |
| 10 Horn Speakers | @ 2 watts | = 20 watts |
| **Total Wattage** | | **= 148 watts** |

If 100-watt modular amplifiers are to be used, then two are needed. The use of two 100-watt amplifiers ensures also that sufficient capacity remains that additional speakers could be added in the future if needed. The extra capacity also allows for the tapping-up of speakers if needed to make the tones or messages more audible in certain areas by moving taps on some speakers from the ½ watt tap to the 2-watt tap for example.

A standby amplifier (identical to the on-line amplifiers) is provided, and an amplifier supervisory unit controls it. In the event that one of the on-line amplifiers becomes defective, it will automatically be removed from the circuit and the standby amplifier will be electronically inserted into the defective amplifier's place.

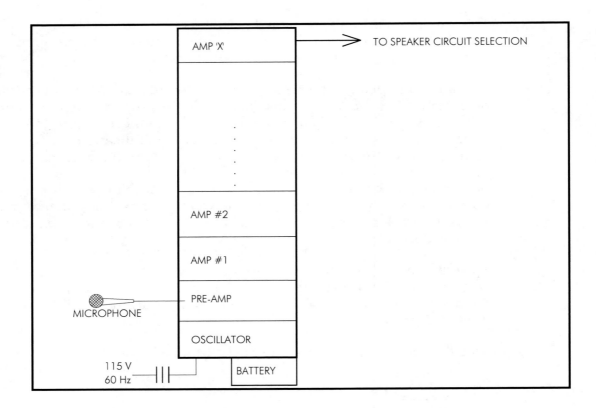

### 7.5.3    Zoned (Modular) Amplifiers

The system of amplifiers described above relates to a small building where all speakers are to receive the same audible alarm tone or the same voice message. Most buildings are sufficiently large that they are required by code to be fitted with speakers that are zoned on a floor-by-floor basis. In a high-rise building, for example, it may be required that the speakers on some floors carry the ALARM tone, whereas the speakers on other floors carry the ALERT tone. This obviously requires that the speakers be wired and controlled on a floor-by-floor basis. In such a case, zoned amplifiers are the best choice. Generally one amplifier (or a small group of amplifiers) would be assembled to power the speakers on each floor or zone.

### 7.5.4    Circuit Power Loss

Power loss in a speaker circuit is as important a consideration as line loss in a bell circuit. Similar questions apply to both:

* How long is the circuit wiring?

* What size of wire is used?

* How many speakers are on the circuit?

* What is the wattage of the speakers?

The designer must refer to manufacturers literature to ensure that the final system design is safely within the limits of signal power determined by line length, power loss because of conductor resistance and the wattage of the signals used to ensure that each speaker operates to its full potential. Refer to Chapter 11 Installation for a discussion on line loss conditions.

## 7.6 The Two-Channel And Three-Channel Concepts

The foregoing information describes a single-channel type of system – a system in which a taped message or a live page or a tone is produced by the amplifiers and distributed to parts or all of the speaker system as required. The disadvantage of this type of system is that there is little flexibility of use. If a voice page is to be given over the fire floor speakers only, then all other speakers in the building would be silent during that period of time. Obviously, this is an unacceptable scenario because it is necessary to be able to convey information to other occupants of the building while transmitting the primary message to the fire floors.

**Two-channel** refers to the use of a system providing two sources of information either one of which can be selected at any time for distribution to any speaker circuit.

In general, one source or channel provides the tone and the second source or channel provides the voice signal from the microphone. Both of these channels are made available at all times.

It is obvious that since two signals are available at any given time (tone and voice), that duplicate amplifiers are a necessity. And since, at any given time, the entire complement of speakers may receive the tone signal or the voice signal, then each amplifier stack must be sized for the full load represented by the total quantity of speakers. If a battery is to be used as the second source of power, then if the two amplifier stacks each require their separate set of batteries and chargers then each battery must be sized to provide the full load of the amplifiers.

This dual channel concept requires slightly different control equipment. The speaker selector switch units must now also contain an on/off switch per speaker circuit that directs the tone out onto the selected speaker zone.

A **three-channel** system can provide an ALERT tone, an ALARM tone, and a voice paging message to different areas in a building simultaneously. This design is obviously superior, as there is no 'silent period' sacrifice to any area of the building while paging, even while both the ALERT and ALARM tones may be sounding in other areas.

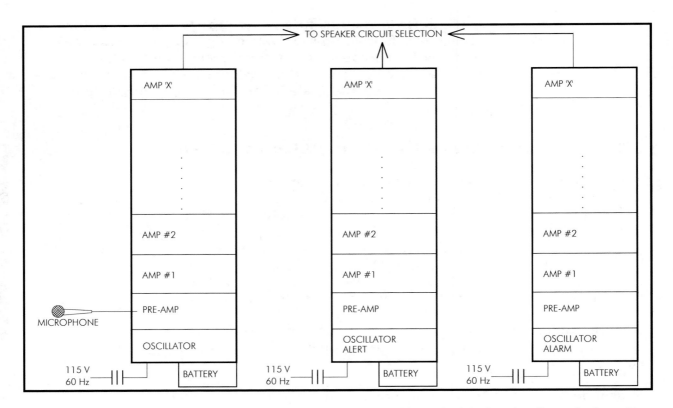

As discussed previously, modular amplifiers would probably be the first choice of the systems designer/installer for this type of system requirement. In this case the proper signal (MESSAGE, ALERT or ALARM) would be directed to the appropriate floor speaker amplifiers.

## 7.7    Emergency Telephone Circuits

The emergency telephone communication system must also be electrically supervised against open circuits or ground faults. To accomplish this, the telephones are connected to typical Class B circuits. An open circuit condition causes the emergency telephone trouble indicator to operate. A fault within any telephone circuit also illuminates the corresponding zone trouble indicator.

The telephone circuit modules send a low supervisory current out over the two circuit wires. The current is stopped from passing through the device by the hook switch. The current is therefore forced to flow to the end of the circuit, pass through the end-of-line device and return via the second conductor to the control panel module. This is typical Class B design.

In the event of an open-circuit condition or a short-circuit condition, the module will detect that the current is either too low or too high and initiate a trouble condition.

©

## 7.8     Common (Main) Control Section

Control Units have many design features - these are listed and discussed below in order of relative importance. Most Control Units now being produced are fully modular, using printed circuit boards that contain both solid-state devices and relays. It is therefore a simple matter for any fire alarm system to have virtually any combination of the many available features.

### 7.8.1     Common Alarm

A fire alarm system may have one or many alarm-initiating circuits. Upon the operation of any remote alarm-initiating device such as station or detector, the control unit must convey this information to other sections of the fire alarm system. For example, bells must be caused to ring, timers may be required for automatic silencing of bells after a pre-set period of operation, signals must be sent to control fire doors, elevators etc. The common alarm section controls all of these various features.  Usually a red indicator, physically located in this section, will be illuminated whenever the Control Unit receives any alarm, and this is called a common alarm indication.

### 7.8.2     Subsequent Alarm

A very important part of any Control Unit is the subsequent alarm circuitry, which ensures that a second alarm, initiated from a field device after the audible devices have been either manually or automatically silenced, will cause the audible alarm devices to sound again. This is true only if the second initiating device is on any circuit other than the original alarm initiating circuit.

### 7.8.3     System Reset

Upon receipt of any alarm initiation from any field device, the common control section must electronically lock into alarm condition and remain so even if the initiating device returns to normal. Operating the panel Reset button restores the system to normal. If the initiating device is still in alarm position when the system reset button is operated, the system will return immediately to alarm condition when the button is released.

### 7.8.4     Common Trouble

The trouble condition has already been fully discussed. A trouble condition exists when an abnormal condition (a ground, short circuit, or open circuit existing in the field wiring, a blown fuse in control unit) exists. A buzzer in the control unit is used to signal a trouble condition and an amber lamp is illuminated

Many control units and system functions are electronically monitored in order to immediately detect an off-normal condition such as:

- Alarm Receiving Circuits: An open circuit or a ground condition on any of the detection circuit conductors will cause a common trouble signal.

- Supervisory Circuits: An open circuit or a ground condition on any of the supervisory circuit conductors will cause a common trouble signal.

- Alarm Signaling Circuits: An open circuit, a short circuit or a ground condition on any of the circuits will cause a common trouble signal.

- Loss of Power: Failure of the primary power feed, or loss or degradation of the standby power source (if battery) will cause a trouble signal.

- Fuse Supervision: A blown fuse in the control unit will be immediately detected and a trouble signal initiated.

- Module Placement: All modules in a control unit must be placement supervised, ensuring that a trouble signal is initiated the moment any module is removed from its proper panel location.

- Signal Control: In the event that the fire alarm signals are automatically silenced by a timer, or if they are silenced by a manually operated switch, a common trouble signal is initiated and as well a dedicated lamp or LED will further indicate the cause.

- Ground Detection: It is a requirement that ground detection circuitry be provided so that it will detect a substantial electrical ground condition and identify such a condition as well as cause a common trouble signal. A substantial ground is a ground fault on any conductor that would adversely affect the system if a second ground of zero ohms appeared.

- Lamp Failure: Incandescent indicating lamps on the Control Unit and on remote annunciators are electronically monitored for burnout, defect and placement. A trouble indication will be generated. In that event, the lamp test push-button will illuminate all good indicators, therefore indicating the defective or missing lamp or LED. It will also test the audible trouble signal.

### 7.8.5   Bypass Switches

Many of the control unit outputs for control of equipment such as fans are provided with a bypass switch and light so that the switch can bypass the output permitting the fire alarm system to be tested without shutting down the fans. After the test, the switch should be reset to its normal position. To ensure that personnel remember to reset

©

the switch to its normal position, it is a design requirement that as soon as the switch is put to its bypass position, a common trouble signal is initiated and a dedicated visual indicator is illuminated.

### 7.8.6    Remote Annunciation

If the system is a zoned system and a remote annunciator is used, then the common control section contains electronic circuitry that assists in the monitoring of, and fusing for, the remote annunciator wiring.  A visual indicator will be illuminated if a trouble occurs in either the remote annunciator or in the interconnecting wiring.

## 7.9    Power Supply

### 7.9.1    Primary Power

Regulations require that an independently fused source of 120 volts 60 hertz feed the fire alarm system. Power must be taken from as close to the incoming mains (the meter) as is possible. A lockable-on, red-painted, fused disconnect switch labeled FIRE ALARM is required.

The fire alarm system must have its source of energy automatically transferred to a standby power supply upon loss of the main power supply in not more than 1 second. Upon restoration of main power, the fire alarm system must have its source of energy automatically transferred back to the main power supply in not more than 30 minutes, except in the event that the standby should fail in which case the transfer is to be instantaneous. The automatic action of switching from normal operating power to the standby or emergency power source must not cause an alarm condition.

Both the main and standby power supplies are to be used for no other purpose than to provide power for the Fire Alarm System. For example, the Fire Alarm System power feed cannot be used to power the equipment (transmitters etc) that connects the building to the off-site monitoring center.

The main power supply must be capable of supplying necessary power for the full operation of the system for an indefinite period.

**Electrical Breaker**          **Electrical Connection FACP**

A step-down transformer and rectifier assembly is used to convert the 120 volt A.C. input to the Control Unit to 24 volts D.C. and the entire fire alarm system operates on this power (except for some audio components). The D.C. output must be electrically isolated from the A.C. input by a two-winding transformer.

### 7.9.2   Standby Power

The standby power supply must be sized to provide supervisory (normal non-alarm) power for not less than 24 hours, followed by full load (alarm) power for:

- 2 hours for all buildings over 36m in height, Group C occupancy buildings over 18m in height, and Group B occupancy buildings greater than three storeys

- 1 hour for all other Group B occupancy buildings not included in the above

- 5 minutes for buildings not requiring an annunciator (single zone buildings)

- 30 minutes in all other buildings

### 7.9.3   Battery Sizing

The battery must be sized to power the Fire Alarm System with charger input disconnected for one rated load cycle. For a Fire Alarm System without voice communication capability, a rated load cycle means the total energy consumed by the maximum possible electrical supervision current plus the trouble signal current for 24 hours followed by the required general alarm load. For a Fire Alarm System with voice communication capability, a rated load cycle means the total energy consumed by the maximum possible electrical supervision current plus the trouble signal current for 24 hours followed by 30 minutes of continuous voice communication (30 minutes continuous is two hour capacity with 25 per cent duty cycle).

For a non-voice Fire Alarm System in a low-rise office building whose supervisory current is 0.315 amps and whose alarm current is 4.6 amps, the battery capacity requirement is determined as follows:

- for supervision power: 0.315 Amps x 24 hours = 7.56 Amp-Hours

- for alarm power: 4.56 Amps x 30/60 hours = 2.28 Amp-Hours

- Total = 9.84 Amp-Hours

A battery rated at 10 Amp-Hours or greater should be selected for this system.

For greater detail relating to the types of batteries and their construction and use, please refer to the 'Course 3 Manual' titled *Basic Electricity For The Fire Alarm Technician.*

### 7.9.4    Engine-Driven Generators

When the standby power supply is an engine driven generator, its design, installation and operation must be in accordance with *CSA C282 Emergency Electrical Power Supply for Buildings.* Trouble signals from engine-driven generators must be automatically transmitted to the Fire Alarm System Control Unit.

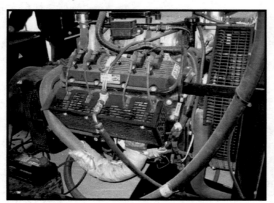 

When the normal A.C. power fails, the 120 volts A.C. feed from the standby generator is connected, through appropriate terminals of a power transfer relay in the control unit, to the primary of the isolating transformer. Proper operation of this transfer relay ensures that only one source of 120 volts A.C. can be fed to the isolating transformer at one time.

Where the Fire Alarm System requires Emergency Voice capability, and the primary power to the Control Unit fails, the switchover to standby power must be immediate. This suggests that the system must use batteries as the standby power because most generators require 15 to 20 seconds to start and to come up to operating speed/power.

Another related point concerns the actual starting of the generator. Most generators are caused to start when the municipal power feed coming into the building is interrupted. On the other hand, Fire Alarm System standby power must be available when power to the system itself is interrupted. Because it is possible for Fire Alarm System power to be interrupted even though there still is municipal power entering the building, then loss of power to the Fire Alarm System must cause the generator to start. This would create problems in many buildings, and probably should not be done. The simpler and perhaps better solution would be to provide battery backup for the fire alarm system even though the building has a generator. In this case, additional security would be achieved by feeding the system from the emergency services electrical distribution network.

## 7.10    Ancillary Circuits

Ancillary devices are building devices or components that are safety-related, but that are not part of the Fire Alarm System. Such devices or functions may include door holder release, maglock release, elevator recall, fan startup or shutdown, and damper operation. These components may be controlled by the Fire Alarm System through the use of relays which typically provide one form C contact (normally-closed, normally-open, and common) for each building control function. Use caution when considering the connection of wires from another system or device. Carefully determine whether the contacts of the control unit relay can handle (is rated for) the incoming power. Perhaps a separate double-voltage relay is required.

**Typical Mag-lock**

**Mag Reset**

The Fire Alarm Control Unit may include switches to individually bypass ancillary circuits. When operated, the switch must also initiate a system common trouble condition.

It is important to note that the Control Unit generally does not supervise wiring to ancillary devices. (It is not a code requirement). Where possible, ancillary devices should be connected in a fail-safe manner, this being of particular concern in the case of electromagnetic locking devices, which could trap building occupants in a fire if improperly installed or controlled.

Fire Alarm Systems are usually required to perform the additional function of sending signals to the fire department or off-site monitoring service. Typically, the Control Unit must transmit three signals to the off-site monitoring service: Alarm,

Supervisory and Trouble. Auxiliary relay contacts (switch bypassable for testing purposes) are included in the Common Control section for this purpose. Upon activation of any alarm, supervisory or trouble conditions, these relays will activate to appropriately notify the monitoring station.

## 7.11 Microprocessors

The operating speed and the inherent power of microprocessors has ensured the future all-pervasive use of microprocessor chips in most Fire Alarm System Control Units. It is probably true that most systems installed today contain some degree of microprocessor technology. In today's large and complex buildings, this type of system has become the norm.

There can be many benefits to using this continuously evolving technology. Individual device identification of field devices, lower installation costs because of less field wiring, improvements in automatic fire detection capabilities, and the ability to quickly produce, and subsequently alter, site-specific operational sequences are examples.

On the other hand, we must be aware that microprocessor technology dramatically alters some of the methods of installation and device/system testing. In addition, errors during custom programming can inadvertently cause unintended system operation that could well be potentially dangerous.

### 7.11.1 Microprocessor Architecture

The Central Processing Unit (CPU) is at the centre of any microprocessor-based system. It interprets and carries out all of the procedures that are defined in the fire alarm system "program". These procedures are individual instructions that are stored in memory, and that define the overall operation and individual functions of the Fire Alarm System.

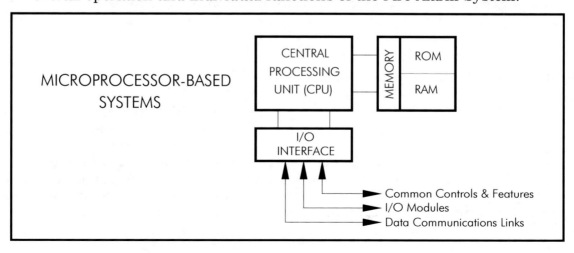

The program is stored in non-volatile memory (the contents of which are not lost during failure of primary and secondary power), and consists of two parts: 'firmware' and 'software'. Firmware is the overall framework program, which would be common to all fire alarm systems of a certain manufacturer and model number. Software, on the other hand, is the portion of the system programming that is building-specific to the application and would include, for example, instructions to activate fan and damper ancillary relay outputs if certain alarm input zones are activated.

As well as the programming for the Fire Alarm System, some amount of memory (volatile) is required for the temporary storage of certain data. This may include such information as an 'events' log, which is a record of the dates and times of all off-normal system conditions.

### 7.11.2    Digital Communication

Microprocessors and their memory support circuitry, function in the digital realm as opposed to the analog world. Instead of a virtually infinite number of possible voltage levels within a range, the CPU recognizes only two voltage levels; one corresponding to 'OFF' or 'FALSE', and one indicating 'ON' or 'TRUE'. These are commonly labeled 'logic 0' and 'logic 1' respectively. Because there are only these two possible states, the mathematical numbering system used by microprocessors is the BINARY system (to the base 2) instead of our commonly used DECIMAL system (to the base 10). Each '0' or '1' value therefore represents a binary digit or 'bit'. These are generally grouped together into eight-bit 'bytes', allowing the microprocessor to process more information simultaneously.

In a previous chapter, it was shown that 'alarm' and the level of its electrical current flow relative to a normal 'window' determined 'trouble' status for a field wiring circuit or zone. This function remains identical in a microprocessor-based system using conventional devices and zoning. Each circuit still has an 'activated' or alarm status, as well as a circuit wiring 'trouble' status.

**Digital Chip
with Logic
Gates**

### 7.11.3    Serial Data Transfer

Reduced wiring is made possible by serial data transfer. This process involves multiple exchanges of information over a two-conductor cable (thus the term 'multiplex'). As an example of the reduction of wiring, consider the use of a microprocessor-based or serial annunciator. Instead of dedicating one wire per zone plus a common for connecting the control unit to the remote annunciator, a serial connection sends multiple circuit status via a two-conductor cable.

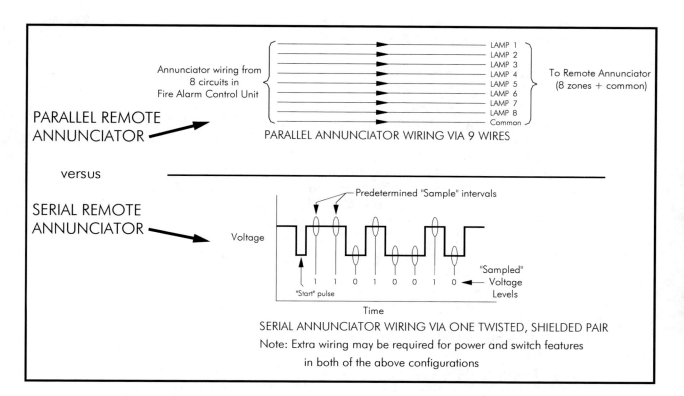

PARALLEL REMOTE
ANNUNCIATOR

Annunciator wiring from
8 circuits in
Fire Alarm Control Unit

LAMP 1
LAMP 2
LAMP 3
LAMP 4
LAMP 5
LAMP 6
LAMP 7
LAMP 8
Common

To Remote Annunciator
(8 zones + common)

PARALLEL ANNUNCIATOR WIRING VIA 9 WIRES

versus

SERIAL REMOTE
ANNUNCIATOR

Predetermined "Sample" intervals

Voltage

1  1  0  1  0  0  1  0

"Start" pulse

"Sampled"
Voltage
Levels

Time

SERIAL ANNUNCIATOR WIRING VIA ONE TWISTED, SHIELDED PAIR

Note: Extra wiring may be required for power and switch features
in both of the above configurations

Data transfer over the two-wire cable can be 'simplex' style with data being sent in one direction only, 'half-duplex' style where data can be sent in either direction but in only one direction at a time, or 'full-duplex' style which allows simultaneous two-way data communications.

## 7.12 Addressable Field Devices

### 7.12.1 Active And Supporting Field Devices

Active field devices are defined as those that can be uniquely identified by the control unit to determine both their presence on the circuit, and their operational status, and which may be commanded to operate or change their operating parameters independently of other field devices sharing a common circuit. Simply put, active field devices can be heat detectors, smoke detectors, manual pull stations, contact monitoring devices (for sprinkler switches), or output ancillary relays, for which the present status can be identified individually at the control unit. Active field devices use serial communication techniques.

Many of these devices (typically up to about 200) can be wired together on a single two-wire circuit (called a Data Communications Link or DCL), reducing field wiring while still providing individual identification (and/or control) of the device in alarm or trouble. Instead of annunciation messages such as "2nd floor alarm", an addressable device may initiate a corresponding message such as "smoke detector, room 202 activated". The benefits of such finite identification are obvious, and for this there is an expected cost tradeoff. (It must be remembered that the *Building Code* contains requirements for 'summary' zoning by building areas.)

Thinking back to conventional systems, where each initiating circuit incorporated built-in lamps or LEDs with typed labels to identify both alarm and trouble status per circuit, this would rapidly become cumbersome in an addressable system having 300 to 400 devices. For this reason, most systems with addressable devices utilize an alphanumeric liquid crystal display (LCD) that presents a preprogrammed 'device/location/status' message corresponding to each addressable device, upon its activation. In the case of multiple simultaneous device activations, additional location messages are stored in an internal buffer through which the operator may scroll, one by one, using a built-in keypad. This LCD feature further reduces the size of the control equipment by minimizing the physical annunciation space required. Note though, that many jurisdictions still require a full LED style annunciation in the Control Unit (in addition to the LCD) for Fire Service use. Also be aware that ULC-S527 requires that, where sequential displays are incapable of displaying eight input events simultaneously, full LED annunciation is required.

A 'supporting field device' is an active field device that monitors other field devices (non-addressable) on a separate supervised circuit and reports the status of that separate circuit to the control unit.

### 7.12.2   Addressable Device Polling

Each addressable device has a predetermined 'address' assigned to it. Addressable devices are "polled" sequentially by the control unit. One by one, the control unit sends the device addresses out over the Data Communications Link (DCL). The devices automatically recognize their own address, and upon recognition, they respond to the control unit via the same DCL wiring. In this manner, all devices on the circuit are interrogated in sequence. After all devices have been checked, the cycle begins again, in a continuous polling process.

### 7.12.3   Automatic And Manual Addressing

Two methods of assigning device addresses have been used - automatic and manual.

Automatic device address assignment (self-configuring) occurs upon system power-up, and does not require the setting of any switches for each device.

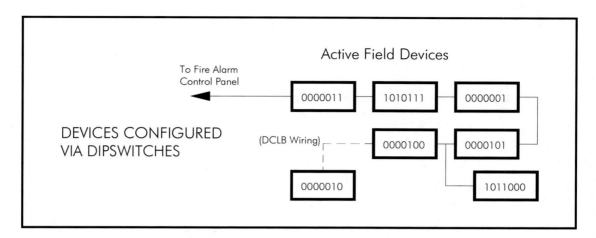

Manual address assignment requires the setting of individual address switches on each device. Device addresses do not have to be physically sequential on the Data Communications Link.

### 7.12.4   Addressable And Analog

As well as there being two types of address assignment, there are two types of addressable device operations: standard and analog. Standard addressables were the first available, and provided one of two responses to the control unit upon being polled – 'normal' or 'alarm' (no response indicates a trouble condition). Analog addressables can provide a full range of device status values. An example would be the actual smoke obscuration levels of a smoke detector being transmitted back to the control unit in a digital format. This is then interpreted, compared to the 'alarm parameters' established by ULC, and processed and acted upon accordingly. These smoke 'detectors' have thus become smoke 'sensors', along with their thermal heat 'sensor' counterparts, and they are dependent on the system's microprocessor for support.

Analog addressable devices offer some additional features to assist building owners and maintenance personnel. Among these are the ability for the control unit to automatically compensate for buildup of dust within smoke sensors, adjusting the alarm threshold accordingly, while still maintaining it within the ULC defined window. At the same time, the control unit can initiate a message on the LCD to indicate that smoke sensor cleaning is required, and specifying the individual sensor(s) needing maintenance.

### 7.12.5   Data Communication Links

The actual wiring for fire alarm systems serial communication is termed a 'Data Communications Link' (DCL). A DCL is the data wiring channel between the CPU and:

• transponders,

- annunciators,

- active field devices, and

- supporting field devices.

A DCL may be configured in one of three ways:

- DCLB wiring, which is similar to a Class B configuration, in that only one end of the circuit is connected to the main control unit,

- DCLA wiring, which is similar to a Class A configuration, connected in a true loop fashion, or

- DCLC wiring, which provides performance superior to DCLB or DCLA.

| System Abnormal Condition | SYSTEM STYLE | | |
|---|---|---|---|
| | DCLB | DCLA | DCLC |
| Single Open | T | A | A |
| Single Ground (a) | A | A | A |
| Wire to Wire Short | - | T | A |
| Wire to Wire Short & Open (Same Link) | - | T | T |
| Wire to Wire Short & Ground (Same Link) | - | T | T |
| Open and Ground (Same Link) | - | T | A |
| Loss of Carrier | - | T | T |

| LEGEND |
|---|
| a  =  Except as permitted in CAN/ULC-S524-06, Clause 4.2.2. |
| T  =  Trouble Indication at the Control Unit |
| A  =  Trouble Indication at the Control Unit and Alarm Receipt Capability During Abnormal Operation |
| -  =  Not Applicable |

## 7.12.6  Fault-Isolator Devices

Although each addressable device can be thought of as a single 'zone', the question must be raised as to how many devices could one afford to 'lose' upon failure of a Data Communication Link. For this reason, *ULC-S524* specifies that the maximum portion of a system affected by a failure shall be one floor area, to a maximum of 2000 m². It can easily be seen that this is reflective of the original code requirements for the maximum floor area of any zone. Systems must therefore employ fault isolators between floors, and between each 2000 m² floor area.

Fault isolators are devices which, when wired in a DCLA or DCLC configuration, will literally disconnect a faulty section of the loop, allowing the remainder to operate normally (a trouble condition would also be initiated at the control unit). Fault isolation must also be used on DCLC network wiring connecting panels in a distributed Fire Alarm System.

©

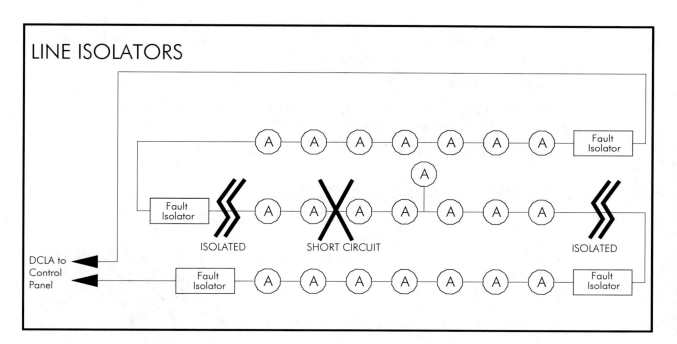

LINE ISOLATORS

The installation standard also limits the number of devices that can be served by a DCL, depending on its A, B, or C configuration. Larger systems may fall into the category of a 'Large Scale System' and additional requirements and restrictions will apply such as requirements for 'Stand Alone' operation.

### 7.12.7  Advantages and Disadvantages Of Microprocessor-Based Fire Alarm Systems

Some of the advantages of microprocessor-based fire alarm systems would be:

*   greater flexibility for special operational sequences such as timers, counters, logic functions, etc.,

*   reduced electronics, which translates to lower cost and smaller physical size,

*   reduced power requirements,

*   reduced field wiring due to serial data exchange,

*   greater ability to provide device-specific information, helping to pinpoint alarms and system trouble conditions, and

*   provision for features that are otherwise impossible (event log, password protection for access to certain control functions, etc.).

There are, however, several considerations (disadvantages) to be aware of with microprocessor-based systems:

*   they may be more easily damaged by static electricity, power surges, lightning, etc.,

- they are much more sensitive to electromagnetic interference 'noise' on the field wiring connecting initiating devices to the control unit, since it can be interpreted as transmitted data,

- some inspection procedures are more intricate and involved,

- intended alterations to the system programming can inadvertently cause other un-wanted/unexpected system changes, and

- the compatibility of field devices is of greater significance.

### 7.12.8  Transponders (Distributed Intelligence)

Transponders, sometimes referred to as Data Gathering Panels or DGPs, can be thought of as slave Fire Alarm Control Units that report the status of their circuits to, and have outputs controlled by, the main CPU.  Functioning similarly to an addressable device, transponders are polled for their status, which is transmitted to the Control Unit in serial data format.
Similarly, the CPU can then send a message to a transponder to activate any of its output circuit functions (signal circuits or ancillary relays).

The advantage of using transponders is once again the reduction in riser wiring.  This can represent a greater savings in large horizontal floor areas as opposed to vertical transponder placement, since floor-to-floor distances are generally about three metres.

Once again, considerations must be made for transponder communications failure.  In the event of a DCL failure, transponders resort to their own fire alarm backup firmware, which generally activates all outputs within that transponder upon reception of any alarm.  This operation is called "stand alone capability" or "degraded mode operation". For this reason, *ULC-S524* requires transponders to house the signal circuits that serve the same area(s) as its alarm initiating circuits.

Another consideration to be aware of is that in stand-alone mode, it may be disastrous for all ancillary relays to activate upon any local alarm. These ancillary outputs could control fans or dampers, and could easily feed oxygen to a fire and pressurize the fire floor.  However, an additional fail-safe ancillary contact for any functions such as these, wired in a normally closed configuration will help to ensure that these systems can not work against the building occupants in the event of fire.

Loss of an audio communications line and alert or alarm tones from the CPU must also be anticipated. If alert and alarm tones are generated at the CPU and distributed to each transponder via audio wiring, provisions must be made for the transponders to incorporate 'backup' tone generators in case of system wiring failure.

Most distributed systems provide operation on a peer-to-peer basis, where each transponder is the equal of all other transponders. Each contains full programming capability.

### 7.12.9  Peripherals

Microprocessor based systems offer support for a wide variety of peripheral equipment, including the following:

**Factory test of Distributed Peer to Peer Transponder and Display Command Centre Network**

- computer display (text messages),

- computer display with colour graphic building layouts,

- touch-screen computer colour graphics displays, and

- printers, including control-unit mounted, computer driven, and stand-alone modems for off-site monitoring via computer.

The operation and features of these peripherals is manufacturer-specific and should be carefully considered at design time.

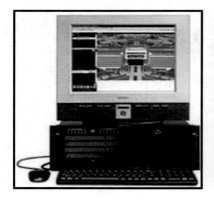  

### 7.12.10  Installation Requirements

The installer of a microprocessor-based system must look to two sources of information and instructions.

The first source of information regarding installation requirements for microprocessor-based systems is the *ULC-S524 Installation Standard*. This standard includes such limitations as the number of devices served by a data communications link, dependent on loop type and system configuration.  Also, transponders served by an emergency generator must nevertheless incorporate standby batteries that are rated to supply supervisory current for a minimum of two hours.  In high buildings classified under section 3.2.6. of the *Building Code*, protection of conductors must also be considered. A one-hour fire separation is required for vertical conductors that form part of a fire alarm or emergency voice communication system. This can be accomplished by a fire-separated wiring shaft using mineral insulated fire-rated cable, or constructing an approved, continuous fire-rated enclosure around the conductors. These are important code requirements.

The other and equally important source of installation requirements is the system manufacturer. The manufacturer may have certain specific wiring needs (for example a particular system may need twisted shielded conductors) to ensure that electromagnetic interference will not enter the CPU via the field cabling.

**Install DCC Cabinets**

### 7.12.11  Design Considerations

With the availability of this high-tech equipment come added features, added possibilities, and added responsibility for manufacturers and for building owners. The most futuristic system is not necessarily the best in a real fire scenario. New systems offer many advantages, but new technology sometimes introduces new concerns, and these must be considered for reliable installation and performance.

**Circuit Integrity Cable
and fire Alarm Cable
Shared Raceway**

## 7.13   Chapter Summary

1.   The Control Unit is the heart and the brains of the Fire Alarm System. It ties all items together into a cohesive unit.

2.   Many aspects of a system installation relate to the integrity of the system, which relates to system reliability.

3.   Because the many alarm initiating and signaling devices sit for month after month without any apparent activity, it is very important that all devices be placement supervised. This is achieved either through electrical supervision or through device addressing.

4.   The basic circuit for most Fire Alarm Systems is the Class B circuit. It electrically supervises the circuit wiring against electrical faults, but also 'placement supervises' all devices connected to it.

5.   Different methods of supervising the circuit depend upon the devices that are connected to the circuit. As an example, bells use a blocking diode, whereas speakers use blocking capacitors.

6.   Line loss possibilities are an important consideration when making decisions relating to the connection of many audible or visual devices onto a circuit.

7.   A wiring fault on any initiating circuit or signaling circuit must initiate a trouble condition on the Control Unit.

8.   The installer must carefully consider the electrical load of the audible or the visual devices that are to be installed on each circuit, to ensure that there will be no excess line loss.

9.   The Fire Alarm System must include annunciation at the designated Fire Service entrance to the building, all in accordance with the *Building Code*.

## 7.14 Review Questions

| # | ? | Question | Section |
|---|---|----------|---------|
| **7-1** | | **Many systems today are based upon conventional current flow device technology, and programming with diodes. The advantages include reduced system wiring costs, yet greater flexibility in the monitoring and control of field devices and ancillary systems.** | |
| | A | True | |
| | B | False | |
| **7-2** | | **A device that can be uniquely identified by the control unit to determine its presence and operating status, and which may be commanded to operate or to change its operating parameters independently of other field devices that share a common circuit** | |
| | A | Ancillary Device | |
| | B | Conventional Field Device | |
| | C | Active Field Device | |
| | D | Control Unit | |
| **7-3** | | **A _____ fault is a series resistance increase that would prevent normal operation** | |
| | A | wiring | |
| | B | Open circuit | |
| | C | Short circuit | |
| | D | All of the above | |
| **7-4** | | **In a _____ system, electrical supervision of initiating conductors is used to ensure that the components remain properly connected to the conventional circuit conductors, and that all wiring remains intact and properly connected to the Control Unit.** | |
| | A | Addressable | |
| | B | Central Station | |
| | C | DVAC control | |
| | D | Conventional | |

©

| # | ? | Question | Section |
|---|---|----------|---------|
| **7-5** | | **Conventional initiating-device circuits not only monitor for the presence of current but they also measure the relative value of current in order to make assessments such as:** | |
| | A | Alarm Condition - a high level of current that exceeds the upper or maximum level of normal current. | |
| | B | Trouble Condition - a low level of current that is less than the lower or minimum level of normal current | |
| | C | Normal Condition - a nominal current level. This is not a specific finite value but a range of current from a definite minimum to a definite maximum, defined as within normal operating parameters for that particular Control Unit. | |
| | D | All of the Above | |
| **7-6** | | **Smoke detectors require a low constant operating current at all times in order that they can perform their detection capabilities. What is the typical constant operating current range?** | |
| | A | 5 to 20 micro-amps | |
| | B | 20 to 160 micro-amps | |
| | C | 5 to 10 micro-amps | |
| | D | 160 to 180 micro-amps | |
| **7-7** | | **Sprinkler Supervisory circuits are very similar to alarm-device circuits except that the output to the common control portion of the Control Unit Initiates:** | |
| | A | A 'supervisory' condition rather than an alarm condition. | |
| | B | A 'open' condition rather than an ground fault condition. | |
| | C | A 'high impedance fault' condition rather than an open condition. | |
| | D | A 'alarm condition rather than an open circuit condition. | |
| **7-8** | | **The operating power required by a signaling device depends upon the type and its operating voltage.  A 24-Volt DC bell will draw 0.075 amperes.  If I have ten of these 24-Volt DC bells how much current will the circuit draw?** | |
| | A | .075 amperes | |
| | B | .75 amperes | |
| | C | 7.5 amperes | |
| | D | 75. amperes | |

| # | ? | Question | Section |
|---|---|---|---|
| **7-9** | | **The power amplifier section of the Control Unit provides amplification for:** | |
| | A | the ALERT and ALARM tones, as well as for the voice messages. | |
| | B | for voice messages as per code | |
| | C | for ALARM tone as per code | |
| | D | All of the above | |
| **7-10** | | **The manufacturer's literature is provided to ensure that the final system design is safely within the limits of signal power. What are the factors that determine power loss?** | |
| | A | Conductor length | |
| | B | Conductor size | |
| | C | The quantity of speakers on the circuit | |
| | D | All of the above | |

©

# Chapter 8: System Operational Principles

## 8.1 Chapter Overview and Key Concepts

This Chapter describes the fire alarm system operational principals for various types of protective signalling systems. The signal processing is the dynamic link between signal input and system response. A control unit will typically receive numerous, varied signal inputs. In addition, outputs can vary widely depending on the specific application of the fire alarm system.

Although signal notification is the last function of the fire alarm signaling process, signaling notification is the most important feature. Understanding the operational principals of the various fire alarm system types is key to ensuring the notification sequence is operating as intended.

## 8.2 Learning Objectives

After successfully completing this chapter, the reader should be able to:

- Discuss the differences between sprinkler supervisory circuits and monitor circuits

- Understand why some supervised circuits cannot detect short-circuits as faults

- Understand the purpose of zoning

- Discuss the location, structure and purpose of a CACF

- Tell why three-channel systems are required in many high-rise buildings

- Tell why modified two-stage systems are used in a high-rise hotel

8: System Operational Principles

## Language defined

Throughout the various codes and standards, certain words and phrases are used to identify specific items, situations, assemblies or processes. Before beginning a study of any of these documents, it is important that the definitions applicable to fire protection are clearly understood. Failure to understand the meaning of a defined term in a code requirement often leads to an incorrect interpretation of that requirement. Also refer to the Main Glossary at the end of this Manual.

| Term | Definition |
| --- | --- |
| **Access-To-Exit** | Those parts of a building, such as aisles, hallways or corridors that provide access to an exit serving that floor area |
| **Alarm Signal** | An audible signal transmitted throughout a zone or zones to advise occupants that a fire emergency exists; also called an EVACUATION signal |
| **Alert Signal** | An audible signal intended to advise designated persons of a fire emergency |
| **Ancillary Device** | A device that performs a life safety related function, but that is not part of the fire alarm system |
| **Authority Having Jurisdiction** | The organization, office, or individual responsible for approving equipment, an installation, or a procedure. Most often, it is the municipal Fire Department |
| **Basement** | A storey or storeys of a building located below the first storey |
| **Building Height (in storeys)** | The number of storeys contained between the roof and the floor of the first storey. An elevator machine room, sitting atop an office building, would not generally be considered a storey in this application |
| **Control Unit** | A device with the necessary circuits or components needed to provide acceptable operating power for a fire alarm system, receive signals from alarm initiating devices, cause audible alarm signals to operate, and electrically monitor the installation wiring and device placement against certain faults and/or removal |
| **Dwelling Unit** | A suite operated as a housekeeping unit, used or intended to be used, as a domicile by one or more persons and usually containing cooking, eating, living, sleeping and sanitary facilities |
| **Electromagnetic Door Release** | A device used to hold doors in the open position, and to release the doors to close automatically when signaled to do so by a fire alarm system or other means |

| Term | Definition |
|------|-----------|
| **Exit** | A facility such as a door, stairs or ramp that leads from the floor area that it serves to an open public thoroughfare, or to a protected exterior open space that has access to an open public thoroughfare. Once in an exit facility, a person should have a continuous path leading to the building exterior |
| **First Storey** | The uppermost storey having its floor level not more than two metres above grade. In certain jurisdictions, it is the storey with its floor closest to grade and having its ceiling more than 1.8 m above grade |
| **Floor Area** | The space on any storey of a building between the exterior walls and required firewalls, including the space occupied by interior walls and partitions, but not including exits and vertical service spaces that pierce the storey |
| **Impeded-Egress Zone** | A supervised area in which occupants have free movement but require the release, by security personnel, of security doors at the boundary before they are able to leave the area, but does not include a contained use area |
| **Interconnected Floor Spaces** | Superimposed floor areas or parts of floor areas in which floor assemblies that are required to be fire separations are penetrated by openings that are not provided with closures |
| **Sprinkler Supervision** | A method of electrically monitoring critical elements of an automatic sprinkler system to detect potentially disabling abnormal conditions, and provide a warning signal |
| **Storey** | That portion of a building which is situated between the top of any floor and the top of the floor next above it, and if there is no floor above it, that portion between the top of such floor and the ceiling (roof) above it |
| **Suite** | A single room or series of rooms of complementary use, operated under a single tenancy, and includes:<br><br>(a) dwelling units,<br><br>(b) individual guest rooms in motels, hotels, boarding houses, rooming houses and dormitories, and<br><br>(c) individual stores and individual or complementary rooms for business and personal services occupancies. |
| **Trouble Signal** | A signal (usually a buzzer and an amber lamp to LED) indicating a fault or an off-normal condition in a fire alarm system |

| Term | Definition |
|------|-----------|
| **Vertical Service Space** | A shaft oriented essentially vertically that is provided in a building to facilitate the installation of building services including mechanical, electrical and plumbing installations and facilities such as elevators, refuse chutes and linen chutes |
| **Waterflow Switch** | A device used to detect the flow of water through some portion of the automatic sprinkler system piping, as will occur when one or more sprinkler heads has operated, and will operate a set of electrical contacts for interconnection to a fire alarm system. An adjustable time delay mechanism may be installed between the paddle-operated stem and the contacts to keep brief water movements from initiating an alarm signal |

## 8.3    General

The primary purpose of a fire alarm system is to save the lives of building occupants. This is achieved by activating audible/visual signaling devices throughout the building whenever a fire alarm initiating device (smoke detector, heat detector, sprinkler flow switch or manual station) is activated. A fire alarm system's secondary purpose is to provide property protection, which is an inherent side benefit of its installation.

Fire alarm systems can also be utilized for emergency control of other building systems, such as supply and return air fans and dampers, stairwell air pressurization fans, electromagnetic door-hold-open devices, and elevator recall.

Lastly, fire alarm system installations may be required to transmit alarm notification to the local fire department or other designated off-site monitoring service.

The key to the proper design and installation of a fire alarm system lies in an emphasis on the operation of the system as a whole, functioning in the specific environment (building) where it is installed. Requirements for fire alarm systems can vary greatly from building to building, making it necessary to carefully analyze the following:

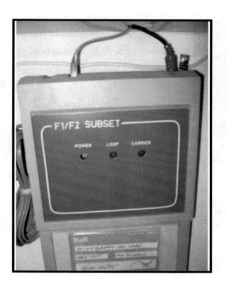

- National, provincial and local building and fire codes

- Type of occupancy

- Building structural considerations

- Special hazards

- Advice of the local Authority Having Jurisdiction

A study of these factors will assist in selecting the detection needs, zoning annunciation, signaling methods, type of operation, and many other design requirements.

## 8.4    Types of System

Once it has been established that a fire alarm system is either required by code (see Chapter 1) or desired by the building owner, the sequence of operation for the system, including the sequencing of audible and visual signals must be determined.

To understand the options, it is first necessary to define two signaling terms:

- An alert signal means 'an audible signal to advise designated persons of a fire emergency'.

- An alarm signal means 'an audible signal transmitted throughout a zone or zones or throughout a building to advise occupants that a fire emergency exists'.

Based upon the foregoing definitions, the two major types of fire alarm systems are described as follows:

### 8.4.1 Single-Stage

A single-stage system sounds an alarm signal throughout the facility on all audible signaling devices, and is activated by any manual station, heat or smoke detector or sprinkler alarm device.

### 8.4.2 Two-Stage

A two-stage fire alarm system causes an alert signal to sound upon the operation of any manual station, heat or smoke detector or sprinkler alarm device. If the alert signal is not acknowledged (via a switch at the fire alarm control unit) within 5 minutes of its initiation, an alarm signal will automatically sound (providing a fail-safe operation). In addition, each manual station is required to be equipped with a key-switch, so that the use of a key will cause an alarm signal to sound.

A two-stage system is intended for use in a building that employs trained and qualified supervisory staff (for example, building security personnel) 24 hours a day, 7 days a week. The first-stage, alert signal, serves to advise the emergency response personnel of a fire condition, so that they can immediately respond. These designated persons may then search for the source of activation, and if it is discovered to be a false alarm, the first-stage may be 'acknowledged' by activating the corresponding switch at the Fire Alarm Control Unit. This switch can perform one or two functions, depending on the system manufacturer and model. It may cancel the 5-minute timer, allowing the alert signal to continue, or it may cancel the timer and silence the signals simultaneously.

©

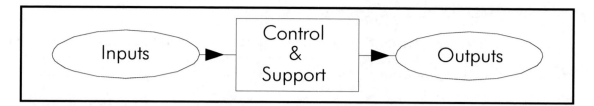

On the other hand, if within 5 minutes, the alert signal is not acknowledged (i.e.- the source of the activation has not been determined), the alarm signal will automatically sound, notifying occupants to leave the building immediately.

If the condition is discovered to be an actual fire, security personnel can activate the alarm signal at any time prior to the expiration of the five-minute timer, using the key-switch included in each manual station. The key-switches are connected to the G.A (General Alarm) circuit in the Fire Alarm Control Unit

The most common signal for the Alert has been a slow signal rate of 20 strokes-per-minute. A fast rate of 120 strokes-per-minute (or continuous). A temporal signal is used for the alarm signal. Of course, the alert and alarm signals may use, or sound on, the same signaling devices, even those with voice reproduction capability. For example the speakers may sound a slow pulsing tone for the alert signal, and temporal pattern tone pulses for the alarm signal. On new systems, the temporal pattern is used.

Two-stage systems also require a fail-safe mechanism with a timing circuit that will automatically initiate an evacuation alarm signal after five minutes if no action has been taken at the Control Unit by supervisory staff. This is meant to ensure that if supervisory staff is for some reason unable to respond to the Alert condition, occupant safety is not compromised. Any two-stage system requires trained, full time staff, who are on watch 24 hours a day, have the ability and authority to investigate and take steps to set in motion an evacuation plan to remove all persons in danger, and to decide whether to sound a general alarm. In many cases, the local fire department will have responded to the building within this five-minute time period.

Generally, the alert and alarm signals must be audible throughout the building to alert personnel. However in large complexes or special occupancies such as hospitals, or correctional facilities, many combinations exist where the alert signal is only heard in specially occupied areas, such as the Security Office, the Engineering and Maintenance Shop, Telephone Switchboard Rooms, and Management Offices. In health-care facilities, the failsafe feature is not required.

### 8.4.3 Modified Two-Stage Operation

One variation of the two-stage system operation is known as 'staged' signaling. Operation of this type can only be used if approved by the local Authority Having Jurisdiction.

In a modified two-stage system, it would be intended that the building be evacuated in phases, or on a floor-by-floor basis. This would usually be due to physical considerations such as the height of a high-rise building, or a high level of difficulty in evacuating hospital patients. In such occupancy, when any fire detection or manual device is activated, the alarm signal sounds in the affected area (or floor), while the alert signal sounds throughout the remainder of the building. The Alarm signaling area may be designated as the fire compartment involved, the floor involved, or the floor involved plus the floors immediately above and below. In this scenario, two-stage manual stations are still provided, allowing total evacuation of the building to be initiated from any floor exit. In addition, the Control Unit provides the capability of evacuating floors individually at any time, and perhaps of delivering voice messages to aid in the evacuation process. Staged systems are used mainly in hotels, some high- rise buildings and institutional occupancies.

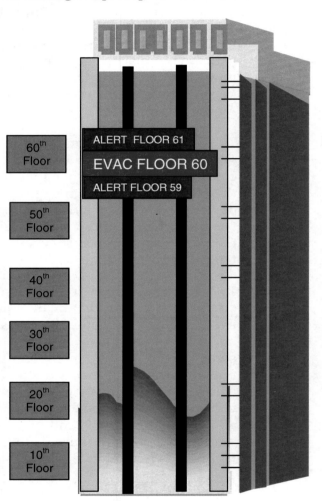

### 8.4.4 Zone-Coded System

Any single-stage or two-stage system can be zone-coded. This system generates different audible codes that are sounded by all signaling devices, and each code describes a particular section or area of the building. Upon hearing the specific code, security personnel will instantly know the location of the fire initiation. Such a code is either produced electro-mechanically or electronically and generates a predetermined,

©

patterned and distinctive signal. The coding mechanism may be integral to the control panel, or may be contained in coded manual stations, or may be a code transmitter to which ordinary initiating devices are connected.

Such a code must be repeated at least four times, and after completion of the coded signals the regular alert or alarm signals are to be sounded.

This type of system is often used in very large high hazard petrochemical facilities. The coded signaling is provided through exterior high power speaker arrays. This prevents the workers from evacuating the industrial facility through the fire-contaminated area.

**Industrial Coded System**

**Industrial Coded System Explosion**

### 8.4.5    Selection

We refer again to the *Building Code* to find the requirements for the proper choice of fire alarm system to use in a specific building:

- A single-stage system must be installed in a Group F - Division 1 building.

- A two-stage system must be installed in a Group B occupancy other than described below.

- A single-stage or a two-stage system may be used in a building three storeys or less in building height used for a children's custodial home, a convalescent home, or an orphanage.

- A single-stage or a two-stage system may be used in all other cases.

This would seem to suggest that there is full freedom of choice - but such is not the case:

- In schools, an immediate general alarm is recommended. Here, the first objective is to immediately warn students and faculty, so that they can remove themselves from any possible danger as rapidly as is consistent with orderly evacuation.

- In dormitories, many apartment houses, and barracks or in any building where people may be sleeping, and where qualified personnel are not constantly on hand to take advance action, an immediate general alarm is also recommended.

- In industrial plants, commercial buildings, and warehouses where workers tend to be scattered, moving about, or in obscure locations, an immediate general alarm is recommended.

- In department stores, and some other types of public assembly buildings, where large occupant loads with persons generally unfamiliar with the building and prone to panic, a two-stage system may be used.

- In most small office buildings, a single-stage system is recommended, however a two-stage system may be accepted by the Authority Having Jurisdiction in a high-rise office building, or major building complex, if there is an acceptable Fire Safety Plan strategy.

Beyond the code requirements, the type of system that can be selected depends on the mobility of the occupants being protected, and should be considered as part of the fire safety plan. The main question regarding occupants is whether they should be evacuated by an immediate general alarm that is sounded on the first actuation of an alarm-initiating device, or should they be left undisturbed until the fire has been investigated and an orderly evacuation procedure becomes necessary and is put into motion by supervisory personnel.

Consult the Authority Having Jurisdiction, and they will assist in determining the most appropriate system sequence.

## 8.5 Fire Alarm Systems - Zoning

### 8.5.1 Input Devices

Each input is represented by a physical 'zone', which consists of circuit wiring to one or more devices serving a part of, or an entire area.

Alarm-initiating zones are electrical circuits wired to field devices such as smoke or heat detectors, manual stations, or sprinkler alarm switches. Activation of any device connected to this type of zone will cause the audible signals to sound in accordance with the approved signaling sequence.

**Zoning Passive Graphic**

Supervisory initiating zones are electrical circuits wired to devices such as sprinkler valve supervisory switches or sprinkler low-pressure sensors. Activation of a device connected to a supervisory initiating zone will obviously not cause the building alert or alarm signals to sound, but will initiate a system supervisory trouble condition at the Control Unit (and remote annunciator if one is required).

Monitor initiating zones simply monitor the status of devices such as the open or closed status of fire dampers, the 'running' status of supply and return air fans, etc. Monitor zones do not activate audible devices or the system trouble signal, but annunciate their status via visual indicators only.

As previously stated, fire alarm devices are usually electrically grouped together, forming 'zones'. The concept of zoning provides a number of advantages and fire safety benefits, and is therefore required by code. Zoning provides a logical breakdown by building area, making it easier and faster to locate an activated initiating device. This reduces investigation time and results in less danger to building occupants and less damage from fire, as firefighting personnel can rapidly respond to the specific area.

Zoning also helps in case of a false alarm to quickly identify the offending device and to overcome such false alarm signals.

Any wiring faults from a broken wire or a ground fault condition can more easily be found if the circuit is in a small zone or area with fewer devices.

Zoning also provides a means to monitor the spread of fire, as smoke or flame may progress from zone to zone.

Lastly, zoning helps to minimize the area of protection loss, should a fire alarm circuit fail or be disabled.

## 8.5.2 Alarm initiating devices

The *Building Code* requires a separate zone for:

- each floor area so that the area of coverage for each zone in a building that is not sprinklered is not more than 2,000 square metres,

- each floor area so that the area of coverage for each zone is neither;

  - more than one storey, nor

  - more than the system area limits specified in NFPA 13 Standard for the Installation of Sprinkler Systems,

- each fire compartment required to have a 2 hr fire separation,

- each shaft requiring fire detectors,

- each air handling system required to be equipped with smoke detectors,

- each contained use area,

- each impeded egress zone, and

- certain fire compartments as further detailed in the *Building Code*.

The *Building Code* does regulate the minimum zoning requirements so that each floor of up to 2000 square metres is a zone. Stairs, garbage chutes, dumbwaiter or elevators shafts, all require separate zones. Since these shafts generally cut vertically through a building, they cannot be connected to a floor zone, as any fire could involve the entire shaft.

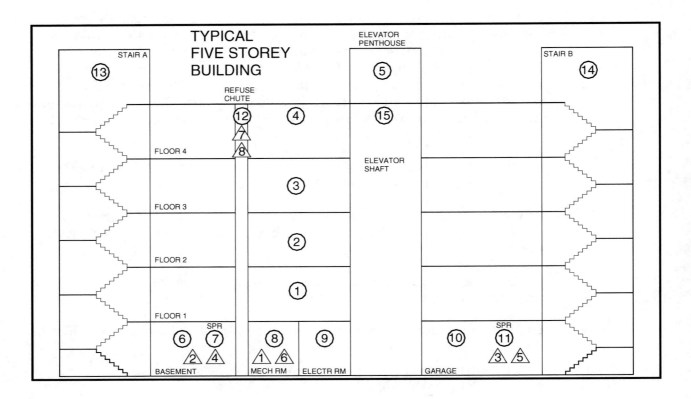

| ◯ ALARM INITIATING ZONES | | △ SUPERVISORY ZONES | |
|---|---|---|---|
| 1. | Floor 1 | 1. | Sprinkler Main Valve |
| 2. | Floor 2 | 2. | Basement Sprinkler Valve |
| 3. | Floor 3 | 3. | Garage Sprinkler Valve |
| 4. | Floor 4 | 4. | Basement Sprinkler Low Pressure |
| 5. | Elevator Penthouse | 5. | Garage Sprinkler Low Air Pressure |
| 6. | Basement | 6. | Standpipe Main Valve |
| 7. | Basement Sprinkler | 7. | Refuse Chute Sprinkler Valve |
| 8. | Basement Mechanical Room | 8. | Refuse Chute Sprinkler Low Pressure |
| 9. | Basement Electrical Room | | |
| 10. | Garage | | |
| 11. | Garage Sprinkler | | |
| 12. | Refuse Chute Sprinkler | | |
| 13. | Stair A | | |
| 14. | Stair B | | |
| 15. | Elevator Shaft | | |

Any room or area, separated by a two-hour fire resistant fire separation, other than dwelling units also requires a separate zone. As fire separations are a prime tool of fire containment, it is logical that such an area should also be separately identified.

©

Smoke detectors, which are required in an air-handling system, also require a separate zone for similar reasons as shafts.

Areas where persons are under legal restraint and are not able to freely evacuate are required to be separately zoned, in order to quickly identify the problem and evacuate as necessary.

When zoning of large areas is required, it is best to remember the reason for zoning, and to think in terms of fast and logical identification of an initiating device. The best zoning breaks are achieved using fire separations complete with fire or smoke barrier doors.

Where a room or space in a building extends through more than one storey, judgment must be exercised in the zoning. Generally, the lowest storey on which access is provided into the room or area should be used as the zoning area. It is also prudent to zone such an area separately from the rest of the floor area, so as to ensure prompt identification of such fires where the floor separations are breached.

Any non-sprinklered building, not more than 3 storeys in building height with an aggregate area of all storeys (including basements) of not more than 2000 m², does not require zoning of the fire alarm system. Again, caution should be used when using this latitude, as even in such buildings, the speedy area identification may help in finding the actual fire or false alarm condition.

Sprinklers need not be zoned as noted above, but must be zoned as per NFPA-13 requirements. The sprinkler maximum areas allowed will vary depending upon the hazard classification: light, ordinary and extra hazard. Light hazard and ordinary hazard has a zoning requirement of a maximum of 4,851 square metres and extra hazard of a maximum of 2,323 m². Such sprinklers are zoned through the use of water alarm switches, which must each be separately annunciated as zones on the fire alarm system. In addition, where floor areas are fully sprinklered, other alarm initiating devices (such as pull stations and smoke detectors) on the floor must be connected to a separate zone that serves the identical area as the sprinkler zone (i.e. 2,000 m² maximum limit is extended to 2,323 m² or 4,851 m².)

### 8.5.3    Supervisory devices

If the fire alarm system uses sprinklers as heat detection devices, then all of the following items are required to be provided with individual zone annunciation at the Fire Alarm Control Unit, and must indicate a supervisory/trouble signal on the building Fire Alarm Annunciator:

- each sprinkler system control valves,

- loss of water pressure,

- loss of air pressure in dry-pipe systems or pressure tanks,

- significant changes in water levels in water storage containers used for fire fighting,

- loss of electrical power to fire pump, and

- low temperature in dry-pipe systems or water containers used for fire fighting.

Similarly, control valves in standpipe and hose systems are also required to be supervised, so that the movement of a valve handle transmits a signal to the Fire Alarm Control Unit for annunciation purposes.

### 8.5.4    Required Annunciation

When more than one zone is required in a building, then zone annunciation must be provided at the designated fire department entrance to the building. Theoretically, the Control Unit could be installed in the Lobby. Good engineering practice suggests that the Control Unit should be located in a dry, warm, protected room such as an electrical room, and that an Annunciator should be installed in the Lobby. The annunciator must provide zone indicators (generally a red indication) for each alarm circuit, and zone indicators (a yellow indication) for each supervisory circuit. Beside each visual indication must be an identification label. The identification labels on an annunciator should use the numbers of the floors that they correspond to and their geographical designations, rather than descriptions of occupant usage, because these will be unfamiliar to fire fighting personnel.

In small buildings less than 2000 square meters and less than three stories high, an annunciator may not be required.

In single-stage systems, supplementary annunciators may be located in other areas such as the manager's or engineer's office.

In two-stage systems, the annunciators must be located to direct the staff, to assist them in speedy investigation of the fire and to help them implement evacuation plans. Therefore, in addition to the main annunciator at the street level entrance that is used for the firefighters' information, annunciators should be located in all key staff locations such as each nursing station, telephone operators' room, administration area, and engineer's office.

## 8.6    Output Circuits

Output circuits are classified by function:

- Signaling circuits

- Ancillary circuits

- Auxiliary circuits

Signaling circuits are those that are wired to, and control, audible and visual signaling devices. Upon activation of any alarm-initiating zone, signaling devices are activated according to the signaling operation sequence for the building. In a two-stage system, programming may be included in the control and support section to send the alarm signal to some signaling circuits, while routing the alert signal to others.

Zoning of signaling devices is not directly addressed in the *Building Code*, unless the building is required to have a voice communication system.

- Obviously in a single-stage system, all signaling devices sound simultaneously. There may be only one signaling circuit needed if there are only a few devices. Or there may be several such circuits. In the latter case, it does not matter which devices are connected onto the different circuits.

- Similarly, in a basic two-stage system, all devices make the same sound at the same time (i.e. all devices sound the alert or all sound the alarm).

- On the other hand, when a modified two-stage system is installed, some devices sound the alert while other devices are sounding the alarm. Signaling devices must therefore be appropriately wired onto the proper circuits.

When a voice communication system is required by code (in a building over 36 m in building height or in a Group B Division 2 occupancy exceeding 3 storeys in height), signaling devices (speakers) are required to be zoned by floor and by stairwell, to allow voice-paging into each of these specific areas.

## 8.7    System Riser Drawing

The purpose of device/area zoning, is that it allows rapid identification of the location of the fire.

This chapter has discussed multiple circuits from an installation wiring point of view for initiating, signaling and ancillary circuits. This information allows the creation of a typical system riser drawing.

The sample typical riser drawing shows probable conduit runs, wire quantities, devices and circuiting.

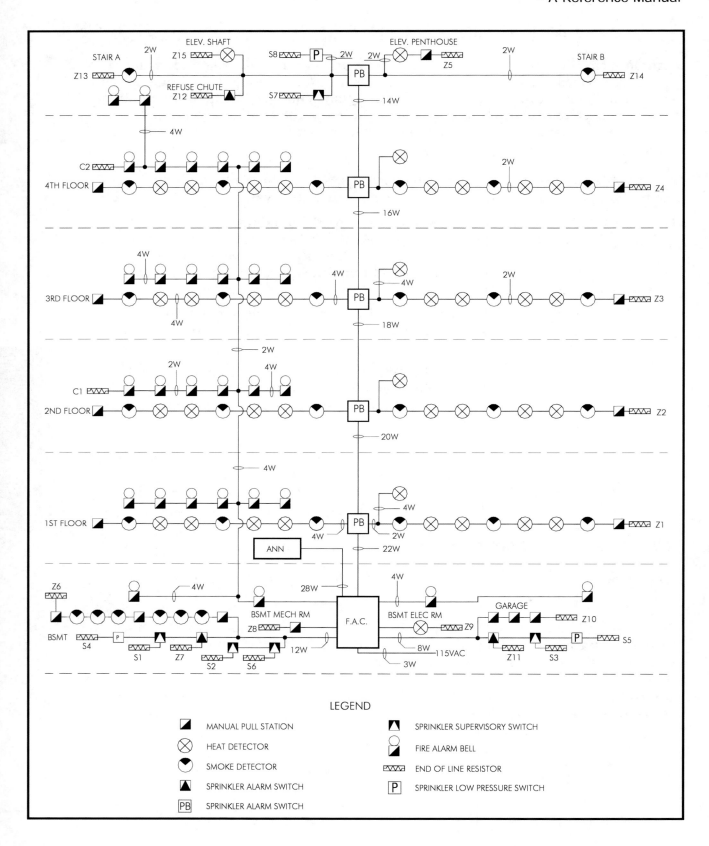

LEGEND

| | | | |
|---|---|---|---|
| MANUAL PULL STATION | | SPRINKLER SUPERVISORY SWITCH | |
| HEAT DETECTOR | | FIRE ALARM BELL | |
| SMOKE DETECTOR | | END OF LINE RESISTOR | |
| SPRINKLER ALARM SWITCH | | SPRINKLER LOW PRESSURE SWITCH | |
| PB | SPRINKLER ALARM SWITCH | | |

©

## 8.8    Emergency Voice Communications

The emergency voice communications system is comprised of both a one-way tone and voice paging system (using speakers as the audible signaling device), as well as an automatic two-way emergency telephone system.

### 8.8.1    Speaker System

The speaker system is a zoned-device, supervised-wire system, with 25 Volt or 70 Volt audio line distribution. Each operating signal zone or area is provided with one supervised speaker circuit. For voice paging, each speaker circuit is activated by a speaker zone selector switch. Operation of any speaker zone switch activates the corresponding speaker circuit for voice paging and illuminates the switch. The wiring to each speaker circuit must be supervised. The emergency paging communications system equipment and wiring must also be electrically supervised against opens, shorts and ground faults. A fault condition within any speaker circuit illuminates the corresponding zone trouble indicators on the Central Alarm and Control Facility. A short across a speaker circuit must prevent this circuit from being selected but does not effect the operation of other speaker circuits. The audible trouble signal is silenced while the microphone is being used or may be continuously silenced by the operation of a trouble silence switch. All trouble indications are extinguished automatically once the trouble condition has been corrected.

### 8.8.2    Handset System

The handset system comprises a remote telephone handset located near each exit from each floor area. Typically, a handset is installed at each manual station location. Lifting a remote handset causes an audible call-in signal and the corresponding floor number indicator flashes. Lifting the master telephone handset silences the audible call-in signal. Operating the flashing zone switch causes the telephone circuit to silence the call-placed tone at the remote telephone, allows two-way telephone communication and causes the zone switch lamp to be steadily illuminated. Lifting of one or more remote telephones from other zones, while a telephone conversation is in progress, flashes the corresponding zone indicators. A call-placed tone sounds on the remote telephones until the flashing zone switches have been operated. The operator is able to select two or more zones for a multiple line conversation.

### 8.8.3    Central Alarm And Control Facility (CACF)

The CACF is more a room than a product or device. The *Building Code* requires that (in certain buildings) a CACF be provided near the Fire Service designated entrance. The CACF room must contain all indicators and controls for all fire/life safety related systems in the building

In general terms the CACF must provide the following functional components:

- A Fire Alarm System Annunciator, showing all alarm and supervisory zone indications.

- Common alarm and supervisory visual and audible indicators

- A microphone with push-to-talk switch. The microphone should be a noise-canceling, hand-held dynamic microphone specifically designed for close-talking operation. The microphone should be constructed of high impact plastic and generally be fitted with a 1.5 m coiled cord.

- One selector switch per operating zone of speakers - usually one circuit/zone per floor and one circuit/zone per stairwell. Circuit select switches are of a maintained position type, for example `push-on push-off'. A separate switch may be provided which cancels or resets all selector switches at once. Associated with each selector switch is the printed circuit board module that provides for both electronic supervision of the wiring to the speakers and also the voice control for that circuit. Also associated with the switch are two visual indicators - one amber LED to indicate circuit trouble and one red LED to show operational power. A pre-announcement tone is provided to transmit an "attention" tone to areas selected by the speaker zone switches or all-call switch, prior to the delivery of voice instructions. The duration of the pre-announcement tone is pre-set by a built-in timer. The fire alarm signals are silenced during the pre-announcement tone and continue to be silenced during the public address announcement. The pre-announcement tone is activated by the operation of the press-to-talk switch on the microphone.

- An all-call switch permits messages to be transmitted throughout the building on all voice/signal circuits simultaneously (without operating individual paging zone select switches). Operation of the all-call switch activates the speaker zone circuit lights and illuminates the all-call switch. All fire alarm signals in the selected paging area(s) are silenced when the press-to-talk switch is operated. The fire alarm signals resound after a three second delay once the press-to-talk switch is released.

- A master handset with cradle switch,

- A selector switch per operating zone of handsets. Usually one zone per floor is provided. Associated with the switch are two visual indicators - one amber LED to indicate circuit trouble and one green LED to show call-in or operational power.

- A visual indicator to show that the paging system cannot be used manually during the initial alarm period. This is often referred to as the one-minute inhibit. The *Building Code* now limits the guaranteed alarm time to 30 seconds, and to 10 seconds for hospitals with supervisory staff on duty 24 hours a day,

- A visual indicator to show that the audible alarm signal has been inhibited by the voice-paging system,

- A switch may be provided in the CACF to allow a private conversation on the handset system, and

- A switch should be provided which will immediately cause a general alarm evacuation tone to be generated over all speaker zones.

These operating control switches, and audible and visual indicators are usually mounted on modular panels in the CACF. Nameplates are used to identify each component.

On the other hand they may be presented on a pictorial graphic layout of the building, with the control switches and visual indicators in the associated areas of the graphic, portraying, at a glance, operational zoning of the system. Such a graphic presentation must, of course, carry a ULC label, as must the entire CACF.

## 8.9    Suppression Systems

Variations of Fire Alarm Control Units are often used as Releasing Panels in special extinguishing system applications. The reliability and dependability of the ULC-Listed control units serves well in the fire detection of special hazards, and the releasing of a suppression agent. Such control units are separately listed by ULC as Releasing Panels.

Such systems are found in computer rooms, electrical control rooms and telephone switching centres. Suppression agents have included halons and other gases, CO2, foam and water. Examples would include pre-action sprinkler systems as well as deluge sprinkler systems.

Most suppression systems control fire through removal of the surrounding air (such as $CO_2$) or by interruption of the continuous chain reaction which we all know as the fourth side of the 'fire 'triangle'.

Designers of these special suppression systems are very interested in early-warning detection capabilities. The intent of course is to detect a fire condition as quickly as is technically possible so that supervisory personnel can immediately intervene in order to manually control the fire situation before the system automatically discharges. Most often, the detection method of choice is the common smoke detector, or the faster acting flame detector.

Most discharges result in a certain amount of clean-up, disruption of the process taking place in the protected area, and a costly re-charge of the system. For these reasons, it is expected that the system will discharge only after a fire condition has been proven.

Smoke detectors are known to be reliable, however nuisance alarms can occur. Several automatic methods of alarm confirmation have been used over the years to ensure that discharge does not take place without first having confirmation of an

8: System Operational Principles

alarm condition. One such system is called Cross-Zoning and another is called Priority Matrix.

Occasionally, the monitoring and controlling of special extinguishing systems is included in the building's Fire Alarm System Control Unit. Generally however, most fire protection designers prefer to have a totally separate Control Unit and system for the special suppression system. The Fire Alarm Technician must be exceedingly careful to understand whether or not the special extinguishing system devices, circuits and controls are completely separate from the Fire Alarm System and Control Unit, or are a part of the Fire Alarm System, before beginning any hands-on inspection and testing of the Fire Alarm System.

### 8.9.1    Cross-Zoned Systems

In rooms to be protected such as Computer Rooms, smoke detectors often are installed alternately on two different circuits or zones. If there are 10 smoke detectors spaced equally on a ceiling, then five would be on circuit 'A' and the other five would be on circuit 'B'. There would also be manual Discharge stations (blue, or orange or yellow) and manual Abort stations installed near the exits from the protected area. Typically the Control Unit would be installed in the room. Lastly, two different audible signaling devices would be in the room: a 'first-zone' bell, and a 'both-zones' horn.

A typical sequence of operation might be as follows: any smoke detector sensing smoke will put the Control Unit into alarm, sounding the first-zone bell. Responding personnel can quickly determine which detector has initiated the alarm, and take action. If the fire condition continues and spreads, the smoke will trigger another adjacent detector putting the second zone into alarm. This will trigger the cross-zoning sequence, sounding the horn and beginning a discharge timer. After the pre-set time, if the Abort Station has not been operated, the suppression agent will be discharged.

Discharge can take place prior to this foregoing sequence if the Manual Discharge station is operated.

### 8.9.2    Priority Matrix

A similar end-result is achieved through installation of a system called Priority Matrix. This is achieved through the use of addressable smoke detectors. Any one smoke detector will put the Control Unit into 'first-detector' mode sounding the bell and identifying the alarmed detector. Subsequent alarm operation of any other device will put the Control Unit into discharge mode.

## 8.10   Chapter Summary

1.   All Control Units are comprised of input circuits, output circuits and both ancillary and auxiliary control sections.

2.   Smaller uncomplicated buildings not containing special occupancies such as health-care tend to use simple single-stage evacuation systems. On the other hand, high buildings and buildings housing mixed major occupancies, or occupancies falling under Group B classifications (as an example) tend to use systems designed around two-stage operation.

3.   Proper and accurate zoning of both alarm and supervisory initiating devices, is extremely important to the responding Fire Service.

4.   Fire Alarm System zoning and sprinkler system zoning areas must correspond to each other.

5.   Ancillary devices and systems are not a part of the Fire Alarm System but they are part of the overall fire/life safety features in any building.

6.   Systems that carry voice messages are valuable because they can carry voice messages in addition to the alarm tones. This allows the Fire Service to convey possibly critical information to building occupants during a fire emergency condition.

7.   A designer can choose between 25-volt and 70-volt speaker systems. It may be a trade-off between possibly longer speaker circuits and the cost of having to install the speaker circuits in separate conduits.

8.   In high buildings, the *Building Code* requires the construction of a CACF in/near the Fire Service designated entrance, because the CACF can allow the Fire Service to be most effective when using all aspects of the buildings emergency and safety systems.

9.   A riser drawing of a proposed system is a great way to quickly understand the general arrangement of the new system

10.   Ancillary features in a building are always monitored or controlled by the Fire Alarm System because they all must function as a cohesive network to have the greatest benefit to building occupants.

## 8.11    Review Questions

| # | ? | Question | Section |
|---|---|----------|---------|
| **8-1** | | **An alert signal means** | |
| | A | 'An audible signal to advise designated persons of a fire emergency'. | |
| | B | 'an audible signal transmitted throughout a zone or zones or throughout a building to advise occupants that a fire emergency exists'. | |
| | C | A 'supervisory' condition rather than an alarm condition. | |
| | D | All of the Above | |
| **8-2** | | **An alarm signal means** | |
| | A | 'An audible signal to advise designated persons of a fire emergency'. | |
| | B | 'An audible signal transmitted throughout a zone or zones or throughout a building to advise occupants that a fire emergency exists'. | |
| | C | A 'supervisory' condition rather than an alarm condition. | |
| | D | All of the Above | |
| **8-3** | | **The system that is intended for use in a building that employs trained and qualified supervisory staff (for example, building security personnel) 24 hours a day, 7 days a week is a:** | |
| | A | Single-stage | |
| | B | Two-stage | |
| | C | Coded | |
| | D | All of the above | |
| **8-4** | | **The signal sequence that best describes when any fire detection or manual device is activated, the alarm signal sounds in the affected area (or floor), while the alert signal sounds throughout the remainder of the building is?** | |
| | A | Single-Stage Operation | |
| | B | Two-Stage Operation | |
| | C | Modified Two-Stage Operation | |
| | D | All of the Above | |

©

| # | ? | Question | Section |
|---|---|---|---|
| 8-5 | | _____provides a logical breakdown by building area, making it easier and faster to locate an activated initiating device. | |
| | A | Transponders | |
| | B | Zoning | |
| | C | Manual stations | |
| | D | Heat Detectors | |
| 8-6 | | **A discrete zone description is code required for** | |
| | A | Duct smoke detectors serving a supply fan unit that serves multiple compartments on multiple levels | |
| | B | Light hazard and ordinary hazard serving a floor area of a maximum of 4,851 square meters | |
| | C | A hydro vault with a two hour separation | |
| | D | All of the above | |
| 8-7 | | **Voice communication system is required by code based on the following:** | |
| | A | A building over 10 m in building height or in a Group A occupancy exceeding 1 storeys in height | |
| | B | A building over 26 m in building height or in a Group C occupancy exceeding 2 storeys in height | |
| | C | A building over 36 m in building height or in a Group B Division 2 occupancy exceeding 3 storeys in height | |
| | D | A building over 16 m in building height or in a Group D occupancy exceeding 13 storeys in height | |
| 8-8 | | **When a Cross-Zoned System is provided protect a Computer Rooms, which of the following statements are true?** | |
| | A | The smoke detectors are installed alternately on two different circuits or zones. | |
| | B | If there are 10 smoke detectors spaced equally on a ceiling, then five would be on circuit 'A' and the other five would be on circuit 'B'. | |
| | C | There would also be manual Discharge stations (blue, or orange or yellow) and manual Abort stations installed near the exits from the protected area. | |
| | D | All of the above | |

| # | ? | Question | Section |
|---|---|----------|---------|
| **8-9** | | **The parts of a building, such as aisles, hallways or corridors that provide a clear path to an exit serving that floor area is identified as:** | |
| | A | Access-To-Entrance Door | |
| | B | Access-To-Garage Overhead | |
| | C | Access-To-Dwelling Unit | |
| | D | Access-To-Exit | |
| **8-10** | | **Fire alarm systems can also be utilized for emergency control of other building systems, such as supply and return air fans and dampers, stairwell air pressurization fans, electromagnetic door-hold-open devices, and elevator recall.** | |
| | A | True | |
| | B | False | |

©

# Chapter 9: Distributed Processing Systems

## 9.1    Chapter Overview and Key Concepts

A great deal of conduit, wire and associated labour is required to install a conventional multi-zone Fire Alarm System. The installation of the zone pairs as well as the annunciation wires, from the different floors down to one central Control Unit, all adds up to a very costly situation.

The benefit of a Distributed Processing System falls out from the reduction in the cost of wire, the cost of smaller conduit systems and the greatly reduced cost of the labour required to properly install all of the above. Basically, the Control Unit can be split up into several sections, located in different parts of the building, and all talking to one another via multiplex communications.

The control unit segments are called 'transponders' and they communicate with one another over a cable referred to as a Data Communication Link (DCL). Early versions of these systems were organized with all control being undertaken by a Central Data Processing Unit.

Be aware that some of these systems may require special trunk cabling (e.g. twisted, shielded pairs) for the central wiring.

The early Master/Slave relationship has now been supplanted by Peer-to-Peer networks, where all individual Control Units share system status information but control their own areas. Centralized control is only initiated via manual operator intervention.

## 9.2    Learning Objectives

Upon successful completion of this chapter, the reader should be able to:

- Understand why conventional systems, particularly in high buildings, are so costly to install.

- Understand the significant survivability advantage offered by Peer-to-Peer systems vs. Master Slave systems.

- Understand the colour coded annunciation requirements for control and status in Command Centres.

- Understand the basic operator interfaces provided by a Command Centre.

## Language defined - Chapter Glossary (Also see Main Glossary)

Throughout the various codes and standards, certain words and phrases are used to identify specific items, situations, assemblies or processes. Before beginning a study of any of these documents, it is important that the definitions applicable to fire protection are clearly understood. Failure to understand the meaning of a defined term in a code requirement often leads to an incorrect interpretation of that requirement. Special terms that will be found in this chapter are listed below. Also refer to the Main Glossary at the end of this Manual.

| Term | Definition |
|---|---|
| **Active Field Device** | A device that can be uniquely identified by the control unit to determine its presence and operating status, and which may be commanded to operate or to change its operating parameters independently of other field devices that share a common circuit |
| **Addressable Device** | A device which can be individually and uniquely identified by a control unit. The address is set using binary/hexadecimal/decimal methods using dip switches, rotary switches or solid-state memory |
| **Alarm Signal** | An audible signal transmitted throughout a zone or zones to advise occupants that a fire emergency exists; also called an EVACUATION signal |
| **Alert Signal** | An audible signal intended to advise designated persons of a fire emergency |
| **Ancillary Device** | A device that performs a life safety related function, but that is not part of the fire alarm system |
| **Authority Having Jurisdiction** | The organization, office, or individual responsible for approving equipment, an installation, or a procedure. Most often, it is the municipal Fire Department |
| **Bonding** | The permanent low-impedance path obtained by joining all non-current-carrying metal parts to ensure electrical continuity, and with the capacity to conduct safely any current likely to be imposed on it |
| **Building Height (in storeys)** | The number of storeys contained between the roof and the floor of the first storey. An elevator machine room, sitting atop an office building, would not generally be considered a storey in this application |
| **Closure** | A device for shutting off an opening through a fire separation. Example: a door, shutter or fire damper |

©

| Term | Definition |
|---|---|
| **Control Unit** | A device with the necessary circuits or components needed to provide acceptable operating power for a fire alarm system, receive signals from alarm initiating devices, cause audible alarm signals to operate, and electrically monitor the installation wiring and device placement against certain faults and/or removal |
| **Dwelling Unit** | A suite operated as a housekeeping unit, used or intended to be used, as a domicile by one or more persons and usually containing cooking, eating, living, sleeping and sanitary facilities |
| **Exit** | A facility such as a door, stairs or ramp that leads from the floor area that it serves to an open public thoroughfare, or to a protected exterior open space that has access to an open public thoroughfare. Once in an exit facility, a person should have a continuous path leading to the building exterior |
| **Fire Compartment** | An enclosed space, separated from all other parts of the building by fire separations having the required fire-resistance rating |
| **Fire Separation** | A construction assembly that acts as a barrier against the spread of fire. A fire separation may or may not have a fire resistance rating |
| **Floor Area** | The space on any storey of a building between the exterior walls and required firewalls, including the space occupied by interior walls and partitions, but not including exits and vertical service spaces that pierce the storey |
| **Ground Fault** | A circuit impedance to ground sufficient to prevent normal operation |
| **Means Of Egress** | A continuous path of travel provided for the escape of persons from any point in a building or contained open space to a separate building, an open public thoroughfare, or an exterior open space protected from fire exposure from the building and having access to an open public thoroughfare. Means of egress includes exits and access to exits |
| **Open-Circuit Fault** | Means a circuit series resistance increase of 10 kOhm or more, unless otherwise stated, resulting from an abnormal condition |
| **Short-Circuit Fault** | A resistance shunt of 0.1 Ohm or less across a circuit, unless otherwise stated, resulting from an abnormal condition |
| **Supporting Field Device** | An active field device that monitors other field devices on a separate circuit and reports the status of that separate circuit to the control unit |
| **Trouble Signal** | A signal (usually a buzzer and an amber lamp) indicating a fault or an off-normal condition in a fire alarm system |

9. Distributed
Processing Systems

## 9.3      Hardwired Systems vs. Multiplex Systems:

### 9.3.1      Hardwired Systems

As we have previously discussed, a typical fire alarm system consists of a number of input circuits and output circuits connected to a central fire alarm control unit. An individual input circuit would monitor the various detection devices in a given fire zone while the individual output circuits would control the various signaling devices in a given fire zone. If the particular fire alarm system is protecting a building with multiple floors, the cost of running wire and conduit all the way from the main control panel to each of the remote zones located throughout the building can be considerably high.

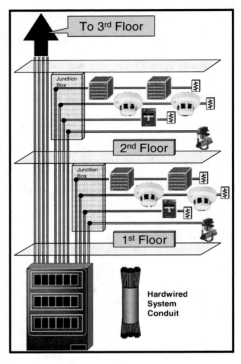

Realizing that each circuit on each floor requires a pair of conductors, the diameter of the conduit that is required to accommodate all of the conductors can become very large. And pulling all of the various conductors from the main floor (or sometimes from the basement if the main fire panel is located there) involves many hours of labour. This cost represents the greatest drawback associated with a hard-wired fire alarm system. As you will discover in this chapter, there is an alternative.

### 9.3.2      Distributed Systems

When the capacity of a given Fire Alarm System reaches a certain point, the cost of installation can be significantly reduced by distributing the monitoring and control capabilities throughout the building rather than concentrating all the equipment in one central location.

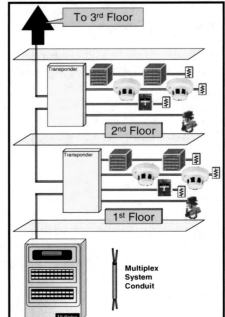

Primarily, the benefit lies with the reduction in the cost of wire, the cost of larger conduit systems and the cost of the labour required to properly install all of the above. With modern fire alarm technology, many separate panels can be installed throughout the building and those panels would still be able to communicate with one another to provide the same functionality as a centrally located system.

The system layout seems quite similar to the previous hardwired system drawing, however, each junction box has been replaced with a "transponder" and the conduit size and wire capacity is significantly less.

### 9.3.3 Master-Slave Distributed Systems

The original "multiplex" systems, that provided a dramatic departure from hard-wired systems, relied on "master-subordinate" (a.k.a. Master-Slave) architecture. The name said it all: Each "system" consisted of one "MASTER" and numerous "SLAVES". These two basic components worked together to create a multiplex system. The "control unit", which is also sometimes referred to as the "main" fire alarm panel, would be considered the "master". All remote fire panels (the Slaves) would be referred to as "Transponders" or Data Gathering Panels (DGPs).

The "master" provided all the "brains" of the system. It would constantly interrogate each of the "slave" panels to gather information that it would use to determine what action needed to be taken. When an appropriate piece of information provided by a "slave" panel was given to the "master" panel, the master panel would initiate commands to the slave panels to activate outputs accordingly. This master-slave communications scheme relied on the "brains" of the master and the integrity of the communications links to ensure success. Without either the master commands or the communication links, the system would not operate.

This "Achilles heel" was due to the lack of "brains" built into the "slave" panels or "transponders". While these "Transponders" could perform monitoring of inputs and they could activate outputs, their intelligence was quite limited. Their true role was to act as slave fire alarm control units that reported the status of their circuits to, and have outputs controlled by, the master panel. They did not perform any decision-making at all. Rather, they functioned similar to an addressable device. For a Transponder in a Master-Slave system, life is fairly simple: Each transponder is continuously polled by the "master" fire alarm control panel for its status. In response, each transponder would transmit their status information back to the "master" in serial data format.

Depending on the information contained in a particular transponder's response from the master's poll, the main fire alarm panel (master) CPU may react by sending a message to a transponder to activate any of its output circuit functions (signal circuits or ancillary relays).

The real advantage of using transponders is, once again, the reduction in riser wiring, raceway size, and installation labour, which reduces overall cost. These two efficiencies can represent a large financial benefit in large horizontal floor areas and in multi-storey high-rise buildings.

Conduit size and wiring for a hardwired system (top) and a multiplex system (bottom) – shown at right

Can you see the difference?

In high buildings classified under section 3.2.6. of the *Building Code*, protection of conductors must also be considered. A one-hour fire separation is required for vertical conductors that form part of a fire alarm or emergency voice communication system. This can be accomplished by

i) a fire-separated wiring shaft

ii) using mineral insulated fire-rated cable, or

iii) constructing an approved, continuous fire-rated enclosure around the conductors.

These are important code requirements.

The other and equally important source of installation requirements is the system manufacturer. The manufacturer may have certain specific wiring needs. For example, a particular system may need twisted-shielded conductors to promote reliable communications between all system components.

Although the cost savings of system wiring can be significant, considerations must be made to allow the system to provide a reasonable level of operation even when a transponder fails to communicate with the master. In the event of a Data Communication Link (DCL) failure, transponders resort to their own fire alarm backup firmware, which often activates all outputs within that transponder upon reception of any

©

alarm from their monitored circuits. This operation is called "stand alone capability". For this reason, *ULC-S524* requires one transponder to house *the signal circuits **and** the alarm initiating circuits* that serve the <u>same building area(s)</u>.

### *ULC-S524*

> *4.2.5 Except as noted in Subsection 4.3, Large Scale Network Systems, in distributed systems employing transponder units with stand alone capability and incorporating both input circuits and output circuits shall be in accordance with the following:*
>
> A *The transponders shall have signal silence, reset, and trouble silence switches with visual indicators, degraded mode and stand alone capability indicators; and*
>
> B *The building area served by such a transponder shall cover the same area for both input circuits and output circuits.*

If you consider what could happen if the signal circuits for a given area were not controlled by a panel that monitored the initiation circuits for that same area, you'd realize that the results could be disastrous. If the communication between all the Slave panels and the Master were not functioning properly, you could have a situation where a fire was detected in one area, but due to a communication fault, the signals (controlled by a separate Slave panel) would not operate!

Another pitfall to realize is associated with default stand-alone mode. If all ancillary relays activated upon any local alarm, results may be disastrous. These ancillary outputs may control fans or dampers and default operation may provide conditions that accelerate the spread of fire rather than provide greater life safety.

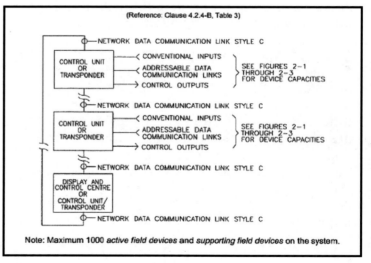

(Reference: Clause 4.2.4-B, Table 3)

Note: Maximum 1000 *active field devices* and *supporting field devices* on the system.

Due to the potential for Master-Slave systems to fail, the ULC standard dictates that their system capacity is limited. The diagram below indicates that a Master-Slave system utilizing Style C wiring be limited to a total system capacity of 1000 points.

## 9.4　　Peer-to-Peer Distributed Systems

Modern "multiplex" systems have improved upon the old "master-subordinate" multiplex systems and their primary downfall: All the eggs in one basket! Rather than relying on one "master" in the system to make all the reactive decisions and to issue all the commands to its subordinate transponders, new systems provide peer-to-peer functionality. Peer, meaning equal, ensures that each and every fire panel connected to the fire alarm network has the intelligence, capability and capacity to monitor all inputs and control all outputs throughout its building jurisdiction. In other words, Peer-to-Peer systems do not have a "master" at all. Rather, they are all equal "peers", and each "peer" can handle its own decisions.

Due to this "equality" among panels, each panel is often referred to as a "node" or "network node" so the term "peer" and "node" are often intermixed. In a true Peer-to-Peer system, each panel (a.k.a. node) has the ability to control all of its inputs and outputs without receiving any commands from a master panel. Instead, each peer responds to information reported by any of the other peers rather than from a command issued by another peer. Keep in mind that each individual peer is not responding to "commands" from another peer. Rather, each peer is responding, on its own, in reaction to "information" being reported by other peers. All responsive action is taken based upon the internally programmed functionality of each individual peer.

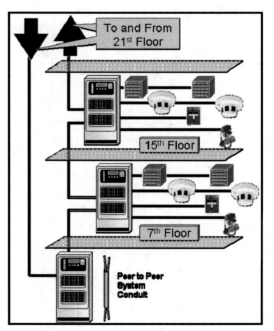

This new type of network provides much more redundancy than a Master-Slave system, as each peer does not rely on the master to operate. Rather, each peer performs its own decision-making and reacts according to the information reported by all other nodes.

This added survivability and functionality of the Peer-to-Peer system over the Master-Slave system is reflected in *CAN/ULC-S524 Installation of Fire Alarm Systems*. Table 3 indicates the maximum capacities of various fire alarm systems – and each capacity varies depending on the type of system being used. If the system is using a Master-Slave operation, the capacity is limited, while if the system is a Peer-to-Peer operation, there is no limit imposed.

**TABLE 3**
**CAPACITIES OF SYSTEMS UTILIZING DATA COMMUNICATION**
**LINKS WITHIN A SINGLE BUILDING**

(Reference: Clauses 4.2.3, 4.2.4, 4.3.1)

| APPLICATION OF DATA COMMUNICATION LINKS (DCL) | MAXIMUM NUMBER OF ACTIVE FIELD DEVICES AND SUPPORTING FIELD DEVICES | | |
|---|---|---|---|
| | DCLA* | DCLB* | DCLC* |
| **PART I**<br><br>EACH ADDRESSABLE DEVICE DATA COMMUNICATION LINK) ORIGINATING IN A CONTROL UNIT OR TRANSPONDER.<br><br>See Notes 1, 3, and 4 | 300** | 200** | 300** |
| | ** This includes all addressable devices on the CIRCUIT | | |
| **PART II**<br><br>NETWORK DATA COMMUNICATIONS LINK INTERCONNECTING CONTROL UNITS, TRANSPONDERS, OR DISPLAY AND CONTROL CENTRES<br><br>See Notes 1, 2, 4 and 5 | Not permitted<br>(See Note 5) | Not permitted<br>(See Note 5) | 1000*** |
| | *** This includes all addressable devices on the SYSTEM. | | |
| **PART III**<br><br>LARGE SCALE NETWORK DATA COMMUNICATIONS LINKS INTERCONNECTING CONTROL UNITS, TRANSPONDERS, OR DISPLAY AND CONTROL CENTRES AS A LARGE SCALE NETWORK IN COMPLIANCE WITH SUBSECTION 4.3, LARGE SCALE NETWORK SYSTEMS.<br><br>See Notes 1, 4 and 5 | Not permitted<br>(See Note 5) | Not permitted<br>(See Note 5) | Unlimited*** |
| | ***Note: This includes all addressable devices on the SYSTEM. | | |

| |
|---|
| General Note: Refer to Table 1 to assist in the selection of the most applicable *data communication links* wiring style shown in this Table, based on the corresponding performance. |
| *Refer to Glossary, Section 2, for definitions of *data communication link style A, data communication link style B*, and *data communication link style C*. |
| Note 1: Refer to Figures 2-1 through 2-5 for examples of Parts I, II and III. |
| Note 2: Where this capacity is exceeded, refer to Subsection 4.3, Large Scale Network Systems. |
| Note 3: Where the capacity is exceeded on a single *data communication link*, additional links shall be added. |
| Note 4: Also refer to other limiting factors such as, response time (refer to Table 2), National Building Code of Canada zoning requirements, and need for *fault isolation modules* (refer to Subsection 4.2, Data Communications Link). |
| Note 5: *Data communication link Style A* or *data communication link Style B* are permitted for dedicated network communication to *annunciators*. |

Peer-to-Peer systems perform better than the older Master-Slave systems when faced with wiring faults such as grounds, short or open circuits. In the past, a shorted pair of communication conductors could knock out an entire master-slave system as no communication could occur between the transponders and the master. One of the major reasons for this liability was inherent with a Class B wiring scheme, which provided just one path for communications between a Master Panel and a Slave Panel. In addition, older Master-Slave systems could not provide "short-circuit" sensing technology that would have allowed them to switch to an alternate communications path if it was available.

## 9.5    Degraded-Mode Operation

Now with peer-to-peer technology, each panel has two paths available on which to communicate with other panels. If the first path fails, a given panel can switch to use the alternate path. Thus, each peer has the ability to divorce itself from faulty segments of the network communication conductors if a shorted circuit is sensed. This wiring topology is called DCLC in the ULC installation standard. The result is that the entire fire alarm system will be completely functional, and able to communicate with all other panels even while the wiring problem is present. While functioning under these circumstances (communicating via alternate wiring path only), the system is said to be working in Degraded Operation.

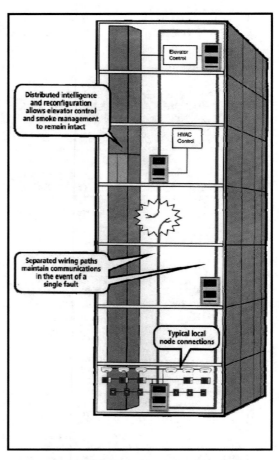

**Preferred DCLC Communications
Routing in High-Rise Buildings**

As noted in *CAN/ULC S524 Installation of Fire Alarm Systems*:

- When control units using transponders or addressable devices serve more than one floor area to a maximum size of 2000 m², a fault within one floor area shall not prevent the normal operation of other input or output field devices in another floor area.

- In systems using Data Communications Links, loss of information shall be limited to one floor area through the use of good engineering practices.

- In distributed systems employing transponder units, the building area served by a transponder shall cover the same area for both input circuits and output circuits.

## 9.6    Testing of DCLC OPERATION

*CAN/ULC-S536 Inspection and Testing of Fire Alarm Systems* specifies the method to be used to test the "redundant" operation of a peer-to-peer network fire alarm system to ensure that the DCLC functionality is working properly.

©

In the standard, it reads:

> 5.6.3 *Where fault isolation in data communication links is provided*
> *between control units or transponders and between transponders,*
> *introduce a short circuit fault and confirm annunciation of the fault*
> *and operation outside the shorted section between each pair of:*
> A    *Control unit to control unit;*
> B    *Control unit to transponder; and*
> C    *Transponder to transponder.*

A diagram showing a testing sequence for peer-to-peer based systems is shown below.

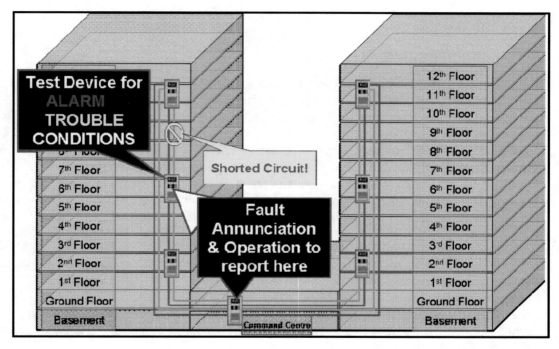

## 9.7    Standalone Operation

If the communication links between peer-to-peer nodes are further compromised and the alternate path is prevented from operating, another term is used to describe panel operation. Within the ULC standard there are other requirements for "stand-alone" operation of peer-to-peer panels. "Stand-Alone" refers to the state of system operation that occurs when both paths of a DCLC communication loop fail. Each panel operating in stand-alone mode must be able to accomplish the same reaction to fire conditions as if it was still communicating with other nodes on the network. The main difference is that it would only react to fire conditions detected by its own monitoring circuits, rather than fire conditions reported by another node's monitoring circuits.

In addition to loss of communication signals, the system must also be tolerant of a loss of audio signals that may originate from another node (possibly the main Voice Command Centre). If alert and alarm tones are generated by the main fire alarm command centre CPU and distributed to each transponder via audio wiring, provisions must be made for the transponders to incorporate "backup" tone generators in case of audio signal failure. The local "backup" tone generators would allow the node that is working in "stand-alone" mode to deliver the same audible alarm signals as if it was still connected to a functioning audio riser.

As stated in the S524 standard:

> 4.3   LARGE SCALE NETWORK SYSTEMS
>
> > 4.3.9   Each transponder and control unit shall provide both alert signal and alarm signal tone generators for degraded mode of operation.

## 9.8   Voice Systems

Systems that utilize peer-to-peer technology are often protecting large buildings and thus, building codes often require these large buildings to be equipped with voice-evacuation systems. In this case, a main annunciator panel or main control and command centre is likely equipped with a paging microphone and various toggle switches or buttons used to control the delivery of ALERT Tones, ALARM Tones, and PAGING ZONE selection for live voice announcement delivery. In these systems, audio riser wiring originates from the main control centre and is distributed throughout the entire peer-to-peer network. The single point of origin for the system ensures that any alarm tones being broadcast will be synchronized, regardless if the tones are being broadcast from different speakers that are connected to different fire alarm nodes.

The remote peers are equipped with Audio tone Generators, but often do not have microphones. To meet the requirement shown above (4.3.9) the remote peers must have built-in sensing technology to determine if the audio signals emanating from the audio signal riser are usable, valid signals. If the audio signal riser is compromised, and the audio signals being broadcast from the Main Voice Command Centre stop arriving at the remote peer, "back-up" tone generators must be available in the remote peer to provide the ALERT Tones and ALARM Tones necessary to alert occupants when required. In this case, the Local Tones may not be synchronized with the Tones being broadcast by other nodes that are using the audio riser source rather than their local audio tone source.

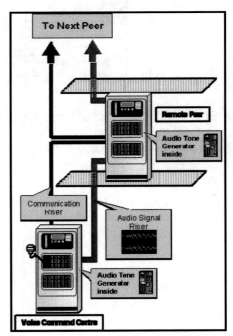

©

It is quite common today to have more than one location available for an operator to deliver voice announcements and control audio tones. In some installations, a remote annunciator is equipped with a paging microphone and control switches, yet all of the signals from the remote annunciator are routed via the main command centre. This design configuration, shown at right, would not represent a good engineering practice. If the main command centre failed to operate properly, or was severed from the network, the remote paging microphone would also surely be inoperative.

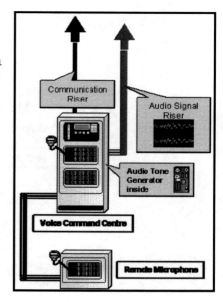

For this reason, many large-scale network systems incorporate a secondary command and control centre that is equipped with its own audio control system, completely independent from the primary audio command and control centre.

When the secondary command centre is used, various controls are activated to "grant" control to the secondary command centre. At that time, all remote peer-to-peer nodes would begin to receive their audio signals from the secondary command centre instead of the primary command centre. This type of set-up provides true redundancy.

## 9.9    Central Alarm And Control Facility (CACF)

In general terms the CACF should provide the following functional components:

- A microphone with push-to-talk switch,

- One selector switch per operating zone of speakers - usually one zone per floor and one zone per stairwell. Once operated, operation remains selected until de-selected. A separate switch may be provided which cancels or resets all selector switches at once. All of the LED indicators associated with each selector switch must follow the colour codes indicated by Table 3 of *ULC-S527 – Standard for Control Panels for Fire Alarm Systems*, depending on the function of each switch. See table, below:

ULC-S527-99                    June, 1999

# TABLE 5

### VISUAL INDICATORS - COLOUR CODE

(Reference Clauses: 3.2.7, 3.11.1.6-A, 3.17.8-D, 3.18.1-D)

| FUNCTION | COLOUR |
|---|---|
| Alarm Inputs | Red |
| *Alarm Signal* | Red with unique identifier |
| *Alert Signal* | Red with unique identifier |
| Page Select | Green |
| Signal Circuit fault | Yellow |
| *Ancillary Device* 'on' | Green or Blue |
| *Ancillary Device* 'off' | Yellow or Blue |
| Telephone Call-in | Flashing Green |
| Telephone Select | Green |
| Telephone Circuit Fault | Yellow |
| Inhibit | Yellow |
| Preannounce | Yellow |
| Supervisory Inputs | Yellow with unique identifier |
| Power - on | Green |
| *Trouble Signal* | Yellow |
| *Alarm Signal* Silence | Yellow |
| Automatic *Alarm Signal* Activation Timer | Green |
| Automatic *Alarm Signal* Timer Cancelled (Acknowledged) | Yellow |

- An "All-Call" switch is provided to permit messages to be transmitted throughout the building on all voice/signal circuits simultaneously (without operating individual paging zone select switches). Operation of the all-call switch activates the speaker zone circuit lights and illuminates the associated all-call LED indicator.

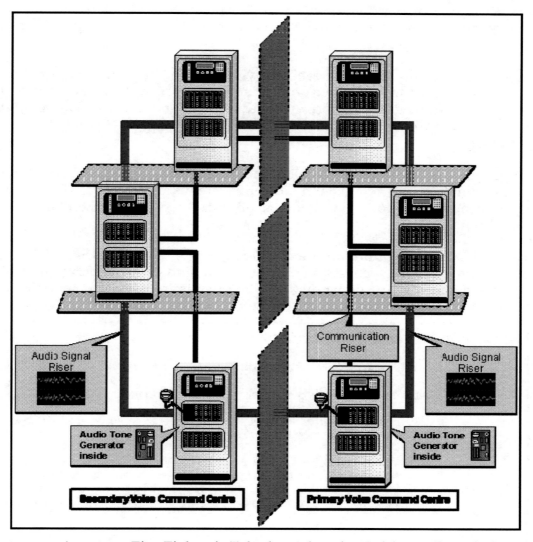

- A master Fire Fighter's Telephone handset with cradle switch

- A selector switch per operating zone of remote Fire fighters' telephone handsets.

- A visual indicator to show that the paging system cannot be used manually during the first minute of alarm - the one-minute inhibit (30 seconds in a hospital). Note that the latest edition of the Building Code permits a duration as short as 30 seconds and permits hospitals with 24 hour supervisory personnel to be only 10 seconds),

- A visual indicator to show that the audible alarm signal has been inhibited by the voice-paging system,

- A switch may be provided in the control centre to allow a private conversation on the handset system

- A switch should be provided which will immediately cause a general alarm evacuation tone to be generated over all speaker zones.

These operating control switches and audible and visual indicators can be physically mounted on modular panels in the control centre. Nameplates are used to identify each component.

Alternatively, all controls may be available via a pictorial graphic layout of the building, with the control switches and visual indicators in the associated building areas depicted on the graphic, portraying, at a glance, operational zoning of the system. Such a graphic presentation must, of course, carry a ULC label, as must the entire CACF.

"Command Centre" redundancy as all of the capabilities and control operations that are available at the main command centre are also available at the secondary command centre – whenever "system control" is granted to the secondary command centre.

The *CAN/ULC-S527 standard for Control Units for Fire Alarm Systems* indicates that when multiple locations are used to provide "command centre" operation for the fire alarm system, certain steps must be taken to ensure these duplicate nodes do not "fight" each other for control of the system.

---

**3.16    DISPLAY AND CONTROL CENTRE**

3.16.1    The *display and control centre* shall comply with the following:

A    All of the requirements of Subsection 3.11.3, Annunciator;

B    Where manual controls are used, they shall meet the requirements of Subsection 3.12, Manual Controls, and the following:

(i)    Controls as defined in Subsections 3.12, Manual Controls, and 3.17, Voice-Alarm Feature, can only be operated from one location at any given time,

(ii)    Indication shall be provided at all *display and control centres* as to which is in control,

(iii)    Complete loss of communication to the *display and control centre* shall not inhibit other communicating *display and control centres* from being able to gain control.

---

In addition to the limitations and requirements for distributed processing systems related to command and control centres, the *ULC-S524 Installation Standard* also stipulates limitations to system capacity dependant upon the type of data communication links being used.

## 9.10    Data Communications Links

The *ULC Standard for the Installation of Fire Alarm Systems* contains many references to multiplexed systems. Because this type of system can monitor thousands of devices covering hundreds of zones in large buildings, design standards must be set to limit the potential for information or system operational loss in the event of data communications failure.

©

The standard accomplishes this via the following requirements:

- The number of initiating devices and signaling output controlled circuits shall be limited by the system data communications link style as follows and as summarized in the table found on Page 7 of this document, for DCL style definitions.

Consider the following excerpts and diagrams for clarification:

- Where the DCL originates in the control unit and serves addressable devices, it is limited by Part I of the table:

| TABLE 3 | | | |
|---|---|---|---|
| **CAPACITIES OF SYSTEMS UTILIZING DATA COMMUNICATION LINKS WITHIN A SINGLE BUILDING** | | | |
| (Reference: Clauses 4.2.3, 4.2.4, 4.3.1) | | | |
| APPLICATION OF DATA COMMUNICATION LINKS (DCL) | MAXIMUM NUMBER OF ACTIVE FIELD DEVICES AND SUPPORTING FIELD DEVICES | | |
| | DCLA* | DCLB* | DCLC* |
| PART I | 300** | 200** | 300** |
| EACH ADDRESSABLE DEVICE DATA COMMUNICATION LINK) ORIGINATING IN A CONTROL UNIT OR TRANSPONDER. See Notes 1, 3, and 4 | ** This includes all addressable devices on the CIRCUIT | | |

- Where the DCL originates in a transponder and interconnects with other transponders, the network DCL must conform to Part II, and the total number of addressable devices on the system must not exceed 1000:

### TABLE 3
### CAPACITIES OF SYSTEMS UTILIZING DATA COMMUNICATION LINKS WITHIN A SINGLE BUILDING

(Reference: Clauses 4.2.3, 4.2.4, 4.3.1)

| APPLICATION OF DATA COMMUNICATION LINKS (DCL) | MAXIMUM NUMBER OF ACTIVE FIELD DEVICES AND SUPPORTING FIELD DEVICES | | |
|---|---|---|---|
| | DCLA* | DCLB* | DCLC* |
| PART II<br><br>NETWORK DATA COMMUNICATIONS LINK INTERCONNECTING CONTROL UNITS, TRANSPONDERS, OR DISPLAY AND CONTROL CENTRES | Not permitted<br><br>(See Note 5) | Not permitted<br><br>(See Note 5) | 1000*** |
| | *** This includes all addressable devices on the SYSTEM. | | |

- Where the DCL originates in the control unit or transponder and interconnects with other transponders and the total number of addressable devices exceeds 1000 Part III of the table applies and the system becomes a Large Scale Network where additional requirements are mandatory:

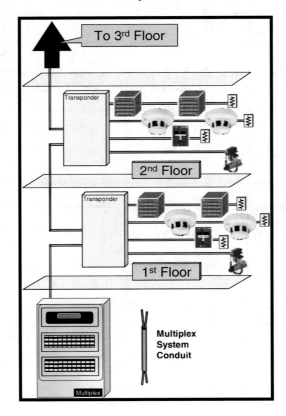

©

**TABLE 3**
**CAPACITIES OF SYSTEMS UTILIZING DATA COMMUNICATION LINKS WITHIN A SINGLE BUILDING**

(Reference: Clauses 4.2.3, 4.2.4, 4.3.1)

| APPLICATION OF DATA COMMUNICATION LINKS (DCL) | MAXIMUM NUMBER OF ACTIVE FIELD DEVICES AND SUPPORTING FIELD DEVICES | | |
|---|---|---|---|
| | DCLA* | DCLB* | DCLC* |
| **PART III** LARGE SCALE NETWORK DATA COMMUNICATIONS LINKS INTERCONNECTING CONTROL UNITS, TRANSPONDERS, OR DISPLAY AND CONTROL CENTRES AS A LARGE SCALE NETWORK IN COMPLIANCE WITH SUBSECTION 4.3, LARGE SCALE NETWORK SYSTEMS. See Notes 1, 4 and 5 | Not permitted (See Note 5) | Not permitted (See Note 5) | Unlimited*** |
| | ***Note: This includes all addressable devices on the SYSTEM. | | |

- Where the DCL originates in the control unit or transponder and interconnects with other transponders and the total number of addressable devices exceeds 1000 Part III of the table applies and the system becomes a Large Scale Network. Large Scale Network have no limit on the maximum number of addressable device There is still a limit of the number of addressable device on one loop as defined in Part I of the Table, the network DCL must conform to Part III and there are additional requirements for Large Scale Networks.

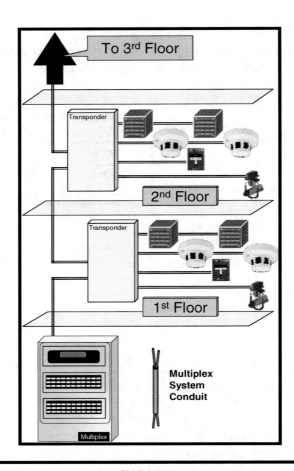

**TABLE 3**

**CAPACITIES OF SYSTEMS UTILIZING DATA COMMUNICATION LINKS WITHIN A SINGLE BUILDING**

(Reference: Clauses 4.2.3, 4.2.4, 4.3.1)

| APPLICATION OF DATA COMMUNICATION LINKS (DCL) | MAXIMUM NUMBER OF ACTIVE FIELD DEVICES AND SUPPORTING FIELD DEVICES | | |
| --- | --- | --- | --- |
| | DCLA* | DCLB* | DCLC* |
| **PART II** NETWORK DATA COMMUNICATIONS LINK INTERCONNECTING CONTROL UNITS, TRANSPONDERS, OR DISPLAY AND CONTROL CENTRES | Not permitted (See Note 5) | Not permitted (See Note 5) | 1000*** |
| | *** This includes all addressable devices on the SYSTEM. | | |
| **PART III** LARGE SCALE NETWORK DATA COMMUNICATIONS LINKS INTERCONNECTING CONTROL UNITS, TRANSPONDERS, OR DISPLAY AND CONTROL CENTRES AS A LARGE SCALE NETWORK IN COMPLIANCE WITH SUBSECTION 4.3, LARGE SCALE NETWORK SYSTEMS. See Notes 1, 4 and 5 | Not permitted (See Note 5) | Not permitted (See Note 5) | Unlimited*** |
| | ***Note: This includes all addressable devices on the SYSTEM. | | |

©

## 9.11 Manufacturers Wiring Requirements

Manufacturers stipulate that certain circuits (emergency telephone circuits for example) must be in separate conduits, or must be installed using shielded cables. Not only is it important to adhere to these recommendations to ensure proper system operation, but also to ensure final system acceptance by the Authority Having Jurisdiction.

The voltage drop on any circuit must not prevent the proper operation of that circuit and has to be within the limitations contained in the manufacturer's installation instructions.

Most importantly, Data Communication Links must be installed using materials and methods that comply strictly with the manufacturers recommendations.

Manufacturers' recommendations must never be in contradiction of any code or standard. Their recommendations however, may be in addition to the minimum requirements, and must be followed.

Manufacturers often provide a mounting box specifically for particular devices. It is important that these be used to maintain the agency listing for the product.

## 9.12 Chapter Summary

1.  Conventional systems can be quite expensive to install, especially in high buildings or in large sprawling low buildings. This is because of the great amount of wiring, size of conduit, and installation labour.

2.  Multiplex communications over minimum wiring can greatly reduce these costs and still provide a reliable system.

3.  Steps must be taken to ensure the dependability of the multiplex systems. This is achieved through the use of special requirements for the materials and installation methods of the trunk communications cable called the Data Communication Link (DCL).

4.  Older Master-Slave systems are disappearing and newer Peer-to-Peer networks are providing solid reliability, because each segmented transponder basically contains the entire program for the entire system and even a catastrophic failure of the DCL will not disable the overall system.

5.  Networked systems can easily provide all of the *Building Code* requirements needed for high-rise structures, including controls included in the Central Alarm and Control Facility (CACF).

6.  Networked systems can also easily provide all of the *Building Code* requirements needed for Emergency Voice Communications systems.

7.  To ensure consistency in presentation of function vs. status, Command Centres must follow the prescribed colour codes dictated by *ULC-S527*.

8.  Multiple Command Centres must be programmed with priorities in mind to ensure that multiple operators do not force Command Centres to "fight" for control of the system.

9.  In a Peer-to-Peer system, audio riser faults should not alter the fire alarm operation from an occupant perspective.

10. Degraded operation in a Peer-to-Peer system should not compromise the system performance at all.

## 9.13 Review Questions

| # | ? | Question | Section |
|---|---|---|---|
| 9-1 | | **Data Communication Links must be installed** | |
| | A | Using materials and methods that comply strictly with the manufacturer's recommendations and CAN/ULC-S524. | |
| | B | Using materials and methods that comply strictly with the Owner's recommendations and CAN/ULC-S525. | |
| | C | Using materials and methods that comply strictly with the Local Fire Official recommendations and CAN/ULC-S536. | |
| | D | Using materials and methods that comply strictly with the Security Technicians recommendations and CAN/ULC-S527. | |
| 9-2 | | **The fire alarm system becomes a Large Scale Network:** | |
| | A | Where the DCL originates in the control unit or transponder and interconnects with other transponders and the total number of addressable devices exceeds 300 | |
| | B | Where the DCL originates in the control unit or transponder and interconnects with other transponders and the total number of addressable devices exceeds 150 | |
| | C | Where the DCL originates in the control unit or transponder and interconnects with other transponders and the total number of addressable devices exceeds 1000 | |
| | D | Where the DCL originates in the control unit or transponder and interconnects with other transponders and the total number of addressable devices exceeds 450 | |
| 9-3 | | **What type of switch is provided to permit live voice messages to be transmitted throughout the building on all voice/signal circuits simultaneously without operating individual paging zone select switches?** | |
| | A | "All-Evac" | |
| | B | "All-Alert" | |
| | C | "Alarm Signal" | |
| | D | "All-Call" | |

| # | ? | Question | Section |
|---|---|---|---|
| **9-4** | | **A system that provides discrete circuits to each floor with a pair of conductors, so that the diameter of the conduit going back to the single conventional control panel can become very large is?** | |
| | A | Addressable System | |
| | B | Two Stage Addressable System | |
| | C | Conventional Hardwired System | |
| | D | All of the above | |
| **9-5** | | **The real advantage of using distributed transponders in a network are:** | |
| | A | The reduction in riser wiring, | |
| | B | Smaller raceway size | |
| | C | Reduction of labour costs | |
| | D | All of the above | |
| **9-6** | | **Distributed peer to peer transponder networks provide much more redundancy than a Master-Slave system, as each peer does not rely on the master to operate. Rather, each peer performs its own decision-making and reacts according to the information reported by all other nodes.** | |
| | A | True | |
| | B | False | |
| **9-7** | | **When control units using transponders or addressable devices serve more than one floor area to a maximum size of 2000 m$^2$, a fault within one floor area shall not prevent the normal operation of other input or output field devices in another floor area. This means that when using a DCL-A circuit to serve multiple floors the devices that must be provided are:** | |
| | A | Terminal Panels | |
| | B | End of Line devices | |
| | C | Short Circuit Isolators | |
| | D | Supporting Field Devices with end of lines on the bells. | |

| # | ? | Question | Section |
|---|---|---|---|
| **9-8** | | **In distributed large scale systems employing transponder units, the building area served by a transponder does not require the same area for both input circuits and output circuits.** | |
| | A | True | |
| | B | False | |
| **9-9** | | **CAN/ULC-S524 Inspection and Testing of Fire Alarm Systems specifies the method to be used to test continued operation of the fire alarm network under a single fault to ensure that the DCLC functionality is working properly.** | |
| | A | True | |
| | B | False | |
| **9-10** | | **If the communication links between peer-to-peer nodes are further compromised and the alternate path is prevented from operating the transponders will then operation in a specific condition:** | |
| | A | Peer-to-Peer | |
| | B | Stand-Alone | |
| | C | Open Protocol | |
| | D | HTML RS-422 Default Mode | |

# Chapter 10: Interface with Other Systems

## 10.1    Chapter Overview and Key Concepts

The basic purpose of a Fire Alarm System is to detect a fire condition, and then initiate audible/visual alarm signalling so that occupants will be aware of the alarm condition, and can take appropriate action.

Of course a Fire Alarm System also does many other things including interfacing with several building systems that have life-safety connotations. Such systems might include the control of elevators, circulating fans, electromagnetic door locks and smoke control doors. In addition, the system might monitor other building systems. Such monitoring might include indications that fans are running (or have been shut down), that dampers have closed or that a smoke-control system has been activated.

This chapter will explore the several different devices/systems that the Fire Alarm System typically will monitor and/or control.

## 10.2    Learning Objectives

Upon successful completion of this chapter the reader should be able to:

- understand the importance of reliable interconnections to, and control of, ancillary systems

- discuss the various types of ancillary systems within different types of occupancies

- identify which ancillary systems need to be controlled by the Fire Alarm System, and why

- discuss how the interconnections between the systems should be completed

- discuss the areas of demarcation between the two systems

## Language defined

Terms that are important to the understanding of this chapter are included below. For a complete listing of such words, expressions and terms, refer to the Main Glossary near the end of this manual. This glossary is not intended to replace or supersede any officially published glossary. It is simply our intent that these be used as a training aid in understanding the contents of this manual. Always refer to the specific code or standard, and to the Authority Having Jurisdiction for the applicable official interpretation.

| Term | Definition |
|------|-----------|
| **Access-to-exit** | Those parts of a building, such as aisles, hallways or corridors that provide access to an exit serving that floor area |
| **Alarm signal** | An audible signal transmitted throughout a zone or zones to advise occupants that a fire emergency exists; also called an EVACUATION signal |
| **Alert signal** | An audible signal intended to advise designated persons of a fire emergency |
| **Ancillary device** | A device that performs a life safety related function, but that is not part of the fire alarm system |
| **Building height (in storeys)** | The number of storeys contained between the roof and the floor of the first storey. An elevator machine room, sitting atop an office building, would not generally be considered a storey in this application |
| **Closure** | A device for shutting off an opening through a fire separation. Example: a door, shutter or fire damper |
| **Electromagnetic door release** | A device used to hold doors in the open position, and to release the doors to close automatically when signaled to do so by a fire alarm system or other means |
| **Exit** | A facility such as a door, stairs or ramp that leads from the floor area that it serves to an open public thoroughfare, or to a protected exterior open space that has access to an open public thoroughfare. Once in an exit facility, a person should have a continuous path leading to the building exterior |
| **Fire damper** | A closure which consists of a normally held open damper installed in an air distribution system or in a wall or floor assembly and designed to close automatically in the event of a fire in order to maintain the integrity of the fire separation |
| **Fire rated assembly** | Commonly used term for an assembly with a fire resistance rating. It may or may not have a fire separation requirement on it |

©

| Term | Definition |
|------|------------|
| **Fire resistance rating** | The time, in hours, that a material or a construction assembly withstands the passage of flame or transmission of heat in accordance with established test procedures |
| **Fire separation** | A construction assembly that acts as a barrier against the spread of fire. A fire separation may or may not have a fire resistance rating |
| **Ground Fault** | A circuit impedance to ground sufficient to prevent normal operation |
| **Means of egress** | A continuous path of travel provided for the escape of persons from any point in a building or contained open space to a separate building, an open public thoroughfare, or an exterior open space protected from fire exposure from the building and having access to an open public thoroughfare. Means of egress includes exits and access to exits |
| **Open-circuit fault** | A circuit series resistance increase of 10 kOhm or more, unless otherwise stated, resulting from an abnormal condition |
| **Public corridor** | A corridor that provides access to exit from more than one suite |
| **Return duct** | A duct for conveying air from a space being heated, ventilated or air conditioned back to the heating, ventilating or air conditioning appliance |
| **Self-closing** | An approved device that will ensure closing after having been opened |
| **Short-circuit fault** | A resistance shunt of 0.1 Ohm or less across a circuit, unless otherwise stated, resulting from an abnormal condition |
| **Smoke compartment** | A space within a building enclosed by smoke or fire barriers on all sides, including the top and bottom |
| **Supply duct** | A duct for conveying air from a heating, ventilating or air conditioning appliance to a space to be heated, ventilated or air conditioned |
| **Trouble signal** | A signal (usually a buzzer and an amber lamp) indicating a fault or an off-normal condition in a fire alarm system |
| **Vertical service space** | A shaft oriented essentially vertically that is provided in a building to facilitate the installation of building services including mechanical, electrical and plumbing installations and facilities such as elevators, refuse chutes and linen chutes. |

## 10.3    General

This chapter will explore the many common devices and systems that exist in many buildings, and that have some connection to fire safety as well as a connection to the Fire Alarm System. We will discuss their purposes, and why (and how) they should be inter-connected with the Fire Alarm System.

We will often use the word 'ancillary' when referring to safety-related devices and systems. The glossary refers to ancillary, as 'a device that has a life safety related function, but is not part of the fire alarm system'. With that definition in mind, we can push towards a better understanding of the interfacing of Fire Alarm Systems with ancillary systems. Generally, all ancillary functions for a given building are located within that building.

There is another type of external circuit that is referred to as an 'auxiliary' circuit or connection. This reference is to the off-site monitoring, by a monitoring service or fire department.

**Typical Mag-lock**

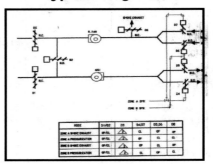

**Two-zone AHU Smoke Control**

## 10.4    Control of Ancillary Systems

Ancillary circuits are provided by, and used by, the Fire Alarm System to control ancillary devices/systems in the building. For example, activation of an ancillary circuit may cause a supply fan to shut down, an exhaust fan to start-up, and an elevator to be recalled to the ground or alternate floor. Or it may release electromagnetically held-open smoke/fire doors, allowing them to close.  These functions are all external to the fire alarm system (i.e. supplementary to the evacuation process) and therefore are identified as ancillary functions.

Generally, all life safety related devices that are intended to operate during an alarm condition, which are within the building, and which are not a part of the fire alarm system, are called ancillary devices or systems. As there are many such systems and/or devices, it is important to take a closer look at their requirements, their operation and their interconnection into the Fire Alarm System. .

Certain basic facts, common to all such devices and connections, must first be understood:

- Normally-closed or normally-open electrical contacts (in the Fire Alarm Control Unit), are used to control most ancillary devices and systems.

©

- These contacts may operate, in common, under any alarm condition, or they may be individually controlled by specific initiating circuits, as part of the system input/output (I/O) programming.

- Power for the ancillary devices almost always is provided from a power source that is separate from the Fire Alarm System power supply. This is the simplest and safest method. However, one must ensure that the ancillary contacts in the control unit are properly sized and rated for the ancillary power that is to be controlled.

- Operating power for these ancillary devices may be taken from the Fire Alarm Control Unit only if the panel has specific power and dedicated terminals available for the purpose, and if the Control Unit is approved for this purpose. The system designer must also take into consideration whether or not the battery is sized to handle the additional load required for the ancillary systems if municipal power fails.

- *CAN/ULC-S524 Installation of Fire Alarm Systems* states that operation of the ancillary device, any device faults, and any electrical faults on the wiring must not interfere with the operation of the Fire Alarm System.

- The connecting means of the devices may be done in a fail-safe manner, meaning that it is designed to return to a safe condition in the event of a malfunction or a failure. Electromagnetic door-hold-open devices are an example. When ancillary devices are controlled by addressable relays it is preferable to locate the addressable relay near the device being controlled. For example, a relay programmed for elevator homing should be installed in the elevator machine room or a fan control relay near the fan control equipment.

## 10.5  Fan Control

By far the most common ancillary feature is 'fan control'. When people speak of 'fan control' they almost always are referring to 'circulating' fans – those fan systems that take air from within the building, condition it (heat, cool, filter, humidify etc) and then send it back into the building. These are usually referred to as 'circulating' systems, but in the past have often been referred to as 're-circulating' systems.

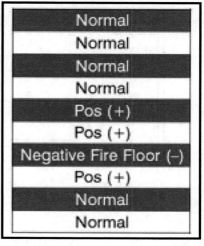

**Sandwich Smoke Control Systems**

### 10.5.1  Circulating Fan Systems

Our Building Codes go to great lengths to ensure that any fire is restricted to the floor area of origin. Fire separations are constructed to ensure that smoke and heat are not allowed to quickly migrate from the fire location to the rest of the building.

Circulating fans must therefore be shut down when a fire condition occurs, when such systems serve:

- more than one storey,

- more than one suite in a storey, or

- more than one zone or fire compartment in an institutional occupancy.

This requirement can be achieved either by an ancillary relay within the air-duct mounted smoke detector or by an ancillary circuit in the Fire Alarm Control Unit. The latter may be controlled by the initiating circuit to which the smoke detector is connected, or indeed by any zone. It generally is considered that fan control from the Fire Alarm Control Unit is preferable to control by individual detectors. As a general rule, if the building is small to medium size, and is a residential, commercial or industrial occupancy, and in the absence of any specific instructions (in the Fire Safety Plan for example) it usually is preferable to shut down all circulating fans upon any alarm condition.

Many smaller buildings would probably have just one or two circulating fans and they should be shut down on any fire alarm condition. There may be a need for two or three ancillary contacts for multiple-fan control.

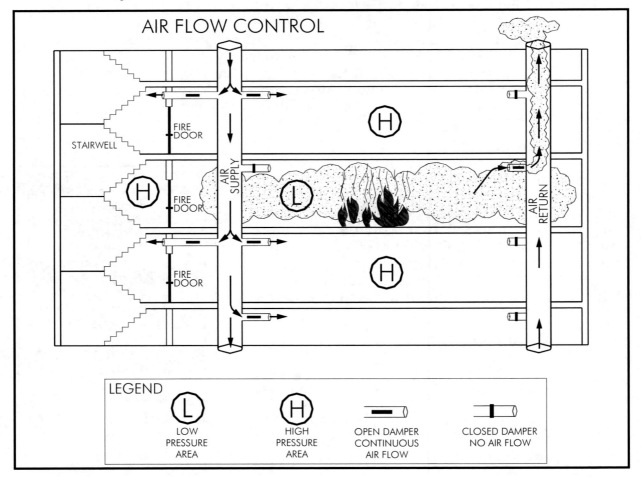

©

However, in larger or more complex buildings such as hospitals or hotels there may be several such fans. In fact, hospitals present probably the most technically involved air-handling systems of any occupancy. Because of operating theatres, intensive care sections, research centres, and concerns about virus control, among others, fan control is best left to the professionals. Hospital management, working with the local fire authorities, will have created a Fire Safety Plan that specifically itemizes precisely how the air-handling systems must operate under fire alarm conditions.

Therefore in some buildings our Fire Alarm System will directly control individual fans, and in other buildings it will control a Building Automation System.

## 10.5.2   Exhaust Fans

Exhaust fans are those that remove air from specific rooms or areas, and expel the air to the exterior of the building. An example would be an exhaust fan in an enclosed underground parking structure would be an example. Often, exhaust fans remain running during a fire condition, because any smoke that might be generated in that area, or that infiltrates from another area, would be cleared away by the exhaust system. The Fire Safety Plan will confirm whether or not the exhaust fans should automatically be shut down under fire conditions.

## 10.5.3   Pressurization Fans

Several conditions may exist in a building requiring that air be forced into a confined space or area. An example would be an exit stairwell in a high-rise building. For example, the *Building Code* requires that, under fire conditions, each exit stairwell must remain relatively free from smoke so as to maintain tenable conditions for occupancy evacuation.

In order to achieve this, a pressurization fan must be present, and must be turned on in order to force air from the outside of the building into the stairwell. This positive pressure will keep smoke from entering the stairwell.

A similar situation holds true for certain elevator shafts, wherein a pressurization fan will force outside air into an elevator shaft in order to maintain tenable conditions within the elevator shaft and cab.

## 10.5.4   Electrical Control of Fans

Most fans (fan systems) operate on 120 volts AC or higher. For several reasons, it is not acceptable or even legal, to bring a second source of 120 volts into the Fire Alarm Control Unit. Therefore, most fan system controllers provide a low-voltage (typically 24 volts DC) control circuit that is used for remote control purposes. This low-voltage circuit from the fan controller is connected through the ancillary control contacts of the Fire Alarm Control Unit.

The control contact should be a normally closed contact while the FACU is in normal operating condition. The contact opens under alarm conditions, and this triggers the fan controller.

### 10.5.5   Building Automation Systems

Often, a Building Automation System (BAS) will exist in buildings with complex needs for acceptable air-handling control, and it will control all fans (and dampers etc) in the building in addition to ensuring the continuing integrity of the air. The BAS will turn on and off fans as needed for the continuing safe operation of the Hospital. In the event of a fire condition, our Fire Alarm Control Unit (through an ancillary contact) will tell the BAS of the 'alarm' condition. The BAS will then initiate whatever fan sequences have been pre-determine by the Fire Safety Plan.

## 10.6   Door-Hold-Open Devices

Electromagnetic door-hold-open devices are typically installed on smoke-control doors in corridors (for example in a health-care facility) and on rated doors or closures in a fire separation. These doors/closures are held open by electromagnetic door-hold-open devices. They are to be released upon a signal from:

- an automatic sprinkler system,
- a heat actuated device,
- a smoke actuated device, or
- the Fire Alarm System Control Unit.

The requirements for electromagnetic locks may vary by National and provincial building codes adopted.

Good engineering practice recommends that the heat or smoke detector should be part of the Fire Alarm System, and control of the door-hold-open device should be from the Fire Alarm Control Unit, and not directly from any detector. The ancillary control circuit in the FACU operates under common alarm conditions, or it may operate as a programmed circuit specifically related to the nearby associated detector.

These door holders simply hold open the door, and release it under alarm condition. Complete operation requires that the door must fully close and latch. This requires therefore that the door be fitted with some type of closer mechanism such as a pneumatic-type of door closer

## 10.7    Electromagnetic Locking Devices

These products are often referred to as 'mag-locks'. They are not a life safety device! In fact they are generally installed in order to block the movement of people as part of a building security system. They are often installed on exit doors (or access-to-exit doors)!

It is of interest to note that the *Building Code* does not require the installation of mag-locks! The *Building Code* requires that, if mag-locks are to be installed in a building, they must be controlled by the Fire Alarm System as ancillary devices, so as to allow the free movement of occupants escaping from a fire condition. The Code states that IF a mag-lock is to be installed, several safety precautions must be provided. For example, mag-locks must be automatically released by the Fire Alarm System. Secondly, a Fire Alarm System manual station must be located on the wall not more than 600 mm from any door fitted with a mag-lock. To ensure that this occurs, there are very stringent requirements contained in the *Building Code*. Many municipalities also have separate requirements relating to the installation and operation of mag-locks.

Almost every installation raises questions as to what methods of interconnection to the Fire Alarm System are acceptable. The recommendation must be that any proposed installation of mag-locks must be discussed with, and approval obtained from, the Authority Having Jurisdiction. In fact many municipalities require that the installer must apply for, and receive, a Building Permit prior to installing mag-locks.

From a Fire Alarm System point-of-view, the electromagnetic locking device must release immediately upon initiation of a Fire Alarm signal.

Many jurisdictions require that each manual station must also directly release the associated mag-lock. The manual station must be part of the Fire Alarm System. If the Fire Alarm System is a two-stage system, then the station associated with a mag-lock must have a contact for the mag-lock, in addition to the two electrical contacts that initiate the Fire Alarm System. The designer and installer must ensure that the manual stations used for this purpose are listed (approved) for this mag-lock application.

Generally, the mag-locks themselves are powered by and controlled by, a separate mag-lock controller. Therefore it is a straightforward proposition for the Fire Alarm System to provide an ancillary contact for interconnection to the mag-lock controller. This would lead to the release of all connected mag-locks. But remember – each mag-lock must also be controlled by the manual station that is located on the associated door. Such a manual station might therefore require three sets of electrical contacts:

- one for First-Stage (Alert) initiation,

- one for Second-Stage (Alarm) initiation, and

- one for releasing the mag-lock on the associated door.

## 10.8 Automatic Elevator Recall

Automatic elevator recall, for all elevators serving storeys above the first storey in unsprinklered buildings, is a requirement of the *Building Code*. One signal is required for all floors, except the floor in which the elevators are generally parked, to initiate a return. A second signal is required when the floor in alarm is the normal elevator park floor, thus returning all elevators to an alternate floor.

Here again, elevators themselves are controlled by dedicated controllers. Therefore the Fire Alarm System, once again, simply provides an ancillary contact that is used to interconnect with the elevator controller which then controls the elevator cabs.

## 10.9 Control of Sound Systems

Obviously, to be effective, the Fire Alarm System signalling devices must be heard above the ambient noise. This may not happen, for example, in some types of entertainment facilities, where the levels of music are very high. For example, music is sometimes played at 100 dB, and the levels of the Fire Alarm Signalling devices is not as loud, or certainly does not achieve the requirement for a minimum 15 dBA above ambient.

Two things can be done to solve the problem. The first would be to install visible (as well as audible) signalling devices in the entertainment area.

The second method (and much more direct) would be to automatically silence the music system during the fire alarm condition. Most amplifier control equipments contain a circuit for remote control, and this circuit should be connected into an ancillary contact on the FACU.

## 10.10 Auxiliary circuits

This term pertains to the automatic connection of the Fire Alarm System in a building to a remote monitoring service or directly to the Fire Department if so allowed. An auxiliary relay contact (switchable for system testing purposes) is included in the system common control section for this purpose. Upon activation of any alarm on the system, this relay will activate in order to send a signal to the monitoring service.

It may be that 'trouble' conditions must also be remotely monitored. In this case two auxiliary relays will be provided.

Connections to the remote service are usually completed over telephone lines. In some cases the FACU connects directly into telephone lines. Refer to CAN/ULC-S524-06 Figure E3.

Most often, however, this method requires that a separate control unit be installed in the protected premises to control communication with the off-site monitoring service. This Controller receives alarm and trouble initiations from the Fire Alarm

©

Control Unit, and then transmits related information to the off-site monitoring service. Fire Alarm Technicians generally should not engage in any way with the Monitoring Controller, nor should the Monitoring Technician make any wiring terminations in the Fire Alarm Control Unit. The question than becomes one of deciding how to handle the interconnections between the two systems. This is easily solved through the installation of a suitable terminal box physically mounted between the FACU and the Monitoring Controller. The Fire Alarm Technician makes connections to clearly labeled terminals in the enclosure, and the Monitoring Technician performs the same function with the conductors from the Communications Controller. Refer to CAN/ULC-S524-06 Figure E3.

## 10.11   Chapter Summary

1.      Ancillary systems within a building are systems that have a fire-safety
        purpose but that are not part of the Fire Alarm System

2.      Fan control is the most common type of ancillary system

3.      Ancillary systems perform useful purposes every day but are controlled by
        the Fire Alarm System to perform specific and sometimes special functions.

4.      Auxiliary connections between the Fire Alarm System and an off-site
        monitoring service must be carefully designed and installed.

©

## 10.12 Review Questions

| # | ? | Question | Section |
|---|---|---|---|
| 10-1 | | **A device that has a life safety related function, but is not part of the fire alarm system is identified as?** | |
| | A | Ancillary | |
| | B | Signalling | |
| | C | Initiating | |
| | D | All of the Above | |
| 10-2 | | **What types of contacts are provided in the Fire Alarm Control Unit to control ancillary devices and systems?** | |
| | A | Secure contacts | |
| | B | Fail open contacts | |
| | C | Normally-closed and/or normally-open electrical contacts | |
| | D | Normally addressable release trouble indicators | |
| 10-3 | | **One of the most common ancillary control feature is?** | |
| | A | Central Vacuum Control | |
| | B | Fan Control | |
| | C | Spark Arrestor Control | |
| | D | All of the Above | |
| 10-4 | | **The best type of fan to maintain a smoke free exit stairwell shaft is?** | |
| | A | Return Fan | |
| | B | Pressurization Fan | |
| | C | Exhaust Fan | |
| | D | All of the Above | |
| 10-5 | | **Electromagnetic door-hold-open devices are typically installed on the following?** | |
| | A | Smoke-control doors in corridors in a health-care facility. | |
| | B | On rated doors or closures in a fire separation from a convention hall. | |
| | C | On rated doors or closures in a fire separation such as doors opening to an exit stairwell. | |
| | D | All of the Above | |

| # | ? | Question | Section |
|---|---|----------|---------|
| **10-6** | | **The Building Code requires that, if mag-locks are to be installed in a building, they must be controlled by the Fire Alarm System as ancillary devices, so as to allow the free movement of occupants escaping from a fire condition.** | |
| | A | True | |
| | B | False | |
| **10-7** | | **Automatic elevator recall, for all elevators serving storeys above the first storey in unsprinklered buildings, is a requirement of what specific Code?** | |
| | A | Elevator Control Code | |
| | B | Electrical Code | |
| | C | Fire Code | |
| | D | Building Code | |
| **10-8** | | **What term pertains to the circuits that provide an automatic connection from the Fire Alarm System to a remote monitoring service or Central Station?** | |
| | A | Supervisory Circuits | |
| | B | Ancillary Circuits | |
| | C | Auxiliary Circuits | |
| | D | Alarm Circuits | |
| **10-9** | | **A closure which consists of a normally held open damper installed in an air distribution system or in a wall or floor assembly and designed to close automatically in the event of a fire in order to maintain the integrity of the fire separation is identified as?** | |
| | A | Fire Alarm | |
| | B | Fire Controller | |
| | C | Fire Damper | |
| | D | All of the above | |
| **10-10** | | **A signal, usually a buzzer and an amber lamp indicating a wiring fault or an off-normal condition in a fire alarm system is identified as?** | |
| | A | Alarm | |
| | B | Supervisory | |
| | C | Trouble | |
| | D | All of the above | |

©

# Chapter 11: Installation of Fire Alarm Systems

## 11.1    Chapter Overview and Key Concepts

Fire Alarm Technicians do not install Fire Alarm Systems! However, Fire Alarm Technicians must be fully aware of what is involved in an installation. The Technician must be aware of the installation requirements contained in *CAN/ULC-S524 Installation of Fire Alarm Systems*, and the contents of the applicable sections of the *Electrical Code*. Basically the *S-524 Standard* tells the Installer how to install the system, and the *Electrical Code* describes the materials to be used.

This chapter looks carefully at all aspects of the *S-524 Standard*, explaining the myriad of details. A Fire Alarm System and all of its component parts including automatic detection devices, signalling devices and all related circuitry, must all be properly located in the specific areas of the building and also must be properly installed, in order for the system to fully perform its many functions, and do so reliably and dependably. The contents of *S-524* must be carefully followed. A proper Verification, therefore, must not only inspect and test the field devices but also must inspect and test the system wiring in accordance with *CAN/ULC-S537 Verification of Fire Alarm Systems*. In Chapter 13 of this manual, you will read that the Fire Alarm Technician must report any discrepancies between what the Technician finds in the field, and the requirements demanded by *S-524*.

## 11.2    Learning Objectives

Upon successful completion of this chapter, the student should understand:

- why system circuits must be isolated above ground
- why circuits must be fitted with an end-of-line supervisory device,
- why conductors and cables must be of a type allowed by the *Electrical Code*
- why each system device must be installed onto an approved electrical box
- the difference between grounding and shielding
- how to calculate line-loss conditions on a signalling circuit
- acceptable methods of providing mechanical protection for system wiring,
- the need to carefully follow the spacing requirements of detection devices
- how to successfully apply the location parameters of signalling devices

## Language defined

Terms that are important to the understanding of this chapter are included below. For a complete listing of such words, expressions and terms, refer to the Main Glossary near the end of this manual. This glossary is not intended to replace or supersede any officially-published glossary. It is simply our intent that these be used as a training aid in understanding the contents of this manual. Always refer to the specific code or standard, and to the Authority Having Jurisdiction for the applicable official interpretation.

| Term | Definition |
| --- | --- |
| **Active Field Device** | A device that can be uniquely identified by the control unit to determine its presence and operating status, and which may be commanded to operate or to change its operating parameters independently of other field devices that share a common circuit |
| **Addressable Device** | A device that can be individually and uniquely identified by a control unit. The address is set using binary/hexadecimal/decimal methods using dipswitches, rotary switches or solid-state memory |
| **Alarm Signal** | An audible signal transmitted throughout a zone or zones to advise occupants that a fire emergency exists; also called an EVACUATION signal |
| **Alert Signal** | An audible signal intended to advise designated persons of a fire emergency |
| **Ancillary Device** | A device that performs a life safety related function, but that is not part of the fire alarm system |
| **Bonding** | The permanent low-impedance path obtained by joining all non-current-carrying metal parts to ensure electrical continuity, and with the capacity to conduct safely any current likely to be imposed on it |
| **Compatible** | The correct electrical, electronic or mechanical interaction between a series of system components that depend on individual unique characteristics that are connected together to meet the requirements of this Standard (e.g. Control Unit and/or Transponder and field devices) |
| **Conventional Field Device** | A field device that is usually connected to a control unit and/or transponder on a common wiring circuit with other devices so that all devices on the circuit provide a common status change information (e.g. fire alarm detection or signalling). Such devices cannot be uniquely identified by a control unit and/or transponder unless there is only one device on the circuit. (Refer to active field device) |

| Term | Definition |
|------|-----------|
| **Dwelling Unit** | A suite operated as a housekeeping unit, used or intended to be used, as a domicile by one or more persons and usually containing cooking, eating, living, sleeping and sanitary facilities |
| **Electromagnetic Door Release** | A device used to hold doors in the open position, and to release the doors to close automatically when signalled to do so by a fire alarm system or other means |
| **Ground Fault** | A circuit impedance to ground sufficient to prevent normal operation |
| **Open-Circuit Fault** | A circuit series resistance increase of 10 Kohms or more, unless otherwise stated, resulting from an abnormal condition |
| **Return Duct** | A duct for conveying air from a space being heated, ventilated or air-conditioned back to the heating, ventilating or air-conditioning appliance |
| **Self-Closing** | An approved device that will ensure closing after having been opened |
| **Service Room** | A room provided in a building to contain equipment associated with building services |
| **Short-Circuit Fault** | A resistance shunt of 0.1 Ohm or less across a circuit, unless otherwise stated, resulting from an abnormal condition |
| **Supply Duct** | A duct for conveying air from a heating, ventilating or air-conditioning appliance to a space to be heated, ventilated or air-conditioned |
| **Supporting Field Device** | An active field device that monitors other field devices on a separate circuit and reports the status of that separate circuit to the control unit |
| **Trouble Signal** | A signal (usually a buzzer and an amber lamp) indicating a fault or an off-normal condition in a fire alarm system |
| **Vertical Service Space** | A shaft oriented essentially vertically that is provided in a building to facilitate the installation of building services including mechanical, electrical and plumbing installations and facilities such as elevators, refuse chutes and linen chutes |

## 11.3    Where it all begins

The installation of a Fire Alarm System (or any addition thereto) is an activity that involves several competencies. From the design and installation of electrical raceways and boxes, to the acceptable locating of system devices, to the selection of electrical conductors, to proper device connections – much knowledge and experience is necessary. The necessary knowledge can be derived from several sources.

### 11.3.1   Codes and Standards

There are various codes and standards that contain requirements relating to the installation of Fire Alarm Systems, and they are as follows:

- The applicable National or Provincial *Building Code,*

- *CAN/ULC-S524 Installation of Fire Alarm Systems,*

- The applicable Canadian or Provincial *Electrical Code,* and (in the case of existing buildings) *the applicable National or Provincial *Fire Code.*

Generally speaking, Fire Alarm Systems (complete systems or simply new extensions to existing systems) must follow the requirements contained in the *Building Code.* (Remember that the Building Code tells us 'what' to do). The *Building Code* also contains a reference to *CAN/ULC-S524 Installation of Fire Alarm Systems* stating that systems installation must meet all applicable requirements contained in the standard. (Remember that Standards tell us 'how' to do it). The standard also states that the installation must comply with the requirements of the *Electrical Code.*

Sometimes the *Fire Code* comes into play regarding an existing Fire Alarm System that is deemed to be unacceptable and must be replaced. The *Fire Code* contains references to the need for the designer and installer to follow the requirements of the *Building Code.*

Therefore in all such situations, the installation of Fire Alarm Systems (in whole or in part) must follow the above codes and standards.

### 11.3.2   Building Permit

In most municipalities, engineered drawings and specifications must be submitted to the local Building Department for review prior to beginning installation.

The permit application process is an important step in ensuring that the design is acceptable, meeting the requirements of the codes and standards as well as the local municipality. There is frequently a comment in the approval process that the installation must still be in full

©

compliance with the *Building Code*. This provides another level of safety to the entire process, providing assurance to the designer, installer and owner.

### 11.3.3    Manufacturers Requirements

It is true that the *S-524 Standard* tells us 'how' to install the Fire Alarm System and its' component parts. However, it recognizes that it cannot, on its' own, state specifically how each individual device must be installed. It must depend upon the manufacturer of the system/devices to provide specific installation instructions relating to each individual device.

Therefore the installer must always check the manufacturer's literature for installation instructions that would include location information, coverage of devices, installation instructions, and other instructions that main pertain to that specific device.

### 11.3.4    The Installation Process

Almost universally across Canada, Electricians must perform Fire Alarm Systems installation work. The educational program leading to the issuance of a Certificate of Qualification as an Electrician contains a segment that relates directly to the installation of Fire Alarm Systems. However, this level of knowledge does not include the high level of detail that a Fire Alarm Technician must have. For that reason, many Electricians have taken the extra step of enrolling in a Fire Alarm Technician educational program in order to obtain Technician status above and beyond their Electrician status.

By the same token, Technicians must be fully aware of each and every installation requirement contained in the *CAN/ULC-S524 Installation Standard* and the *Electrical Code*. We can be assured that a system will continue to function for many years only if it is installed in accordance with all applicable codes and standards. When a Technician sees a facet of an installation that is not acceptable under the codes, then the Technician must bring that situation to the attention of the installer, expecting immediate correction.

## 11.4 Installation Details - General

### 11.4.1 Common Requirements

#### Raceways

As you learned in *Course 3 Basic Electricity for Fire Alarm Technicians*, all *Fire Alarm System* wiring must be of a type acceptable under the Electrical Code. In addition, all conductors must be:

- installed in metal raceways of the totally enclosed type,

- incorporated in a cable having a metal armor or sheath,

- installed in rigid non-metallic conduit where embedded in at least 50 mm of masonry or poured concrete, or

- installed underground, or installed in electrical nonmetallic tubing where embedded in at least 50 mm of masonry or poured concrete.

There are exceptions for buildings of combustible construction

#### Grounds

Fire Alarm Systems must be free of grounds except parts of circuits or equipment that are intentionally and permanently grounded to provide ground fault detection, or circuit protective grounding. They should be designed so that they do not depend upon the effectiveness of any ground connection except at the control unit. A single ground must be detected and a trouble signal initiated.

#### Electrical Supervision

Each alarm or supervisory initiating device, signalling device and emergency telephone must be connected to the field wiring in such a way that it is not possible to remove the device from the circuit without causing a trouble signal. Each circuit conductor entering a device box must be cut and individually terminated to the dedicated screws. Conductors must not be extended, un-cut, onto and beyond the device. There should be no, or as few as necessary, joints in the wiring.

#### End-of-Line Devices

Install the End-of-Line device, for each supervised circuit, in a separate box beyond the last device. Alternatively, if there is only one device on a circuit, then the End-of-Line device may be installed inside that device.

©

### Mounting Boxes

Each system device must be installed onto an approved electrical outlet box of the type specified by the manufacturer of the device. Such box, connectors and other installation materials must be of a type approved for use with the type of conduit used. Such boxes must be large enough to handle the device itself and provide ample space for the wiring connections.

### Device Guards

When device guards are deemed to be necessary, ensure that the guards are ULC-Listed for use with the device.

### Ancillary Control

It is permissible to provide operating power for ancillary devices from the Control Unit provided sufficient primary and secondary power is available to operate the devices and that any such devices do not interfere with the full operation of the Fire Alarm System. In addition, the Control Unit must be approved and Listed for the purpose. Very importantly, the *Electrical Code* prohibits power conductors from more than one source from being installed in a common conduit, except at a dual-voltage relay/enclosure where the ancillary device is connected and controlled.

In most instances, the Fire Alarm Control Unit simply provides non-powered contacts for the control of ancillary devices and systems.

### Special Requirements

Manufacturers may stipulate that certain circuits (e.g. telephone circuits) must be installed in separate conduits. Some manufacturers require that such circuit wiring must be shielded conductors. Not only is it essential that these requirements are followed to ensure full and proper operation of the system, but also to ensure final acceptance by the Authority Having Jurisdiction

## 11.5    Installation Details – Control Units

Several common-sense guidelines apply to the installation of Control Units:

- Locate the Control Unit in a well-lit, dry room where there is a low dust level and the temperatures are in the range of normal indoor temperatures.

- Locate it away from transformers, high-voltage cables and other such high electrical 'noise' equipment

- Do not use the Control Unit as a junction box
- Enter all field wiring as close to its connection points as possible, and secure all conductors.
- Tag all conductors and cables in a logical and orderly fashion.

## 11.6    Initiating and Signalling Devices

Many specific requirements apply to the installation of field devices, however several general comments also apply:

- Install devices to approved and acceptable electrical outlet boxes, ensuring a minimum of 15 mm clearance between the walls of the box and the device terminals. Ensure that the mounting box is acceptable to the manufacturer of the device.
- Install electrical boxes to permanent structures such as walls, ceilings etc. Devices must not be installed directly onto ceiling tiles.
- Install all devices such that they are readily visible and accessible.
- Cover all smoke detectors during construction so that they do not become contaminated with construction dust.
- Ensure that devices are not accidentally painted during construction/reconstruction.

### 11.6.1   Manual Stations

- Manual stations are to be mounted at height of 1200 mm to 1400 mm above the finished floor, to the centre of the station. Keep in mind that there may be other codes (Provincial or Municipal) that may alter the height requirements. Some jurisdictions stipulate that, in a barrier-free environment, the manual station must be no higher than 1200 mm above the floor.
- Manual stations are typically installed at exit points from a fire zone, usually at a door. The manual station must be visible at all times at a maximum distance from the door of 1500 mm. It is good practice to install the manual station on the latch side of the door; however manual stations may be installed on the hinged side as long as it remains visible when the door operates or is in the open position.
- Large doorways exceeding 12 m in width must have a manual station on both sides of the doorway.

### 11.6.2   Fire Detectors

There are many types of detectors as well as installation criteria. All fire detectors that require power to operate (smoke detectors for example) must be compatible with the Control Unit. This is to ensure that these fire detectors operate as intended, and that power requirements of either

©

the detectors or the Control Unit does not hamper the operation of the entire system.

- Each detector is to be accessible for periodic maintenance and testing. Exceptions to this requirement are areas deemed to be safety related like High Voltage room, hazardous material areas. In these areas alternate detection methods could be used such as beam detectors.

- Confined-area devices must have remote visual indicators installed in a visible location. Each device must meet the criteria for the area in which it will be installed. An example of this would be installation of a fixed-temperature type heat detector (not a rate-of-rise type) above a boiler, or in a commercial kitchen where ambient temperatures fluctuate dramatically.

- Most fire detectors are installed on ceilings. With the many types of ceiling designs and heights, come different types of installation methods. The following are the different types of layouts that are covered in *CAN/ULC-S524 Installation of Fire Alarm Systems*.

  - Smooth Ceiling

  - Sloped Ceiling (Peak Type)

  - Sloped Ceiling (Shed Type)

  - Galleries, Mezzanine & Interior Balconies

  - Partitions

  - Corridors

- Spot fire detectors must be installed so that they are not in the direct airflow or closer than 450 mm from a supply air outlet or from an exhaust outlet measured to the edge of the detector. [Figure 11.6.2a]

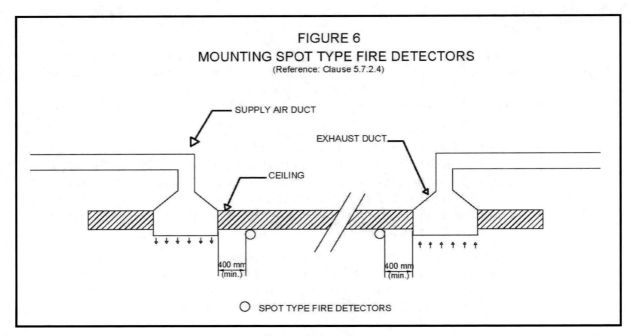

Figure 11.6.2a

- For smooth ceilings, the distance between spot type fire detectors must not exceed their rated flat ceiling spacing, and there must be [detectors within a distance of 50 % of the detector spacing, measured at a right angle, from the walls or partitions reaching to within 450 mm of the ceiling. The maximum distance from a spot type detector to the furthest point of a side wall or corner within its zone of protection [Refer to CAN/ULC-S524-06 Figure 9] must not be greater than 70% of its spacing.

- For irregularly-shaped areas, the distance between detectors may be greater than the specified detector spacing [Refer to CAN/ULC-S524-06 Figure 10], provided that the distance from the detector to the furthest point on a side wall or corner within its area of protection does not exceed 70 % of the detector spacing.

- Generally, detectors must be installed so that a clear space of at least 450 mm is provided between the device and any obstruction. [Refer to CAN/ULC-S524-06 Figure 4]

## 11.6.3   Heat Detectors

*CAN/ULC–S524* provides many specific requirements for the installation of heat detectors:

- Heat detectors must be mounted on the ceiling as per *CAN/ULC-S524*. Note there have been exceptions to this rule that have involved the Authority Having Jurisdiction as well as design engineers, where heat detectors were permitted to be installed on side walls as it was not feasible to mount at ceiling locations.

- Temperature ratings of heat detectors are to be selected from Table 4 of *CAN/ULC-S524*.

- When ceiling heights exceed 3,000 mm to 9,000 mm, the spacings of detectors must be greatly reduced. [Refer to CAN/ULC-S524-06 Figure 15] On average, heat detectors that are above 3,000 mm lose 13 % of their range for every 1,000 mm above 3,000 mm.

- It is recommended that with very high ceilings, other fire detectors should be considered.

- On a sloped ceiling that is less than 30°, heat detectors should be spaced according to the height of the peak. For a sloped ceiling greater than 30°, the average slope height shall be used rather than locating the heat detectors in the peak. [Refer to CAN/ULC-S524-06 Figure 15]

- In Beam-type construction the following requirements are to be met: beams that do not project lower than 100mm below the ceiling are to be installed as a smooth ceiling space. For beam construction that exceeds 100mm but less than 450mm the heat detector spacing shall be to a maximum of 66% of a smooth ceiling detector height at right angles to the beam construction. [Refer to CAN/ULC-S524-06 Figure 16]

- An alternate method of calculating heat detector spacing is as follows: If beam depth to ceiling height ratio is greater than 0.1 and beam spacing to ceiling height is greater than 0.4, heat detectors must be placed in each beam pocket. Likewise if beam depth to ceiling height is less than 0.1 or beam spacing to ceiling height is less than or equal to 0.4, heat detectors must be placed on the bottom of the beam construction. With beam construction the coverage of heat detectors would be further reduced for high ceiling requirements as discussed earlier.

- Where girders, support beams or joists cross each other and are within 300mm of the ceiling they should be considered as beams.

- Where beams and/or joists cross each other and the minimum measurement in the compartments are less than 2400mm across the heat detector should be mounted at the cross point of the beams at a maximum of 66% of its rated spacing for smooth ceilings.

## 11.6.4   Smoke Detectors

Always make sure that the smoke detector being used is designed to meet the environment that it is protecting.

- Smoke detectors must be compatible with the Fire Alarm Control Unit. This means that smoke detectors must be ULC-Listed for use with the specific Control Unit.

- Smoke detectors may be installed on vertical surfaces such as walls, between 100 mm to 300 mm from the ceiling. [Figure 11.6.4a]

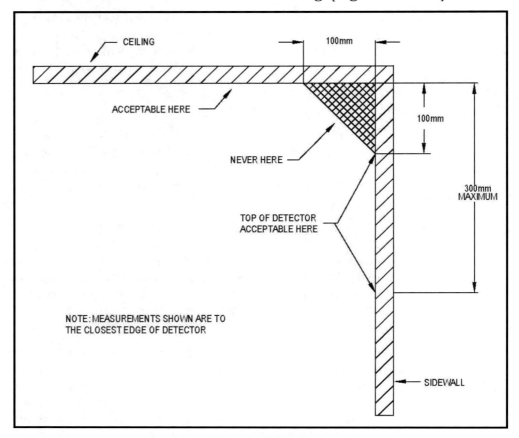

**Figure 11.6.4a**

- Smoke detector spacing is not affected by ceiling height.

- Smoke detector coverage should not exceed 83 m² per detector.

- In a ceiling with beam construction the following requirements are to be met: Beams that do not project greater than 100 mm from the ceiling should be treated as smooth ceiling space. If the beams project more than 100 mm but less than 300mm below the ceiling and the ceiling height is less than 3600 mm the smoke detectors are to be installed at right angles to the direction of the beam to a maximum of 50% of the smooth ceiling spacing. If the beams project greater than 300 mm below the ceiling or the ceiling height is greater than 3600 mm each bay area formed by the beams should be treated as a separate area.

- A smoke detector must be mounted at the highest point of the exit stair shaft as required by the National Building Code. In addition, exit stair shafts exceeding 18 m in height measured from the lowest point to the highest point of the shaft must have additional smoke detectors installed at every 3rd level.

- Smoke detectors in areas with high air movement must not be installed directly in the stream of the air supply. [Refer to CAN/ULC-S524-06 Figure 23]

### 11.6.5 Air-Duct Smoke Detectors

These detectors are designed to detect the presence of smoke in a circulating system and to shut down the system so as to prevent the spread of smoke to other areas of the building. Duct smoke detectors do not eliminate the necessity for open area detectors.

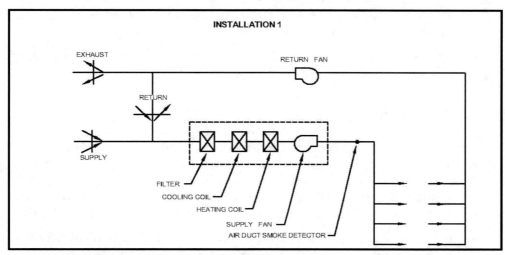

- Duct smokes are usually mounted in the main supply duct, however if the duct smoke cannot be installed in the main duct supply, duct smoke detectors are permitted to be installed in each branch line, as close to the main supply as possible.

  - Where air velocity exceeds 1.5 m/s, one air duct smoke is to be installed for every 1.5m² of cross sectional duct area. When air velocity is less than 1.5 m/s, one air duct smoke detector shall be installed for every 0.5m² of cross sectional duct area.

  - Air ducts are usually mounted outside the duct utilizing sampling tubes that are installed within the duct in such a way as to allow for adequate air movement for proper sampling of the air. In addition these duct smoke detectors must also allow for verification of airflow from the duct to the smoke detector. All duct smoke detectors must permit access to the entire assembly.

  - Air duct smoke detectors must be mounted in a straight section of the duct. [Refer to CAN/ULC-S524-06 Figure 25]

  - When subject to both positive and negative airflow, the raceway entry points and other openings must be sealed.

## 11.6.6   Beam-Type Smoke Detectors

Location and spacing of these detectors is to be as manufacturer's documented installation instructions. It is recommended that beam detectors be installed near the ceiling, free of obstructions, such as to allow for smoke and other fire related gases to pass through the beam.

Beam type smoke detectors should be located near the ceiling above the open grid ceiling where the following conditions prevail:

- The minimum opening in the grid is 6mm or larger.

- The thickness of the grid material does not exceed the maximum dimensions of the opening: and

- The openings constitute 70% or more of the area of the ceiling material.

## 11.6.7   Air-Sampling Detectors

Location and spacing of these detectors is to be as per the manufacturer's documented installation instructions. Air sampling type networks should be designed on the basis of sound dynamic fluid principles. Network design must include calculations showing the flow characteristics of the piping network and for each sampling tube.

- Air sampling pipe networks must be airtight, permanently fixed and conspicuously labeled as a smoke detector sampling tube.

- Air sampling detectors should initiate a trouble signal when the airflow is outside the manufacturer's specific range.

- Sampling port and filter are to be kept clear in accordance with the manufacturer's documented instructions.

## 11.6.8   Flame Detectors

Location and spacing of these detectors is to be as per the manufacturer's documented installation instructions. Very different from smoke and heat detectors, flame detectors are line-of-sight devices. Because the triggering energy from a flame travels at the speed of light, flame detectors can react almost instantaneously to the appearance of a flame.

Spacing and positioning of the flame detectors should be so that no point requiring detection in the hazard area is obstructed or is outside the field of view of at least one flame detector. Distances from the viewing surface and acceptable cones of vision are to be found within manufacturers instructions.

©

### 11.6.9  Other Fire Detectors

Location and spacing to be based on the principal of operation and an engineering survey of the condition anticipated in service and in accordance with documented manufacturer's recommendations.

### 11.6.10  Fault Isolators

Fault Isolators are used to restrict the effects of a single electrical fault such as a short-circuit, to the zone or area of the fault, to ensure that the data communication link does not become totally useless over its' entire length, causing more than one zone not to operate. [Figure 11.6.10a]

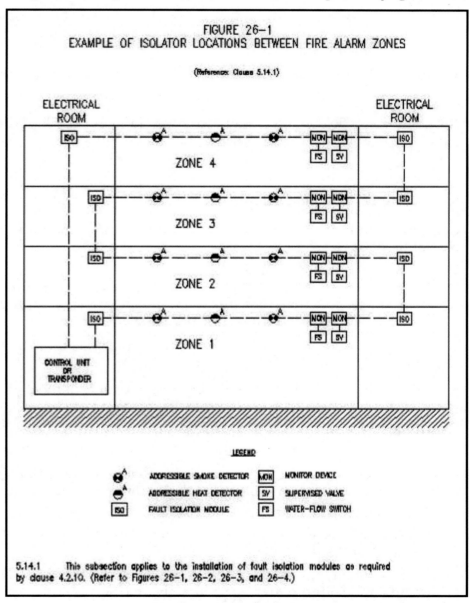

**Figure 11.6.10a**

- Each fire alarm zone that is fire separated, must be protected by one isolator when entering and one when leaving the zone. [Refer to CAN/ULC-S524-06 Figure 26-3] For open large areas that have more than one fire zone, a single fault isolator between zones may be utilized.

- Separate fault isolators must be mounted in a separate box, visible and accessible at all times.

- Fault isolators incorporated within a field device must be mounted in accordance with the requirements of the device.

- Fault isolators for an exit or vertical service space must me mounted on the floor area side.

- Fault isolator modules installed on opposite sides of the same fire separation must be offset horizontally by 400 mm and not located within the same stud space.

- Fault isolators must be identified by a label on the cover plate or device.

Note that some field devices may contain isolation capability, therefore possibly negating the need for separate isolation modules. [Refer to CAN/ULC-S524-06 Figure 26-1 and Figure 26-2]

## 11.6.11  Signalling Devices – Audible and Visible

Some of the specific requirements relating to audible and/or visible signalling devices are as follows:

- Where ceiling heights allow, install audible signalling devices so that they will not be less than 2300 mm above the floor measured to the top of the device. Note that this requirement does not apply to in-suite signalling devices that incorporate silencing means.

- Wall-mounted audible devices must be installed so that the top of the device is 150 mm below the ceiling.

- Signalling devices that are subject to obvious mechanical damage must be protected by a compatible, listed, accessory.

- Audible and Visible signalling devices must be supported independently of their attachments to the circuit conductors.

- Audible and Visible signalling devices must be installed in sufficient numbers to meet the audibility and visibility requirements of the Building Code.

- Signalling devices must be installed in accordance with the manufacturers' instructions.

- Audible signalling devices within a building must generate similar sounds and sound patterns when activated.

## 11.6.12  Audible Signal Devices

The *Standard* contains a reference to Appendix C Sound Level Measurements of the Standard for recommended installation criteria. Other items are:

- Audible signal devices must be installed in accordance with manufacturer's instructions.

- Good intelligibility means that more low-power audible devices are beneficial and also means that speaker layouts may be different than bell or horn layouts.

- Audible signal devices must be wired with the same polarity.

## 11.6.13  Visible Signal Devices

- Visible signal devices must be rated not less than 15 cd.

- Two or more visible signalling devices in corridors or rooms in the same field of view must be installed as if the corridor was a room of those dimensions.

- Wall-mounted visible signalling devices must be installed such that the entire lens is not less than 2000 mm and not more than 2400 mm above the finished floor.

- Wall-mounted visible signal devices must be installed in accordance with Table 5 using one of the following:

  - A single visible signal device; or

  - Two visible signal devices located on opposite walls; or

  - Two or more visible signal devices in the same room or adjacent space within the field of view that flash in synchronization.

- In square rooms with wall-mounted visible signal devices centered at the midpoint of the wall, spacing must be in accordance with this table. [Refer to CAN/ULC-S524-06 Table 5 and Figure 3]

- In rooms with visible signal devices not centered on a wall, the effective intensity (candela) from one wall-mounted visible signal device must be determined by maximum room size dimensions obtained either by measuring the distance to the furthest wall or by doubling the distance to the furthest adjacent wall, whichever is greater, as required by the above table. Refer to CAN/ULC-S524-06 Appendices D1, D2, and D3.

- Where a room configuration is not square, the square room size that allows the entire room to be encompassed or allows the room to be subdivided into multiple squares must be used.

- Where multiple wall-mounted visible signal devices are used within a room, room must be subdivided into multiple squares and the selection of the device output and location must be in accordance with CAN/ULC-S524-06 Table 6 and Figure 3 and Appendices D1, D2 and D3.

- Ceiling-mounted visible signalling devices must be suspended or mounted at not more than 9000 above the finished floor level. [Refer to CAN/ULC-S524-06 Table 6]

- Where the ceiling-mounted visible signal device is not located at the centre of the room, the effective intensity (candela) must be determined by doubling the distance from the device to the farthest wall to obtain the maximum room size.

- Installation of visible signal devices in corridors greater than 6000 mm wide must comply with the spacing requirements for rooms in accordance with rooms of a similar size.

- Installation of visible signal devices in corridors 6000 mm or less in width must be in accordance with the requirements of CAN/ULC-S524-06 Table 7.

- Visible signal devices must be located not more than 4600 mm from the end of the corridor with spacing not greater than 30 m between adjacent signalling devices.

- Where there is an interruption of the concentrated viewing path, such as a fire door, an elevation change, or any other obstruction, the areas must be treated as a separate corridor.

- Wall-mounted visible signal devices in corridors will be permitted to be installed on either end wall or the sidewall of the corridor with spacing requirements of above.

## 11.6.14 Combination Audible/ visible signal devices

- Where combination audible/visible signal devices are installed, the location of the device must be determined by the requirements of 11.7.11 *Signalling Devices – Audible and Visible* and 11.7.13 *Visible Signal Devices.*

- Note that further installation criteria should be referenced in Appendix C *Sound Level Measurements* and Appendix D *Visible Signal Devices* of the Standard.

## 11.6.15 Emergency Telephones

The Installation Standard provides the following specific installation requirements:

- Telephone handsets must be installed in a lockable enclosure and provided with a means for gaining access to the telephone without a key. In areas where telephone handsets are not subject to tampering and vandalism, the handsets need not be installed in lockable enclosures.

©

- The enclosures must be installed in an accessible location between 1350 mm and 1500 mm above the finished floor measured to the centerline of the enclosure.

- Handsets must be compatible with the associated Control Unit or Transponder.

### 11.6.16 End-of-Line Devices

End-of-line devices are installed to enable electrical supervision of a circuit. This is usually a resistor that allows a small electrical current to flow. The Fire Alarm Control Unit constantly monitors this current. If the supervisory current decreases to a specific level, the Control Unit initiates a trouble condition.

- End-of-line devices are to be installed in separate enclosures at a height less than 1800mm above the finished floor measured to the centre of the end-of-line device, and located beyond the last device on the circuit.

- The end-of-line devices for a circuit with only one field device on it may be located within that field device.

- End-of-line devices must have an identifying label securely attached to the front of the cover plate, listing the zone or circuit served by the device.

## 11.7    Circuit Power Loss

Electrical power loss in a circuit is determined by:

- the quantity of signal appliances,

- the current draw of each appliance,

- the size of the electrical conductors,

- the length of the conductors, and

- the location of the devices on the circuit.

Note that the length of wire is not just the length of conductor from the control unit to the end-of-line device, but the combined length of both conductors. Usually this is twice the length from the control unit to the end-of-line device.

It is common practice to perform line loss calculations assuming all devices are connected at the end of the circuit. This method is obviously slightly inaccurate but the error is on the side of safety. And it is a much simpler calculation. The greatest accuracy is obtained by performing the calculation for each bell location on the circuit and then compiling the total of the losses. This amount of detail is seldom needed or performed.

Example calculation:

- quantity of devices:         9
- type of device:         24 volt DC bell
- current draw/requirement:  0.15 amps per device
- length of circuit:        100 metres
- size of conductors:      14 AWG
- conductor resistance:    2.57 ohms/300 metres

Line Loss = (quantity of Devices x Individual Device Current) x (Conductor Length x Conductor Resistance)

= (9 x 0.15) x (2 x 100 x 2.57/300)
= (1.35) x (1.71)
= 2.3 Volts

**This value of power loss in the wiring is just within the maximum allowable loss of 10% of signal rated voltage and is therefore acceptable.** This example also assumes that all signalling devices are grouped at the end of the circuit. It is probable that the devices would be installed at various locations along the circuit length and the resultant line loss would be somewhat less than shown in our example.

## 11.8    Additional Points relating to Installation

There are some devices and or other elements of a Fire Alarm System where there may be a keen eye to detail required to ensure these small but important installation requirements are upheld.

Ultimately, the installation of the system and all of its components will be under the direction of drawings approved by an engineer, approved by the municipality's fire prevention and building departments, and installed as agreed upon between the site and the installation organization as outlined in a binding contractual agreement.

Along the line, in this process, the various codes and standard references will also be quoted or incorporated into the system's design. This is where small but significant things can be detected (if you are knowledgeable) or missed when you don't know what you are looking at or for.

### 11.8.1   A/C Power Disconnect Means

In terms of the fire alarm system's A/C (alternating current) power disconnecting means shall be clearly identified as the fire alarm power in a permanent, conspicuous and legible manner and shall be coloured red and lockable in the 'on' position.  Specifically from the standard for installation of fire alarm systems, CAN/ULC-S524-06 3.2.1.5 the standard also references "lockable".  This refers to the need for the disconnect switch to have a means of locking or being secured in the closed ('on") position (by means of a padlock through a hole in the switch handle, breaker lock over a breaker in a distribution panel, or the distribution panel door that can be locked with an available key). However, again it may be suggested to <u>use</u> such lockable features to secure the system's A/C power supply.

### 11.8.2    Accessibility of Junction Boxes

The making of joints and splices into conductors is governed by the installation standard, 3.4.10, which refers to the *Canadian Electrical Code*, Part I, section 12, which in-turn states that joints and splices in wires and cables shall be accessible. This can be interpreted as ensuring the connections to conductors have to be placed in such a way that access can be arranged for service to the conductor. In the process of inspection, junction boxes must then be in a place where they can be accessed (not concealed behind walls without providing access/service doors).

### 11.8.3    Raceways

Not only should attention be paid to a system's detection devices, signaling appliances and wiring supervision devices, such as end-of-line devices and isolators, but also the wiring raceways and their condition.

The raceways, which deliver the conductors from a fire alarm system control panel or related transponder(s) to its associated devices, should not be overlooked in our inspection of a system. Typical raceway issues that are common include, but are not necessarily limited to support issues, termination and transference issues, acceptable types in use, and sizing issues.

Proper raceway support is a large concern for our systems. Should the support for the raceway fail, the supporting members of the system become the conductors contained therein. This risks the connectivity between the system and its devices.

Termination and transference issues are common sources of errors in raceway installations. Raceways must terminate at a device utilizing a fixture box in a proper, approved manner. The termination method is based on the instructions of the manufacturer of a given raceway. The termination point allows for proper support to the raceway and is a source of strength for the bond between the raceway and the fixture box, provided that the fixture box is also mounted properly. This termination also prevents conductors from exposure to external damage. Surface raceway is usually decorative in nature, but still must provide protection to the conductors within the raceway.

Joints in the raceway must be in accordance with the manufacturer's direction, using approved fittings for the application. Proper joints prevent the conductors from exposure and potential damage. Attention must be paid to proper joints and terminations to ensure conductors are

©

not exposed. Transferring raceway is an area where one raceway type may marry with another type. Typical sources of raceway transfer occur where a decorative surface type raceway changes to a more utilitarian/functional type of raceway, such as an EMT, rigid type, flex or armored type raceway.

The connections made between the two types of raceway must be correct. These transfer points can and usually occur on walls, just above suspended ceiling tiles. A quick check above a ceiling tile may prove to be a good double check to ensure that the transference of one type to another type of raceway was done properly.

### 11.8.4   Class A Installations

A Class A circuit is defined as a circuit having one continuous path connecting all components on the circuit and terminating, through an alternate connection path, in the source enclosure. The intent of such a wiring method is to provide greater reliability.

Remembering that a Class B circuit automatically detects an open-circuit fault, or a ground fault (and in some cases a short-circuit fault), and that with such a single fault, the devices on the circuit may, or may not, operate, depending on the location of the fault on the circuit.

A Class A circuit guarantees that, with a single such fault, all devices on that same circuit will still operate.

Strenuous installation requirements relate to this style of circuit. The alternate wiring circuit (i.e. the return of the two-wire circuit to the source) must be in separate raceways or cable assemblies having a separation of at least 300 mm [Refer to CAN/ULC-S524-06 Figure 1-1] where the cables are installed vertically, or 1200 mm where the cables are installed horizontally.

There are exceptions to the above:

- for a distance not to exceed 3,000 mm where the primary and return conductors enter or exit field devices, control unit or transponders. [Refer to CAN/ULC-S524-06 Figure 1-2]

- single wiring drops to individual field devices [Refer to CAN/ULC-S524-06 Figure 1-3]

- single drops to multiple field devices installed within a single room not exceeding 110 m² [Refer to CAN/ULC-S524-06 Figure 1-4]

Class A wiring may be used for Conventional field devices, Addressable field devices or for DCL connections between Control Units and Transponders.

©

## 11.9    Chapter Summary

1.    Fire Alarm System installations are performed by Electricians and not by Fire Alarm Technicians.

2.    CAN/ULC-S524 *Installation of Fire Alarm Systems* is the document that directs all aspects of installation materials and methods.

3.    All field devices must be installed onto acceptable electrical outlet boxes. Such boxes and all interconnecting wiring and raceways must be installed in accordance with *Standard S-524* and the *Electrical Code.*

4.    *Standard S-524* contains instructions relating to the location of all field devices, including the need for multiple devices in given rooms and spaces.

5.    Proper selection of detection devices, and proper locations, are very important for the successful and prompt detection of a fire condition.

6.    For building occupants to be made aware of the operation of a Fire Alarm System, it is imperative that audible and visible signalling devices be installed in accordance with spacing parameters provided in *Standard S-524*.

7.    The use of Class A wiring for field devices adds one more level of reliability over that of a Class B wired system.

8.    All systems Control Equipment, and all field devices, must be installed in accordance with Manufacturer instructions.

9.    During a Verification, it is the responsibility of the Fire Alarm Technician to inspect the installation materials and methods used, to ensure that they are in full compliance with *Standard S-524* and the *Electrical Code.* If they are not, the Technician must bring the matter to the attention of those in charge of the building so that the matter will be corrected.

10.    Only full attention to, and complete compliance with, *Standard S524* and the *Electrical Code,* will ensure a totally reliable installation.

## 11.10   Review Questions

| # | ? | Question | Section |
|---|---|----------|---------|
| **11-1** | | **Fire Alarm Technicians do not install Fire Alarm Systems!** | |
| | A | True | |
| | B | False | |
| **11-2** | | **Typically the Occupational Health and Safety Code comes into play regarding an existing Fire Alarm System that is deemed to be unacceptable and must be replaced.** | |
| | A | True | |
| | B | False | |
| **11-3** | | **In most municipalities, engineered drawings and specifications must be submitted to the local Building Department for review prior to beginning installation.** | |
| | A | True | |
| | B | False | |
| **11-4** | | **Universally across Canada, Engineers must perform Fire Alarm Systems installation work.** | |
| | A | True | |
| | B | False | |
| **11-5** | | **Fire Alarm Systems must be free of grounds except parts of circuits or equipment that are intentionally and permanently grounded to provide ground fault detection, or circuit protective grounding.** | |
| | A | True | |
| | B | False | |
| **11-6** | | **If there is only one device on a circuit, then the End-of-Line device may be installed in the electrical box for the device.** | |
| | A | True | |
| | B | False | |

©

| # | ? | Question | Section |
|---|---|----------|---------|
| **11-7** | | **It is NOT permissible to provide operating power for ancillary devices from the Control Unit even if sufficient primary and secondary power is provided to operate the devices and that any such devices will interfere with the full operation of the Fire Alarm System.** | |
| | A | True | |
| | B | False | |
| **11-8** | | **Locate transponders and control units away from transformers, high-voltage cables and other such high electrical 'noise' equipment** | |
| | A | True | |
| | B | False | |
| **11-9** | | **Manual stations are to be mounted at height of 1200 mm to 1400 mm above the finished floor, to the centre of the station.** | |
| | A | True | |
| | B | False | |
| **11-10** | | **Smoke detectors need not be compatible with the Fire Alarm Control Unit. This means that smoke detectors can be connected to any Control Unit and they will operate as intended.** | |
| | A | True | |
| | B | False | |

# Chapter 12: Verifications

## 12.1    Chapter Overview and Key Concepts

A verification is an extremely thorough, systematic inspection and testing of an entire, or a portion of a Fire Alarm System, to ensure it has been installed correctly, programmed or configured correctly, meets all applicable standards, works properly and is in accordance with the project design documents (plans and specifications.

A verification is carried out by technically-capable personnel who understand Fire Alarms Systems, the rules and regulations, and the operations of the particular brand of system being verified.

A verification is a legal requirement just about everywhere in Canada. It must be performed as directed by the Provincial *Building Code*, which dictates that it must be done in accordance with the *ULC standard CAN/ULC-S537 Verification of Fire Alarm Systems*, applicable at the time the design was approved.

It needs to be well planned, uninterrupted by stops to 'fix problems', and it must be complete. It must be documented at length and in full detail. It needs to be signed off by the Verifier(s) and by the attending Designer, who share responsibility for the system's compliances and integrity.

## 12.2    Learning Objectives

After studying the contents of this chapter, the reader should be able to do the following;

- Understand the strategic importance of a verification
- Understand how a high work ethic leads to improved performance
- Understand the structure of the verification standard
- Identify the proper approach to overall system performance tests
- Perform adequate tests of the installed wiring
- Determine precisely what tests to apply to the detection devices
- Measure the acceptability of audibility and intelligibility
- Understand the importance of accurate and complete written test documentation
- Recognize when a greater degree of product knowledge (such as factory-authorized training) is necessary to perform an acceptable verification

## Language defined - Chapter Glossary (Also see Main Glossary)

Terms that are important to the understanding of this chapter are included below. For a complete listing of such words, expressions and terms, refer to the Main Glossary near the end of this manual. This glossary is not intended to replace or supersede any officially-published glossary. It is simply our intent that these be used as a training aid in understanding the contents of this manual. Always refer to the specific code or standard, and to the Authority Having Jurisdiction for the applicable official interpretation.

| Term | Definition |
|------|-----------|
| **Active Field Device** | A device that can be uniquely identified by the control unit to determine its presence and operating status, and which may be commanded to operate or to change its operating parameters independently of other field devices that share a common circuit |
| **Addressable Device** | A device that can be individually and uniquely identified by a control unit. The address is set using binary/hexadecimal/decimal methods using dipswitches, rotary switches or solid-state memory |
| **Alarm Signal** | An audible signal transmitted throughout a zone or zones to advise occupants that a fire emergency exists; also called an EVACUATION signal |
| **Alert Signal** | An audible signal intended to advise designated persons of a fire emergency |
| **Ancillary Device** | A device that performs a life safety related function, but that is not part of the fire alarm system |
| **Authority Having Jurisdiction** | The organization, office, or individual responsible for approving equipment, an installation, or a procedure. Most often, it is the municipal Fire Department |
| **Candela** | The SI or metric unit of measure for luminous intensity or candlepower of a light or strobe |
| **Check, Inspect And Test** | **CHECK** - A visual observation to ensure the device or system is in place and is not obviously damaged or obstructed |
| | **INSPECT** - A physical examination to determine that the device or system will apparently perform in accordance with its intended function |
| | **TEST** - the actual operation of the device or system to ensure that it performs in accordance with its intended operation or function |

| Term | Definition |
|---|---|
| **Control Unit** | A device with the necessary circuits or components needed to provide acceptable operating power for a fire alarm system, receive signals from alarm initiating devices, cause audible alarm signals to operate, and electrically monitor the installation wiring and device placement against certain faults and/or removal |
| **Fire Alarm System** | A system comprising both manually operated devices and automatic fire detectors, alarm signalling devices and a control unit, all electrically interconnected in order to detect fire conditions and to warn the occupants of the building |
| **Fire Detector** | A device that detects a fire condition and automatically initiates an electrical signal, and includes heat and smoke detectors |
| **Fire Detector — Heat** | A device for sensing an abnormally high air temperature or an abnormal rate of increase of temperature |
| **Fire Detector - Smoke** | A device for sensing the presence of visible or invisible particles of combustion, the concentration of which exceeds a pre-determined level |
| **Flame Detector** | A detector that is designed to sense the radiation emanating from a flame. It may also sense the modulated flicker of the flame, which generally must be sustained for a period of time before the detector is activated. Two common types of flame detectors are 'infrared' and 'ultraviolet' detectors, so named because of the frequency range of radiation looked for by the detector design |
| **Ground Fault** | A circuit impedance to ground sufficient to prevent normal operation |
| **Manual Station** | A device that initiates an alarm condition in a fire alarm system, when actuated manually. The station will remain in the operated condition until it has been reset to normal using a special tool |
| **Open-Circuit Fault** | Means a circuit series resistance increase of 10 kOhm or more, unless otherwise stated, resulting from an abnormal condition |
| **Owner** | Any person, firm or corporation controlling the property under consideration |
| **Short-Circuit Fault** | A resistance shunt of 0.1 Ohm or less across a circuit, unless otherwise stated, resulting from an abnormal condition |
| **Sprinkler Supervision** | A method of electrically monitoring critical elements of an automatic sprinkler system to detect potentially disabling abnormal conditions, and provide a warning signal |
| **Suite** | A single room or series of rooms of complementary use, operated under a single tenancy, and includes: |

| Term | Definition |
|------|------------|
| | (a) dwelling units, |
| | (b) individual guest rooms in motels, hotels, boarding houses, rooming houses and dormitories, and |
| | (c) individual stores and individual or complementary rooms for business and personal services occupancies. |
| **Supply Duct** | A duct for conveying air from a heating, ventilating or air-conditioning appliance to a space to be heated, ventilated or air-conditioned |
| **Supporting Field Device** | An active field device that monitors other field devices on a separate circuit and reports the status of that separate circuit to the control unit |
| **Trouble Signal** | A signal (usually a buzzer and an amber lamp) indicating a fault or an off-normal condition in a fire alarm system |
| **Waterflow Switch** | A device used to detect the flow of water through some portion of the automatic sprinkler system piping, as will occur when one or more sprinkler heads has operated, and will operate a set of electrical contacts for interconnection to a fire alarm system. An adjustable time delay mechanism may be installed between the paddle-operated stem and the contacts to keep brief water movements from initiating an alarm signal |

## 12.3    The Purpose of a Verification

You already know that Fire Alarms Systems are life-safety systems, which people depend upon every day to give them the earliest possible warning of a developing fire condition so they can protect themselves. In that way, Fire Alarm Systems are a bit like parachutes, or air bags in cars...they simply MUST work when they are needed...they are 'mission-critical' so-to-speak.

But Fire Alarm Systems can be complex and extensive. They involve a number of different stakeholders at various times, each of who has responsibilities in making a Fire Alarm System "happen". Building owners have obligations to protect the occupants. Engineers & Consultants have an obligation to understand the nature and use of the buildings they are working on, and to design and specify Fire Alarm Systems that at least comply with the provincial *Building Code* and the standards it references.

Installing Contractors (often) have the obligation to purchase and install Fire Alarm Systems that comply with the Engineers' specifications, and to install them in compliance with the *Building Code* and the standard *CAN/ULC S524 Installation of Fire Alarm Systems*. Of course Fire Alarm System manufacturers are relied upon in their "promise" to provide reliant, compliant systems that are properly type-tested by ULC according to the appropriate standards.

Finally, there are also the Fire Officials and Authorities Having Jurisdiction, trying to ensure that adequate, compliant systems are installed and working reliably.

With all these players involved, you can understand why there are many opportunities for something to go wrong. But that can't be allowed to happen on a Life Safety system!

That is why, once all the designing, specifying, configuring, estimating, bidding, buying, approving, installing and initial testing are all done, it is critical  to very thoroughly and completely inspect and test the entire Fire Alarm System from end to end to ensure that the Fire Alarm System was installed:

- in compliance with *CAN/ULC-S524*,
- in compliance with the appropriate *Electrical Code*, and
- in compliance with the Designer's specifications and drawings,

The verification must also confirm:

- that the system design and operation is fully and properly documented, so that the users know what to do, and so future tests, inspections, design changes, and re-verifications can be reliably carried out
- that everything works properly,
- that all the detectors detect,

- that signals are sent and received where they are supposed to go,

- that automatic responses take place as they are supposed to,

- that annunciators indicate the correct conditions,

- that audible signals sound audibly in the right place with the right tones,

- that voice evacuation equipment works properly, audibly and intelligibly,

- that monitoring stations and Fire Authorities are notified quickly,

- that logging of events happens properly, etc., etc.

All of the above and more, must happen so that building occupants can rely 100% on getting that critical early warning if a fire event occurs.

## 12.4    The Criticality of High-Quality Work and Complete Documentation

Verifications can sometimes be long, difficult and onerous affairs, especially on large systems. Some parts are repetitive and potentially boring. Other parts can be difficult and complicated. Still other parts are awkward and frustrating. One has to deal with pressures from many quarters....

Owners and Contractors press for completion to get occupancy. They may demand Certificates and Reports well before they can reasonably be ready. While Verifying, one may uncover quite a number of things that are incomplete or not operational, meaning the whole process, or at least a good part of it, may have to be repeated at a later time or at least resumed after a delay. During partial verifications, coordination of tenant and building routines with testing schedules can slow the process considerably. And the Verifier's boss often wants to know when this one will be finished because another one awaits.

So Verifying Technicians may find themselves under the gun, and from time to time may be asked to "speed things up" or even to "cut corners". It is critical that Verifiers adamantly insist that they be allowed to do a complete, thorough verification, and to document it fully. It can be a matter of life and death.

In some provinces there are new laws that hold Technicians responsible for the integrity of their work, and levy fines and jail sentences for negligence or failure to act responsibly. So it is very important to know the laws and regulations in your province, and to resist at all costs, pressures to do anything less than a very thorough job.

Furthermore, at a later time, when annual inspections are performed, or when extensions and modifications are made to the fire alarm, or even when an inquest is being held following a fire incident, it is very important that the records of verification are complete, clear and available. So it is worth taking the trouble to 'document' fully and accurately up front.

©

## 12.5    The Applicable Codes and Standards

The National Research Council, in Ottawa, oversees the development of the *National Building Code*. The *Building Code* is then either adopted, or it is adopted when modified somewhat, by each Province and Territory. Provincial building codes govern the requirements for various aspects of Fire Alarm Systems, including verification. To do so, the *Building Code* refers to ULC's standard *CAN/ULC–S537 Verification of Fire Alarm Systems*, citing the applicable edition of that standard, and directing that it govern verification activity.

### 12.5.1    Structure and Content of the *CAN/ULC-S537* Verification Standard

The *CAN/ULC-S537 Standard* is actually a reasonably brief document that, after defining its 'terms', simply lists all the inspections and testing that must be done. It speaks initially to the "Procedures" in general, and to the documentation requirements. Then it stipulates the extent and type of examinations and tests required for each part of the Fire Alarm System including; the system wiring, Control Units and Transponders, large-scale-network systems, power supplies, printers, all field devices, including automatic detectors, pull stations, sprinkler supervisory devices, signaling devices, emergency telephones and end-of-line devices

The standard concludes with requirements for verifying system modifications, and concludes with tables that outline the requirements for abnormal system condition behaviours, response times, and colour codes for visual indicators.

The standard has (informative) Appendices that describe other aspects of testing in more detail, and provide sample forms for documenting verification results.

### 12.5.2    Other Relevant Standards

If it were as easy as following just one standard, things would be simpler. *CAN/ULC S537* itself refers to other ULC standards, including *CAN/ULC-S524 Installation of Fire Alarm Systems, CAN/ULC-S536, Inspection and Testing of Fire Alarm Systems*, and *CAN/ULC-S529, Smoke Detectors for Fire Alarm Systems*. So to properly undertake a verification, one must also be familiar with these referenced standards. Therefore, in order for technicians to fully understand Verifications, it is essential that they must understand all of the Standards mentioned above.

The intent of this chapter is not to simply repeat the contents of those Standards, but instead to complement the Verification Standard so that the purpose and context of its prescriptions can be better understood. The Standard dictates WHAT, and a very little bit of HOW. This Chapter attempts to explain HOW and WHY and offer some supplemental advice and information.

### 12.5.3    Ensure That You Use the Applicable Versions

Be aware, that the building codes and the ULC standards are constantly under revision, and that the relevant versions of those documents must be used at all times. Even if the current *National Building Code* is dated 2005, unless the province has adopted it and published it or some version of it, the applicable Provincial *Building Code* may have an earlier date. The building codes refer to various ULC standards related to different aspects of Fire Alarm design, application, installation and testing. Refer to Table 1.3.1.2 in Division 1 of the *Building Code* to determine which edition of each standard is the edition being referenced. The most recent edition may not be the edition referenced. Be aware that addenda to the *Building Code* are issued periodically and may include revisions to the table to update references. However they no longer stipulated the specific issue or revision date of those standards, and you will need to know the currently applicable dates of those standards, perhaps by referring to ULC's website. You may also wish to consult a code consultant to ensure you have the correct versions for reference.

## 12.6    Qualifications of Verifying Personnel

### 12.6.1    Minimum Qualifications – All Systems

Appendix A of *CAN/ULC-S537* speaks to qualifications for people who perform verifications, however the section is extremely brief, simply stating;

> *"Any person who performs the verification of a fire alarm system should be familiar with this standard and have received suitable formal training or sufficient experience acceptable to the authority having jurisdiction."*

While this statement implies that it is basically up to the "AHJ", it is important that common sense and reasonable judgment prevail. For even the most basic Fire Alarm Systems, competent verification requires a good knowledge of basic electricity, basic electronics, Fire Alarm Systems in general, the specific system being tested in particular, and an understanding of the applicable Codes and Standards.

This implies some post-secondary education either in applied technology, in engineering, or in an electrical trade, plus some further learning/accreditation in Fire Alarm Systems, in the *Building Code*, and in a number of relevant ULC standards, including *CAN/ULC-S524 Installation of Fire Alarm Systems, CAN/ULC-S527 Fire Alarm System Control Panels*, and yes, *CAN/ULC-S537 Verification of Fire Alarm Systems*.

Furthermore, it would be very unwise for inexperienced technicians to undertake a verification by themselves without having done one before.

©

Prior to handling or supervising a verification alone, one should have actively participated in several previous verifications under the supervision of a knowledgeable and experienced technician.

It is also critical that technicians doing a verification can read and understand the Fire Alarm System design documents and drawings. They must also be able to understand and apply the fire alarm manufacturer's instructions, applications guides, specifications and shop drawings. They must be able to understand the intended operation of the system, and how to develop comprehensive test sequences that exhaustively prove that the system is installed as designed, and is in compliance with *CAN/ULC-S524*. They must be able to clearly, quickly and accurately record all appropriate test data, and be able to interpret it for AHJs, building owners and system designers.

Familiarity, with safe handling and operation of Fire Alarm Systems, with electrical safety, and with construction site workplace safety procedures, are also basic qualifiers for verifiers.

While neither the *Building Code* nor the *CAN/ULC-S537 Standard* specifically require the minimum qualifications outlined above, one can anticipate that the Authority Having Jurisdiction will demand them.

## 12.6.2    Essential Qualifications – Software-Based and Networked Systems

### Software-Based Systems

Today's larger fire alarm systems are typically "addressable", often "intelligent", but just about always micro-processor and software based. This means that 'software' and 'firmware' will determine how the fire alarm works, how it responds to different inputs, how it will decide if alarm or trouble conditions exist, how it signals, how it annunciates, what it prints out, and what sequence of operation it follows.

Technicians performing a verification of such a system will be effectively putting the software and firmware through their paces, and so their familiarity with how that software is configured for the application in question, how it is designed to respond, i.e. how it works, for the specific system under test, is essential. This implies a need to be able to read programming documents, operating sequences, 'matrices' and input/output correlation schedules for the specific make of system at hand. Hence the need for some degree of training from the manufacturer, and some experience with that manufacturer's systems, is essential.

(Note that "firmware" refers to programs that are "hard coded" into the system, that are standard for the type and model of system, and that are not field modifiable'. Neither the Designer nor the Owner or even the Servicer of a Fire Alarm System can alter the "firmware", although a factory-trained and factory-authorized technician may be able to download newer versions of the firmware in the field under strict conditions. Hence, a verifier need not be expert on a system's firmware in order to do a proper verification.)

### Networked Systems

Systems so extensive they require more than one fire alarm control panel to handle the I/O, functions and number of zones involved, are often synthesized as networks of basic control panels (also referred to as 'nodes' or 'data gathering panels'), all hooked into one or more 'Command and Control Facilities'. The need to establish and manage high speed real-time communications among nodes of a networked system adds another layer of complexity onto that brought about by software-based detection, annunciation, control and signaling. The required extensive testing of the reliability and 'survivability' of the network under real operating conditions, when verifying a larger scale system, implies the need for the verifier to be familiar with the communications operations of the specific make and type of system being verified. Typically, an AHJ will absolutely require that someone verifying or overseeing the verification of a networked system have factory training and certification for the specific system involved.

### 12.6.3  Objectivity – Avoiding Conflicts of Interest

The Preface to the S537 Standard says the following in its third paragraph:

> *"The requirements of this Standard contemplate that the verification procedure described herein will be conducted by an organization other than the installing contractor and designer, and that the verification will be carried out by qualified personnel in the employ of an organization acceptable to the authority having jurisdiction."*

Reliability in verifying the integrity of a Fire Alarm System is critical, since a Life Safety System is involved, and lives are at stake. Therefore it is important that the verifier not only be qualified, but totally impartial as well. Theoretically, verifying technicians should have no stake in the outcome of their testing and inspections, so that their results are in no way shaded or unduly influenced. This means the Installer and Designer are disqualified as verifiers (the ULC Bulletin 2006-03 discusses this topic).

The Installing Contractor is typically the electrical contractor that physically installs the wire, conduit, devices, boxes and panels that make up the Fire Alarm System. But who is the designer? Occasionally this is less clear. Normally, a Consulting Engineer or Code Consultant who specifies the type, components, layout and operation of the Fire Alarm

©

System is considered the designer. Under this (the usual) assumption, in provinces where technicians may oversee verifications, technicians employed by the manufacturer or the company who sold the fire alarm equipment to the installer or owner, may verify the system, even though these latter organizations tend to have a stake in its successful commissioning.

The advantage gained in engaging technicians employed by the manufacturer or seller of the fire alarm equipment is typically that those technicians will be knowledgeable and well qualified to verify the system because of their familiarity and experience with it. This solution is acceptable to the majority of AHJ's, in the majority of jurisdictions,

However some feel the manufacturer's or seller's employee cannot be totally impartial, and those AHJ's insist that a party not involved in the supply or install of the system must verify it. However, qualified and knowledgeable technicians are still required, so authorities will often recommend that another company, which is an authorized representative of the manufacturer of the system involved, be engaged to do the verification. Some people actually carry out two verifications, one by the manufacturer's technician, and another by an uninvolved service company. These duplicated verifications are often referred to as "Third Party" verifications.

In some jurisdictions, verifiers are required to have specific professional designations. In some jurisdictions, a verification must be carried out by, or under the direct supervision of, a Professional Engineer

## 12.6.4   Integrity in Self Assessed Qualification

As mentioned above, the building codes and ULC standards do not dictate the specific qualifications required for verifying fire alarm systems, they simply state 'assumptions', and indicate that it is the AHJ who must accept the credentials of prospective verifiers.

AHJ's may or may not have extensive fire alarm knowledge, technical or otherwise, so they will typically ask for some evidence of qualification. A CFAA Technician-Registration Card may support the qualification to 'work on' Fire Alarms Systems under a Provincial *Fire Code*, but it is not aimed at comprehensively qualifying anyone to verify newly installed or modified fire alarms. When specific benchmarks are missing, one may be faced with 'self-assessing' one's own capability to competently perform a verification.

If you are faced with such a situation, you should challenge yourself as rigorously as you can about the various areas of knowledge and experience mentioned above, before deciding you should take on such a critical function. It is important not to go to extremes or frivolously disqualify yourself, but it is equally important that you are firmly convinced you know enough and are experienced enough, before you accept a verification challenge. In a Life Safety situation, integrity and reliability greatly outweigh ego and financial gain. Compromise is simply not worth it.

Deciding to take on the responsibility of a verification is not the only area where integrity is crucial. When carrying out the work, or when supervising others when they do so, integrity in doing a complete, thorough and accurate job of testing, inspecting and documenting is paramount. Verifications are difficult, painstaking tasks. They are often done at the tail end of a construction project, under lots of pressure from Owners, Contractors and even Fire Officials to finish quickly. Details are often painstaking to obtain in circumstances of short schedules, confusion on the job site, and stakeholders who view Fire Alarm Systems as nothing more than necessary evils.

It is an absolute requirement that verifiers be resolute and unswerving in their dedication to doing a 100% complete and accurate job, ensuring that the entire Fire Alarm System has been put through all the required paces, and that everything has been clearly and accurately recorded. Filling in blanks and ticking off boxes is easy. Doing the work of obtaining real and meaningful data to support form-filling can be a much bigger challenge, but it is critical all the same.

Let's now move forward to the technical aspects of verifying.

## 12.7    Verification Procedures and Processes

### 12.7.1    Understanding the Terminology

The fire alarm industry is populated by many customers, companies, products, technicians, engineers, designers, salespeople, managers and other stakeholders. Each company and product has its own nomenclature for various devices, panels, assemblies, functions, procedures, operations, labels, features, differentiators, techniques and models. When all the jargons from all the players mix in the marketplace, very large numbers of different acronyms, abbreviations and references evolve into a kind of industry-specific 'lingo'. However the meanings to all these industry participants of acronyms and expressions is far from common. The same word(s) can mean different things to different people, and confusion arises when these different people try to communicate.

Because it is critical that there be no confusion or misunderstanding of the codes and standards, glossaries of terms are typically provided, and the *CAN/ULC-S537 Standard* is no exception to this rule.

At the beginning of the *CAN/ULC-S537 Standard*, a variety of terms are defined for purposes of clarifying the Standard itself and the meanings of its clauses. It is very important that all the terms listed be read and understood. Even if there the Verifier disagrees with the absolute correctness of a definition in terms of their own knowledge, for the purposes of the Standard and in the context of how it uses the listed words and phrases, the definitions must be accepted as correct and important. The descriptors for devices, display types, annunciators, circuits, operating modes etc., are all very particular and specific, and are all very relevant to proper effective communication and documentation.

The definitions will of course not be listed here, however you should not proceed with this chapter until you have obtained and reviewed the S537 Glossary, since the Standard and this text use the defined terms frequently.

### 12.7.2    Understanding the Timing

Clause 3.1.5 of the *CAN/ULC-S537-04 Standard* says;

> *"Each component of the fire alarm system shall be verified in accordance with this Standard before occupancy of a building, except as noted in Clause 3.1.6"*

Clause 3.1.6 discusses 'partial occupancies' or 'replacements of a fire alarm system in stages', wherein parts of a system may be verified individually, and occupancy only of areas for which the fire alarm has been verified and is operable, may take place. Upon completion of the last partial verification, all of the fire alarm must be re-tested and inspected, in accordance with *CAN/ULC-S536 Inspection & Testing of Fire Alarms*.

In other words, a building can't be occupied until its fire alarm has been verified, and the system cannot be verified until all the installation, initial testing, troubleshooting and discrepancy rectifications have been completed. The latter point is important to understand clearly. On occasion, as a large Fire Alarm System is being installed, there is a temptation to test the system in pieces and phases, uncover deficiencies, correct them, re-test, document and consider that a part of the verification has been completed. This approach is not valid, because the verification is intended to be just that, a process of proving everything is working, not a process of testing to uncover deficiencies to be fixed.

To be valid, a verification must be done after the installation has been completed and tested by the installer and the commissioning team. Otherwise, the 'bit-by-bit' verification could take many months to complete, and by the time the last 'bit' is tested, problems and troubles may very well have developed in the segments 'verified' earlier on. To be certifiable as verified, it must be verified that all parts and functions of the fire alarm are working at the same time.

The partial verification scenario is a concession only to the very specific situation in which distinct, pre-defined phases or areas of a building are to be occupied in steps because it is not feasible to occupy the building in its entirety in a single stage, or because commercial interests dictate that parts of the building are to be occupied so that rent cheques can flow. The tests and reports for each phase must be complete, accurate and documented before occupancy of that phase occurs, and as mentioned, the entire building must be inspected and tested again once the last phase has been verified/occupied.

The staged replacement scenario can be similarly understood, in that it is unlikely an Owner can empty the entire building all at the same time to replace the Fire Alarm System, so similar principles to partial occupancy apply there as well. Note, however, that in staged replacements, parts of the old and parts of the new systems must work together at the same time to ensure the entire (occupied portion) of the building has protection 100% of the time.

### 12.7.3    Understanding the Scope of a Verification

A verification must include anything and everything required to do the following:

- Demonstrate that the fire alarm system has been completely and properly installed in accordance with the applicable *Building Code*, *CAN/ULC-S524 Installation of Fire Alarm Systems*, and with the design provided by the Engineer or Fire Alarm System Consultant.

- Inspect all the components of the fire alarm including initiating devices, input circuit wiring, control panels (displays, panel control devices, annunciators, sounders, labeling, mounting etc.), output wiring, signals, relays, amplifiers, speakers, remote annunciators and controls, power supplies, batteries, power connections, remote monitoring interface equipment and transmitters, ancillary devices, etc., to ensure they are all of the correct type and rating, all properly and securely mounted and connected, in good condition and in working order.

- Test all the functions, operations, sequences, annunciations, tones, and responses of all initiating devices, control panels, signals, annunciators, displays, peripherals, communication lines, and subsystems of the fire alarm to ensure they all operate as required by the *Building Code*, the *Standards* and the Design.

- Record and document, as described in the Standard, all device identification, locations, addresses, inspection findings, test results, operating sequences, measurements such as response times, detector sensitivities, sound pressure levels/audibility readings, etc. A Verification Report confirms that the system has been installed properly and is operating properly, it is not intended to be a punch list of deficiencies and failures to be rectified by the supplier/installer. Such deficiency punch lists should be cleared well before a Verification is begun. Excessive problems uncovered in a Verification

©

argues for a complete restart -verification after problems have been cleared.

### 12.7.4   Staged Occupancies

When a new building is being erected, and a complete new fire alarm system is being installed, the entire fire alarm system should be verified in a single continuous process, especially if the initial occupancy will be a complete occupancy. Verifying in bits and pieces is poor practice, and may be refused by the Authority Having Jurisdiction. However, occasionally buildings are erected in stages, and occupied in stages.

Alternatively, an existing Fire Alarm System may need to be replaced in stages for practical reasons, and so it may be necessary for the system to be verified and made operational in stages as well. This can be done, but each portion of the Fire Alarm System corresponding to each 'stage' must be fully verified per *CAN/ULC-S537*, and then, after all stages are completed over time, before a verification certificate for the whole building may be issued, the entire new fire alarm must be completely re-inspected and re-tested in accordance with *CAN/ULC-S536 Inspection and Testing of Fire Alarm Systems*.

This ensures that all the various portions of the total Fire Alarm System have maintained their integrity and proper working condition as time has passed and as successive stages have been added. It is, in a sense a 'double-check'. Re-testing per *CAN/ULC-S536* is not as intensive or extensive as the full Verification procedure, so this requirement is not as extreme as it may sound, it is just 'due diligence'.

### 12.7.5   Verifications in Existing Buildings – Additions, Modifications, Replacements

Any time a fire alarm system is modified or extended from its original design/configuration, it is very important to ensure that the changes and additions function properly per the new, modified design, and also that the act of changing or extending the system has not compromised the operation of the un-altered portion. To address this requirement to ensure that changes are made while maintaining full system integrity, a specific procedure has been pre-scribed in Section 6 of *CAN/ULC-S537*, that dictates that some limited re-testing of the unaltered portion of the Fire Alarm System must be carried out along with full verifications of the new portions. Again, this is not really very onerous, and is necessary to ensure that nothing has been corrupted in the change process. This will be reviewed in more detail later in this chapter.

### 12.7.6   Documentation Requirements

A Verification is an extensive, detailed initial inspection and test of a critical life safety system. On larger systems, it can be complex, somewhat convoluted, and time-consuming. A Verification also establishes a "baseline" for future reference, for additional annual inspection and testing, for later troubleshooting and for 'forensic' review in case a post-incident failure diagnosis is required.

It is a very serious and important task, and therefore, it is just as important to document a Verification very fully, in an organized way, that will provide the reader of the Verification Report with a complete picture of the system, all its components, all the things that were tested, all the measurements that were taken, and any and all special functions, conditions and operations that were noted during the process.

Unfortunately, different Verifiers will have different perspectives on what constitutes good record-keeping, so the developers of the *CAN/ULC-S537* have put together a set of standard forms, that are exhibited in Appendix C. While the Standard refers to the Appendix as 'informative', most Engineers and Authorities Having Jurisdiction expect to see a report that is at least as comprehensive as the appendixed report.

The forms try to take as much of the guess-work out of the Verification process as possible, posing mostly questions that require a 'Yes', 'No', or 'Not Applicable' check-box to be checked. However, there is nothing preventing the professional Fire Alarm Technician from improving upon the information provided in the standard forms by adding pages of explanations and additional information, which might be helpful to future readers in understanding the system.

The Verification Report is the primary product of the Verifier, take pride in it, and aim for excellence in preparing it!

## 12.8   Verification Procedures - Breaking It Down Into Parts

Let us now examine the required approaches to verifying the various sub-systems that make up a Fire Alarm System. What follows refers to the sections of *CAN/ULC-S537* entitled "WIRING", "CONTROL UNITS & TRANSPONDERS", & "FIELD DEVICES"

This section attempts to explain the requirements listed in the *Standard* - not at repeating those requirements. It is assumed that as you study this chapter, you have a copy of the standard to which to refer.

©

## 12.8.1  Wiring

### Survivability

Wiring links just about all parts of a Fire Alarm System together. Wiring in a Fire Alarm System can be compared to the nervous system in the human body. Cut or destroy wiring, and you can cripple a Fire Alarm System, just as broken nerves can cripple a person! So good verification of the wiring is critical.

The standard refers to 'Supervised Circuits'. Because it is so critical to keep fire alarm wiring working, just about all the circuits in the system are supervised, and trouble indications must be provided when a wiring fault occurs.

Before beginning you verification of the wiring, it is advisable to review the Design, the Riser Diagrams, the Layout Drawings, and the Specification provided for the fire alarm system by the Engineer or Consultant to familiarize yourself with the types of wiring and circuits designated for the system. It is also advisable to become familiar with the manufacturers' literature/cut sheets to note the wire sizes that may be connected to their equipment.

All supervised wiring must be inspected and verified for compliance with required wire sizes, cable types, fire/thermal ratings, polarities and terminations. The routing and raceways used must be per the applicable *Electrical Code*, and per requirements of *CAN/ULC-S524 Installation of Fire Alarm Systems*, properly mounted in appropriate compartments. Wire sizes must be adequate for the loads carried, and within the gauge ranges specified by the manufacturers of each device to which they connect. This requirement is referred to in various sections of the Standard, stated in different ways.

In addition, specific types of tests must be done on each kind of circuit to ensure that the supervision is working, that trouble signals result when faults are imposed upon those circuits. Conventional device circuits can be tested by (safely) opening the circuits at appropriate places. Addressable circuits can be tested by removing addressable devices as well as by opening the circuits.

End of Line devices for both Conventional Input Circuits and Signal Circuits must be fully tested in all fail modes to ensure appropriate trouble conditions are annunciated at the fire alarm control panel.

Of course additional survivability is afforded when Class A wiring is installed, but it must be tested to ensure that alarms can be initiated by any device on a Class A circuit when an open circuit occurs. The Standard refers to an 'electrically remote' point in the circuit as being appropriate to open for testing purposes. The intent here is that you determine the 'worst case' open circuit situation, one that will require signals to travel over the longest possible wire runs (or over the longest possible portion of the unbroken circuit) in order to initiate the alarm. The logic is that if that test passes, alarm functions over shorter distances under single open circuit conditions are bound to function.

In addition to open circuits, all circuits must be tested to ensure that a Ground Fault indication occurs when a ground fault is applied (to either side) at the "electrically furthest" point.

## Loading and Adequacy of Electrical Power in Fire Alarm Circuits

It is also required to ensure that circuit lengths and wire gauges as installed, allow every device in the system to receive and operate at its rated power consumption without excessive voltage drop. It is necessary to be familiar with methods of calculating voltage drop along circuits for various distributed loads of known wattage (i.e., amperages at specified voltages). This should have been done by the Engineer as part of the design, however take the time to look up consumptions of the various devices (initiating devices or signals) on a circuit, the gauge and type of wire used, and if you become doubtful about any circuit in particular, make a measurement to check it out, and/or discuss it with the Engineer.

## Data Communication Links

The Standard very clearly itemizes the tests required to ensure that Data Communication Links (DCL) are properly designed, wired, and supervised. It refers to a Table (at end of the Standard) entitled 'Abnormal System Conditions' that summarizes the required response of the fire alarm for each type of fault on the DCL wiring.

The concept of verifying survivability of a short circuit is introduced in the DCL Testing section because such wiring links typically interconnect transponders or subsystems on different floors of a building or in different zones, and *Code* requirements are such that any fault in a circuit on one floor, zone, or compartment, should not inhibit the circuits on another floor or in another zone or compartment from initiating alarms and trouble signals. Therefore the design will have short-circuit isolating devices installed between such zones, and DCL tests must ensure they function as required.

## 12.8.2   Verification procedures

## Control Units and Transponders

This section focuses on testing not only the Fire Alarm Control Panel itself, but also on ensuring that everything connected to it initiates the

©

correct panel response per the program or correlation matrix configured for the specific system.

To that end, the initial two sections (somewhat redundantly) specify the minimum testing requirements for various input circuit types, but they recognize that sounding an alarm when operating each and every input device can be onerous and impractical, so it is stipulated that at least one of each device type on each circuit must initiate the alarm circuit operation, but that outputs may be inhibited when testing the rest of such devices on each circuit.

The section also requires that a hard copy of the 'Input to Output Software Correlation Report' must be included with the Verification report. It is expected that such reports (which will differ from manufacturer to manufacturer) will clearly indicate what output or logical event should result from activation of each initiating device. This reinforces the test results in explaining the fire alarm operation, and as well provides a guide for later inspectors, testers and trouble shooters to determine the expected response of the system to various conditions.

As for wiring, it is necessary to become thoroughly familiar with the design documentation in advance of verifying the Control Panels & Transponders. Become familiar with the requirements of that design, the locations of various panels, and the intended functioning and operation of the system. Obtain a design documentation package and have it available when it is time to inspect and test the system.

It is required to inspect the control panels and transponders to verify they have been installed in the right places, at appropriate heights, securely fastened, properly protected from any unfriendly elements, and easily accessible to those intended to use them (building operators and firefighters as the case may be). The panels should be properly identified, clearly labeled, visible, and all controls reachable. Again, the *ULC/S524 Standard for Installations* and the *CAN/ULC-S527 Standard for Fire Alarm Control Panels* must be referred to ensure proper ULC labeling and compliances, regardless of the fact that the Engineer/Consultant and the manufacturer(s) are also obligated to do so.

## Control Unit & Transponder Inspections

This section of the Standard lists a number of visual/ manual inspection items for Control Panels that really amount to common sense and good practice in checking out any electronic system.

Indication lamp colours are required to conform to the 'Visual Indicators – Colour Code' Table at the end of the document.

Of particular note in this section is the requirement to record the version and date of firmware and software loaded on the system. You may want to verify with the panel manufacturer's representative regarding the firmware version if it is not clearly marked on a chip or on a document accompanying the panel.

Also in this section it is stipulated that it must be verified that for transponders with standalone and degrade modes of operation, inputs and outputs "serve" the same zone(s), and that they have their own signal silence, trouble silence and reset switches, along with indication of operating mode.

Again, record your observations, and record your concerns for later review, as and when they occur....

## Control Unit and Transponder Tests

The Verification Standard once again pretty clearly and specifically lists all the tests that must be done on the Control Unit and Transponders. The list addresses all the standard indications, signals, responses and operations common to all fire alarm control panels that are ULC listed.

- It requires that all visual and audible indications related to alarm and supervisory functions operate as designed.

- It stipulates the testing of all alarm and supervisory functions of input circuits as mentioned earlier, and all output circuits, in accordance with the design and *Code* requirements.

- It stipulates the verification of automatic and manual alarm sequences (alert-to-alarm transition, signal silences, signal silence cut-out timer function, signal silence inhibit, re-initiation of silenced signals on subsequent alarms, coded signals, etc.) as well as smoke detector 'status change confirmation'.

- It stipulates testing of Reset functions, and the inspection of ancillary devices for proper rating and compatibility with the fire alarm system.

- It stipulates testing of the transfer from normal to emergency power, and

- It stipulates complete testing of the Remote Monitoring function at the "signal-receiving centre".

Performing all these tests will require that you are able to sound alarms to the minimum degree stipulated, and to operate all parts of the Fire Alarm System. Therefore, it is critical to plan such testing well in advance, coordinate well with the Engineer, building Owner and Contractor, and be ready with enough personnel to make all the observations necessary to comply with the standard.

Also, record the results as the testing occurs - not after the fact....

©

## 12.8.3   Voice Communication System Tests.

The section in the Standard on Voice Communication Tests is also a list of all the required functions to be tested on systems equipped with voice evacuation systems. Once again, it really is important to become familiar with the design, layout, configuration and operation of the Voice portion of the system so as to enable complete testing. Not all architectures are the same. Some systems have centralized amplifier banks with long speaker risers and runs. Others have distributed amplification with amplifiers located near or adjacent to transponders that serve several floors and/or zones of a facility. Some have multiple channels to handle concurrent tones of different types in different zones and paging in yet other zones.

So begin by understanding the Voice system, it will save you lots of time later.

The functions to test, as stipulated by the standard in this section, include;

- all visual and audible indicators and switches for power, trouble signals, silence functions

- output circuits activation and indication for all call and for selective paging and troubles

- microphone, and initial page inhibit timer for alert and alarm signals

- all call operation on emergency power, automatic switchover to standby amplifier(s)

- operation and indications for emergency telephones, including trouble indications

The list above and in the Standard may not include all the functions designed into the Voice Evacuation system. Multiple-channel operation, auxiliary-channel operation, paging from different Control and Display Centres through 'give-control/take control' functions, Stand-Alone and Degrade modes of paging and tone generation, synchronization of tones in neighbouring zones, and a variety of other operations, may apply to the system you are verifying. Again, test everything, and record as you go.

## 12.8.4   Response Time Tests

One of the most frustrating problems fire alarm operators faces is that there is typically a delay between the time they push a button, throw a switch, or touch a keyboard, and the beginning of the event or response they are trying to evoke. Somewhat like pressing an elevator button many times when it doesn't come right away, an operator may inadvertently initiate unwanted multiple events, or assume that a system isn't working, because things don't happen instantly.

©

Another delay-related challenge is the phenomenon that occurs when an occupant activates a manual station upon discovering a fire, but because the alarm does not sound immediately, the occupant hesitates to leave the building by the nearest stairwell, and might even go back toward the fire to look for another manual station.

For these reasons and others, time limits have been placed upon the occurrence of output functions when inputs are initiated. Current time limits ('response time' requirements ) are listed in a Table at the back of the standard, and the "Response Time" section of the Standard simply lists the various times to be tested that appear in the table.

The scope of this section includes signaling to the Remote Monitoring Center and Releasing Start of sequence, as well as signal sounding-to-input initiation delays.

By studying the specifications of the specific fire alarm system you are verifying (both manufacturer's and Engineer's specs.), you can get an idea of the polling times for input circuits, the clock speed of the Control Unit Central Processing Unit, and the activation process for output circuits, which may allow you to anticipate expected time delays, and recognize when something isn't operating as it should.

## 12.8.5   Large-Scale Networks

Large scale networks are defined for purposes of the standard as those systems that have more inputs, outputs and other devices than the allowed maxima for a single fire alarm panel, per the *CAN/ULC-S524 Installation standard*. In order to handle more devices than the limits allow, more panels are provided, and these panels are interconnected in a 'Network' so that they may operate as a single system.

The testing requirements for such extended fire alarms include;

- verifying that each 'node' or transponder serves a defined area, that its inputs and outputs are in that same area, to allow for stand-alone operation, and to limit the impact of a failure of a single transponder to the protection in one (corresponding) area.

- verifying that transponders with stand-alone capability have the indications and controls required for a standalone fire alarm 'head end'.

- confirming through direct testing that the various possible failure modes (open circuits, ground faults and shorts) on a communication link result  in the correct operation of the transponders and the network as a whole, and

- verifying that the 'network' and its nodes or transponders continue to function as two or more sub-networks when the network cabling is opened or shorted in one or more places, and that within sub-

©

networks, alarms, troubles, and inter-panel functions continue to operate correctly when initiated.

You may seldom, or even never, be faced with Verifying a Large-Scale Networked Fire Alarm System, however the trend toward networked systems continues, and when you do get the opportunity, it will be important to be prepared. Read up on the specific manufacturer's system, its network characteristics, its network wiring options, and how it is supposed to perform under single and multiple failure scenarios. Learn as much as you can by communicating with the manufacturer's rep., and with the Engineer, and by consulting books and web-sites that provide information about network operations. The more you know, the better your verification will be.

## 12.8.6   Power Supplies

Power supplies for fire alarm systems typically consist of;

- a main transformer whose primary side is connected through appropriate over-current protection and disconnecting means to a separate A.C. supply circuit dedicated to the Fire Alarm System.

- AC/DC rectification circuitry to provide the (nominal) 24VDC power to the fire alarm electronics

- DC voltage and current control circuitry to provide correct voltage for both circuit operation and battery charging operations

- back up batteries, typically located inside the fire alarm control cabinet itself, or occasionally in an adjacent metal-enclosed battery compartment, and

- output over-current protection devices and connectors/terminals and/or wiring harnesses to distribute DC power to the fire alarm system electronics.

Each Control Unit and Transponder will typically enclose its own dedicated power supply, and often, in addition, 'booster' power supplies are deployed remotely from control panels in circuits needing additional power not available from the main panel.

Because of the 'essential service' nature of Fire Alarm Systems, their power supplies must be 'on' and available through just about every imaginable circumstance, including power outages, failure of an A/C source of supply, etc. For that reason the A/C supply to fire alarm systems in many types of buildings must be connected to a source of 'Emergency Power', which may include an emergency power generator or even an 'Uninterruptible Power Supply'.

In addition, the fire alarm system must have its own batteries to keep it operating in 'supervisory' and 'alarm load' conditions.

The requirements for emergency power and for battery back up capacity for fire alarms are defined in *CAN/ULC-S524* and *CAN/ULC-S527*. The design, construction and connection of the power supply systems must also comply with the *Canadian Electrical Code*, and CSA standards governing the design and installation of emergency electrical power supplies.

## Verifying the Power Systems

The S537 Standard is explicit and detailed in terms of what needs to be inspected, tested and recorded in terms of fire alarm power supplies. It is important that you become familiar with the Design and the power requirements specified by the Designer, in addition to the *ULC Standard* requirements and the wiring and specific configuration of the power supply(ies) for the system being verified.

Initially the power supply electronics, labeling, cabling, batteries, over current protection and disconnecting means should be carefully inspected to ensure compliance with the drawings, the spec., and the standards. Undersized distribution wiring can constitute serious fire hazards if their current carrying capacity is less the over-current protection to which they are connected. At the same time, failures or anomalies in other electrical systems in the building should not interrupt power to the Fire Alarm System, hence the requirement for separate supply circuits.

If 'Ancillary Devices ' are connected to the Fire Alarm system, they either need to be powered separately, or need to be connected to panels/power supplies specifically sized to handle their loads in addition to main Fire Alarm System loads.

The capacity of each power supply must of course be adequate to supply the electronics load and to recharge depleted batteries within the time frames dictated by the standards. The batteries themselves must be of an adequate size and type, and compatible with the Fire Alarm equipment as specified by the manufacturer and as ULC-listed.

## Batteries

Battery voltages and currents must be measured and recorded under the conditions outlined in the S537 Standard, and proper, safe-charging must be checked, without undue heating of batteries. Proper ventilation is essential to prevent build up of dangerous battery emissions.

The capacity of the batteries to keep the Fire Alarm System going for the prescribed lengths of time in supervisory and alarm load modes must be tested and documented, as well as the system's capacity to recharge depleted batteries to prescribed levels. The S537 standard is helpful in describing methods of simulating different load conditions so that Silent

©

tests can be undertaken to measure performance under alarm conditions without having to physically sound the audible signalling devices.

It is important to take adequate time to ensure proper, adequate charging cycles that comply with the battery manufacturer's and the control unit manufacturer's specifications. Quick voltage measurements don't ensure that charging voltages are properly controlled and charging currents are properly limited to avoid over-charging, which is as harmful and dangerous as under-charging.

### Emergency Power Sources

Emergency power generators also need to be tested, and it must be verified that the Fire Alarm System continues to function smoothly through power failures and back-up generator starting sequences. Again, the standard is simple but clear on the testing requirement. Of course, ensure a properly trained and authorized person carries out the generator testing and operation and any transfer switching functions in a well planned and coordinated manner. Document the generator nameplate data, operating characteristics, as well as the dates, times and results of tests carried out.

### 12.8.7   Annunciation and Trouble Signalling

As part of making sure the fire alarm control, display, and warning systems are all working properly, it is required to test all the annunciators, both those on control units or transponders and remotely mounted units. Each annunciator must provide certain minimum indications, which include;

- Power On

- a common "Trouble" signal

- a "Lamp Test" function (or the equivalent for LCD-type annunciators)

- a visual indication of "Alarm Signal Silence" *

- a visual indication of Alarm Signals *

- correctly labeled alarm and supervisory input zone status indications, and

- visual indicators for ancillary functions *

    *      (Required on Display and Control Centre annunciators and control units but not all annunciators)

On Display and Control Centres, a Control Unit or a CACF, there must be switches and controls to allow manual activation of alarms, alarm acknowledgement, alarm silencing (as well as a full complement of display controls where LCD or CRT type displays are used). In addition, the design should be reviewed and checked for the requirements for other control and switch functions such as ancillary device operation, fan and damper operation, bypass functions, etc.

In addition to Annunciators, it is required that Remote Trouble Signal Units operate correctly, including both visual and audible trouble indications, and trouble signal silence functions.

Nothing can replace the Verifier studying the design and learning in detail the intended operation of each fire alarm system he/she verifies. The fire alarm system response to a complete range of possible events and conditions needs to be simulated and proper annunciator indications verified. This is often very difficult to do while a building is partially occupied, because of the need to trigger alarm, trouble and supervisory events in order to ensure the right annunciations take place. It also requires at least two and sometimes more people to undertake the testing, and to observe responses at each system annunciator of each type of event in each zone.

*CAN/ULC-S537* prescribes the minimum testing required in circumstances where multiple annunciators provide the same indications of the same events, simply in different locations. Because observing the annunciation of every type of event at every annunciator can be extremely time consuming, the Standard allows some relief if it can be demonstrated by the nature of the system design that like events will cause identical indications at separated locations.

### 12.8.8   Printers

Fire Alarm Systems often have system logging/event printers, whether built into the FACP or separately connected. It must be verified that the printer is of the correct and appropriately listed type, that it is properly connected, and supervised by the fire alarm panel where required; that it prints the correct information when events occur. A printer is in effect another form of annunciation, and deserves the same degree of thorough testing as fixed indicating or LCD/CRT based annunciators.

As with the other parts of the system, the specified operation of the printer(s) must be determined and tested, including specific report generation operations as required by the design. Some larger systems have more than one printer, each dedicated to printing certain types of events, or even events that arise in certain specific zones or building areas (vectored printer functions). Consult the designer and/or the manufacturer's technician to become familiar with the specific printer operations required.

### 12.8.9   Items and Functions not listed in the Standard

The Verification Standard is both specific and general at the same time. It cannot possibly anticipate and discuss all the variations of design and display that appear in the various manufacturers' control panels. Many systems use LCD and other Digital Displays to portray graphic representations of the building and the fire alarm system operation, or to display alarm events themselves, with additional information helpful to an operator. The way in which alarm events print out or appear on a display may vary from panel type to panel type, and additional enquiries, reports and displays may be available to an operator when responding to a fire event, or tracing events after the fact.

For this reason it is important to become familiar with the specific type of Control Unit or Transponder being verified before undertaking the prescribed tests. Everything must be tested, not just what is listed in the Verification Standard.

## 12.8.10  Verifying Initiating Field Devices

### Preparing to Test

Before they are put through their operational paces, all field devices connected to the fire alarm need to be carefully inspected for proper installation in the correct locations as indicated in design drawings, in accordance with the requirements of the currently applicable version of the *CAN/ULC S524 Standard*. Each device must be clearly and properly identified, and have its type and identification number along with its physical location, 'address' and 'loop number', or circuit number as applicable, recorded neatly in the appropriate places in the Verification Report, as well as in related design drawings or diagrams. Each device must be clean, in good condition, and firmly and permanently held in place, without weighing down or otherwise stressing the wiring connected to it.

During construction, some types of field devices are fitted with protective caps or covers to keep dust and other foreign material from entering. Presumably when you are verifying a Fire Alarm, construction is virtually finished, and the building site is clean and ready for occupancy. So in order to properly verify all devices, protective caps and covers must be removed, so that unrestricted air flow or people access, as appropriate, is provided.

### Testing

Whatever the device type, it needs to be initiated or operated in each of its possible modes, and the appropriate response, indication annunciation and sequence of events verified to have taken place, at each display location in the Fire alarm system. Depending on the device type and purpose, the intended response to activation (or disconnection) may be an alarm signal, a supervisory signal, or even a trouble signal). You need to ensure you know what the correct operation and response is, and that you also know how the device manufacturer intends that the device be tested.

Wiring supervision must be verified at each conventional device, and appropriate trouble indications must be checked to have taken place when connections are lifted. On Class A circuits or on redundantly wired loops or links, the device's ability to transmit an alarm must be demonstrated to survive a single fault of each type on either side of the device connection, as dictated by the circuit type and design intent.

## Manual Stations

In addition to operating all stages and /or modes of each manual station and verifying correct responses by the Fire Alarm system for each stage or mode, make sure that the station is mounted at the correct height per the applicable code and standard, is accessible, and is of a construction appropriate for the environment. Outdoor manual stations must be weather-proof, and likely mounted under protective transparent covers. Reset key mechanism should be tested and verified to be free of obstructions or dirt.

## Heat Detectors

Heat detectors are of various types, as you likely recall from other parts of this text and other texts you have learned from. For testing purposes, it is very important to understand the difference between a 'one-time non-restorable' heat detector and a 'restorable' heat detector.

The 'one time' unit applies the principle that at a certain temperature, an element melts that causes an electrical state change in the detector, either through a mechanical link or by having the melting element in the electrical circuit. Obviously one cannot test such devices using a heat source to cause the melting to occur when doing a verification, so instead, the electrical operation of the detector must be simulated at the terminals where it connects to its input circuit, and the correct responses checked.

Restorable units may be of various types and designs, either conventional bi-metal types or electronic thermistor-based units. The operation of these units must be by a controllable, safe heat source (NOT via open flame). The manufacturer of the detector in the instructions or manual accompanying the unit will likely provide some direction as to how to test the detector, those instructions should be followed. Hair dryers, heat lamps, or even designed-for-the purpose calibrated heating instruments can be used. It is of course important to know the 'trip' points of the detectors, and to monitor the temperature at which change-of-state occurs.

©

'Rate of Rise' heat detectors must be demonstrated to function if the temperature around their detection elements changes more rapidly (in degrees per minute) than the design/alarm rate for the unit. Rapid rise in temperature can be simulated by ensuring a low initial temperature and introducing warm air close to the sensing element (of course without damaging it physically or thermally). By knowing the approximate temperature difference between the initial ambient and the warm air stream, and by measuring time-to-trip, the rate of rise can at least be verified to function. Again, calibrated heat sources designed specifically for detector-testing can provide easy and accurate test results.

Finally, thermal sensors in 'intelligent analog' devices can provide actual temperature information to a compatible fire alarm control panels, such that the temperature at the device itself can be observed during a (non-destructive!) test, and the detector and/or panel algorithm can be verified to trigger an alarm if the rate-of-rise or the absolute temperature levels are reached.

While proper testing of detector function may seem onerous initially, seasoned verifiers have acquired the right tools and the right methods to perform the correct tests in a timely manner without compromise.

## Smoke Detectors

In order to verify a smoke detector, it is required to introduce smoke or a non-destructive equivalent of smoke into the detector's chamber, and observe the initiation of an alarm signal. In general the detector manufacturer will list acceptable 'canned smoke' types or makes, and will even provide some guidance as to how to introduce such 'test gas' properly into the detector chamber and how much to use. Some time will be required for the detector to respond, it is important not to 'over-apply' the gas in an effort to trigger the detector.

Smoke detectors operate within a specific range of 'sensitivities', in other words, they are set to initiate at a level of obscuration (% per foot) that falls within the range stipulated in the appropriate ULC standard. It is required to measure the sensitivity level of each smoke detector, and ensure that it lies within the operating range indicated on the detector itself or in its accompanying documentation. The sensitivity level measured, must be recorded, along with its 'in-range' status.

Smoke detectors can become too sensitive, or not sensitive enough, as a result of dirt build up over time. If a detector is too sensitive, it will be subject to false-alarming. If it is not sensitive enough, it will not detect smoke quickly enough, or perhaps it will not detect smoke at all.

If the detector can be cleaned by the user, then cleaning is one remedy to a detector whose sensitivity is found to be out of range. If cleaning doesn't help, then the detector should be replaced.

Be careful to ensure that the smoke detector is meant by the manufacturer to be opened in the field, and cleaned in the field. Older ionization detectors, especially high voltage models, are not meant to be opened, but should be returned to the factory or properly disposed of in accordance with the handling and disposal regulations governing ionization devices.

## Multi-Sensor Detectors

Some more modern fire alarm systems employ advanced-design smoke detectors that have been engineered for enhanced detection capability for target hazards or for improved rejection of 'deceptive phenomena' expected in the specific environment in which they are installed. These detectors may use multiple sensors (photo, ion, thermal) in combination, and as well 'multiple criteria', such as absolute signal levels, rate of signal change, integration of signals, rate of signal fluctuations, etc., to apply algorithms that more effectively differentiate between real fire-associated developments and false-alarm drivers. These devices likely don't have fixed or simple thresholds to go into alarm upon simple and sudden introduction of test gas.

Therefore you might find such detectors will not go into alarm when normal smoke-testing is undertaken, and you will have to read the manufacturer's instructions carefully to determine how to do a smoke test, and how to measure sensitivity. For instance, one manufacturer's detector can have a number of different algorithmic settings possible depending on the environment of the intended location. To do a smoke test, one must 'turn off' the algorithms/settings and put the detector into 'standard photo' mode in order to verify the chamber response.

So, it is not only important to test per the manufacturer's instructions, it is also critical to restore the operating settings and measure/record the effective sensitivity at the control panel after doing so.

Remember, write it all down as you're doing it !

## Remote Indicators:

Indicators connected to smoke detectors but located remotely for better visibility need to be checked for both operation and clear visibility at the appropriate location.

## Status Change Confirmation (Alarm Verification)

Some manufacturers include in their designs the ability to set the control panel to automatically verify the steadiness and consistency of an alarm condition by requiring a detector status to change for a given length of time, before deciding a real alarm exists. This is intended to counter false alarms from detectors in areas or conditions where they are subject to

©

spurious, momentary occurrences of high obscuration readings. While this feature is commonly applied in the U.S., it is far less commonly allowed by an Authority Having Jurisdiction in Canada, and it may only be implemented with the Authority's knowledge and written permission.

The main concern is that real alarm conditions should not be delayed from being annunciated/sounded. It is also critical to note that a delay for Status Change Confirmation is only permitted for smoke detectors, and that one must verify that no other types of initiating devices have any delays imposed upon their state changes causing alarm signals to sound.

Therefore be very careful to ensure that if Alarm Verification is in use, it only affects smoke detectors, and that its use has been approved by the AHJ!

## Air-Duct Smoke Detectors

Placing smoke detectors into enclosures that collect air samples from ducts, and route them through the detector's chamber, is a very effective way to quickly detect the presence of smoke or carriage of smoke from one part of a building to another. However, the Duct Detector assembly must be verified to be installed correctly, unobstructed, with the correct orientation and air flow direction. Also, since smoke detectors have very specific air-flow limitations to their operation, it must be ensured that the right detector model has been applied along with compatible enclosure and tubing.

As always, it is very important to review and follow the manufacturer's instructions and to test accordingly with conditions as 'live' as possible without causing damage or difficulty as a result.

## Beam-Type Smoke Detectors

In certain areas of buildings, where traditional spot-type smoke detectors cannot be applied, either because the building contour will inhibit smoke flow to such a device, or because access to such a device for maintenance and testing would be extremely difficult, 'Beam Type' smoke detectors are sometimes applied. Such devices typically have emitters, target reflectors and receivers, and are set to detect specific levels and durations of interruption of their beams.

These devices must also be verified to be properly installed and aimed, and tested very carefully following the procedures and settings prescribed by the manufacturer. Since these devices have specific sensitivity settings, the sensitivity must be measured and recorded just as for any smoke detector.

## Flame Detectors

Occasionally, in situations where smoke detection will not cover a fire hazard situation effectively, flame detectors are applied. As their name implies, they respond to the presence of flame, using infrared or ultraviolet sensing technologies alone or in combination. They typically are watching for radiation in specific frequency bands, and EM radiation sources that have 'flicker rates' characteristic of open flames.

The set-up and test of flame detectors is typically not trivial, and requires careful review, full understanding of, and strict adherence to the manufacturer's instructions, however they must nevertheless be fully verified by a qualified person as part of the *CAN/ULC-S537* requirement.

Flame detectors are often installed in industrial environments where there may be very special and dangerous fire hazards. Flames being guarded against may include some not visible to the naked eye (hydrogen fires), and so it is extremely important that a verifier fully understand the environment and hazards in any area she/he must go to test, and ensure they are accompanied by and supervised by personnel specially qualified to work in such situations.

## Other Automatic Detectors

The principals that govern verification of smoke and flame detectors also apply to any other type of fire detector. You must;

a)  verify proper installation, location, orientation and identification,

b)  test all functions and alarm triggering per manufacturer's instructions,

c)  measure sensitivities,

d)  record location, identification, all observations, test results and sensitivities, and

e)  write it all down as you do it!

## Sprinkler/Water Extinguishing Systems

Sprinkler and other water-extinguishing systems are required to be monitored and supervised by Fire Alarm systems, at the very least in all new sprinklered buildings, and in those being brought up to current codes and standards.

Devices involved include;

a)  water flow detection switches (paddle or pressure types) whose operation is assumed to imply a fire, and is required to initiate a fire alarm, and

©

b)      supervisory devices, applied to signal an off-normal condition in the sprinkler/water system that requires the attention and response of a building operator or maintenance person

Water Flow switches need to be inspected for proper installation, and tested by introducing water flow through or at the device, to ensure they cause the required alarm signaling via the Fire Alarm system. If a signal timer is installed to delay signal transmission through momentary pressure changes, the timer function must be tested and the actual delay time recorded.

Supervisory devices may include;

a)      Valve Position Switches, which must be tested to operate and cause a trouble signal, for a twenty-percent (20% of full travel) movement from the normal valve position (that position in which the extinguishing system may operate/provide waterflow).

b)      Pressure Switches, which must be tested to initiate a trouble signal at the (low) pressure setting per the design, and to re-set at the normal/high pressure setting to allow adequate 'dead band' per the design (settings and trip points to be recorded).

c)      Level Switches, which must be tested to operate at the design-low-water level if possible by physically lowering the water level to do so, otherwise via causing a change in the switch contact state, and verifying the required trouble signal is initiated.

d)      Low and High Temperature Switches, whose operation must be tested via "electrical simulation" by changing contact states and observing the occurrence of the required signals.

e)      Power-Loss Switches connected to the electrical supplies of Fire Water Pumps and Air Compressors, which must be tested by operating the power disconnect switch or breaker upstream of the pump or compressor, and observing the required trouble signal.

For other types of fixed extinguishing systems, it is important to become familiar with how they operate, what output they provide to the Fire Alarm System, and to ensure that operation of that output causes the required signal/annunciation at the Fire Alarm Control Panel.

A General Word of Caution: Extinguishing Systems are intended to put out fires, and it is critical they always be ready to do so. However they very often cause extremely serious damage if they release in an uncontrolled or an un-intended fashion. Water can cause massive, very expensive damage if during testing procedures, it is allowed to flow where it is not meant to go, or to flow when it is not meant to flow. Gases, foams and chemicals may or may not cause similar damage if inadvertently released, but they will typically be very expensive to clean up and/or to replace.

Not only can there be damage to property, there can actually be injuries to people, and damage to the environment, about which the local municipality will not be pleased.

So make sure you understand how your 'wet' or 'dry' testing may be safely undertaken, that you know that discharged water will flow to a safe place, and that you coordinate your testing with building officials, operators and tenants.

A little extra thought and effort can prevent a major problem, when testing and verifying any system.

## 12.8.11 Verifying Signalling Field Devices

### General

Signalling devices connected to Fire Alarm Systems are typically audible or visible, or a combination of both. Verifying signaling devices requires application of the many of the same principles as verifying initiating devices;

a)    verify proper installation, location, orientation and identification,

b)    test all functions and verify manufacturer's data to ensure all unit ratings and (tap, candela, etc.) settings are as required by the design,

c)    measure sound pressure levels and visibility of strobe-type signals with respect to the applicable codes and installation standards,

d)    note locations, identifications, all observations, test results and levels, and

e)    write it all down as you do it.....!

For audible signals, it is required to measure and record audibility using a sound pressure level meter, using the dBA scale at appropriate distances, and to make sure that minimum dB levels per the *Building Code* are provided at the most 'acoustically distant' part of a zone or suite, and recorded in the Verification Report.

### Residential Occupancies

Specific rules apply to the operation and survivability of signaling circuits that connect in-suite signals in a residential building.

First of all, it must be tested and verified that the occupant is able to silence the alarm signal(s) inside her/his suite for ten minutes. The alarm should automatically re-sound (if it has not been silenced or reset at the fire alarm control panel in the mean time) after the ten minutes. The *Building Code* allows the intent of this requirement to be achieved in

©

a couple of ways, one involving providing in-suite silencing modules, the second relying upon the fire alarm control panel to provide in-suite silencing and alarm re-sounding functions. It is important for one to determine which approach has been taken, and to test and verify all functions accordingly.

The second requirement related to residential buildings is that it must be ensured that the in-suite signals are connected such that fouling, tampering or disabling of a signal in one suite will not inhibit the ability of sounders in any other suite from operating if an alarm occurs. Currently, the *Building Code* also allows the intent of this requirement to be achieved in three ways. One involves the use of suite isolators that will trip and isolate a suite from the rest of the suites on the same signal circuit, should a short circuit occur on that circuit in that suite. If this approach has been used, it is important to test, verify and record the correct functioning of the isolators.

Another method is for the suite signals to be wired on a Class A circuit separate from that driving the corridor signals (i.e. at least two signal circuits per floor). If this approach is used, a dead short on the suite signal circuit in one suite will indeed inhibit the function of signals in other suites, however an open circuit or cut wire in one suite will not affect the others. Again, test, verify and record accordingly.

The third option is to wire each suite on a separate signal circuit.

For residential suites, the Verification standard allows for Audibility Levels Testing to be done for each type of suite configuration only, enabling the verifier to save a great deal of measuring time, however the operation of signals in every suite must be tested and verified.

*CAN/ULC-S537* has appendices that provide excellent guidelines for various device tests and measurements. In particular, Appendix G describes in reasonable details methods, approaches and caveats concerning measurements of sound pressure levels. It should certainly be consulted and followed by Verifiers and AHJ's alike.

## Intelligibility

Verification of signals and tones, as well as announcements, from speakers in fire alarm systems provided with Voice Evacuation systems must all be tested, verified and recorded as well.

While very specific measurements and minimum levels have been prescribed for Audibility, the Codes and related Standards don't yet prescribe specific measurements for Intelligibility, which relates to one's ability to understand a message or announcement. While intelligibility is not very applicable to "tones", it is very applicable to Voice Messages, and while specific tests are not prescribed for this, a Verifier should always satisfy her/himself that each message type emitted from a Voice

Evacuation system is clearly understandable in all parts of each zone served by the system. Unintelligible instructions can cause confusion and even panic, and are therefore not an option as part of a properly verified fire alarm system.

## Synchronization

When stroboscopic lamps are used as visible fire alarm signals, there are often two or more placed in the same zone or area of visibility. If these strobes are set to flash independently, their outputs can combine or interfere with each other and cause effective light flashes at frequencies that can be harmful or dangerous to certain epileptics. Therefore the firing of strobe lights concurrently visible by one person must be synchronized to occur at exactly the same time. While most fire alarm systems are specified this way, it is important to verify that synchronization is provided where required.

A similar requirement applies to audible signals applied such that two or more are concurrently audible anywhere in a building, since acoustic interference or reinforcement can garble signals, both tones and voice messages. Therefore a similar requirement for synchronization applies, and must be tested, verified, and recorded.

## Emergency Telephones

Each telephone must be inspected and tested for clear two-way voice communication, appropriate indication at the FACU that a handset has been lifted, that the 'in use' or 'system operable' tones are heard in each remote handset, and that the enclosures, locks, instruction labels and other "mechanical" arrangement for each telephone are per design and in good working condition. Where two or more handsets are connected into the same circuit, it is required to test that they can both work at the same time.

## 12.9    System Modifications

While it is reasonably obvious that complete new fire alarm systems need to be completely tested, verified, and documented from end to end, what to do when modifications or additions are made to an operating fire alarm system, after the initial Verification , for some reason is less obvious to many, and needs proper understanding.

The intent of the Verification Standard is to ensure that the complete Fire Alarm is working as designed, at all times, and that the various requirements it has for inspections, tests and recording procedures, if carried out as described, will ensure that everything works.

Ask yourself, if I change something on a Fire Alarm system, what might be affected by the act of making that change?

©

The obvious one is if the new device or function is defective, the fire alarm won't work...so I had better at least test every new device, function or sub-system that I add or replace on a fire alarm, to ensure that the whole system will work post-modification.

Less obvious is what else I need to test in case the new or replacement item affects another part of the system in some unintended way, or in case I make an error in making the modification.

For instance, if I connect something incorrectly, or address something incorrectly, or program something incorrectly, what do I have to test and what do I have to re-test on the system  in order to make sure in "brute force" fashion that I catch and correct such a mistake.

The Verification Standard outlines the minimum inspecting, testing and re-testing that is required if certain parts of a fire alarm are modified or if something is added.

- It stipulates that it must be verified that the load ratings and capacities of the system are not exceeded and that the power systems are adequate to handle any additional load.

- It stipulates the conventional devices and circuits that must be verified and re-verified if modifications are made to such circuits, taking into account the way in which new devices are wired into those circuits.

- It requires the verification (or re-verification) of all devices that serve or are linked to a fire alarm system through a "data communication link" that is added or modified.

- It requires the COMPLETE verification of a Control Unit or Transponder that is added to or replaced in a fire alarm system, PLUS the re-testing of all existing devices connected to such a replacement (or added) control unit, in accordance with *CAN/ULC-S536 Inspection and Testing of Fire Alarm Systems.*

- It stipulates the requirement to verify all circuits, functions and subsystems that could be affected or are affected by any modification to a control unit.

A review of the 'System Modifications' section of the Standard will reveal the sense and intent of what is needed.

## 12.9.1   Software Changes

What if the 'Configuration' programming of a software-based fire alarm is revised and re-installed on the system?

The extreme point of view is that since a revision to the job-specific configuration program or data base can theoretically drive extensive change to the way a fire alarm system operates, when such software is changed, the operating logic of the entire system including all responses, alarm conditions, annunciations, signals, control-by-event sequences, "matrices", etc. should be re-verified. However this implies a huge amount of costly work, especially on larger fire alarms, and is typically impractical, since the only things certain in life are death, taxes, and software changes.

So the Verification Standard leaves it to the integrity of the verifier to either:

- Re-verify all system functions that could be affected by the modifications (except wiring supervision), or

- Test all modifications indicated as having been made in a comparison listing of the "before" and "after" configuration programs.

In doing limited verification/testing based on a software comparison (in fact in any testing done after a software modification), it is critical to fully document both the changes and the functions and system tested with ensuing results, in a re-verification/subsequent verification report. Should a failure of a fire alarm occur, forensic investigation will certainly pursue all of the verification documents, and records of system modifications and related tests. Absence of such documents could lead to a presumption that required testing was not carried out, and NO-ONE wants to go there!

### 12.9.2   Firmware

Firmware is typically embedded software that is the same for every fire alarm system of the same type/model number. It typically can NOT be accessed or changed in the field by the user, operator, designer or installer. It typically must be updated according to a well-controlled, prescribed process, by the system manufacturer, after full testing of such an update or 'firmware revision' has been carried out at the factory.

Firmware changes will not typically alter the way project-specific configuration software functions, and therefore, will not typically imply field re-verification after a firmware update. However, it is the manufacturer's responsibility to ensure that a firmware update will not drive altered system operation, and to inform the end User/Owner, the Engineer/Designer, the Installer and the Verifying parties if such altered operation will (unavoidably) result, and ensure arrangements are made for re-testing/verification of the altered functions.

## 12.10   Ancillary Devices and Systems

During the study of this chapter you have come to understand the role that a Verification plays in ensuring that the Fire Alarm System functions in accordance with the applicable codes and standards, the project design documents and the manufacturers instructions.

Upon completion of the Verification, every single aspect of the Fire Alarm System has been exercised and found to be completely functional and compliant. This includes the functional testing of the ancillary (relay) contacts in the Fire Alarm Control Unit (FACU). The contacts were tested and found to 'reverse' from normally-open to normally-closed and/or vice-versa.

From reading previous chapters in this Manual, you will understand the importance of ancillary devices and systems, and therefore you will understand how essential it is that all such systems operate in total compliance with the applicable codes and standards, the project design documents and the manufacturers instructions.

We need to look at these situations in detail.

## 12.10.1  New Construction Verifications

*CAN/ULC-S537 Verification of Fire Alarm Systems* does not require that the Fire Alarm Technician test/verify any ancillary devices during a Fire Alarm System Verification. In fact a statement to that effect is found in the standard. There is also a cautionary note, to that effect, on the suggested report format. It really can be no other way, because the Fire Alarm Technician cannot be expected to be knowledgeable on the intricate workings of the air-handling systems within a hospital, the elevator controller in a high-rise condominium, or the mag-locks security system in an office tower.

Therefore, it is very important that all players in this situation (building owners, Authorities Having Jurisdiction etc) understand that the Fire Alarm Technician has no further responsibility than to verify that the ancillary controls/contacts in the FACU operate as required by the design documents, that the interconnection wiring entering the FACU from the ancillary device/system is acceptable and is properly terminated in the FACU, and that the voltage appearing on the ancillary control conductors is acceptable and within the electrical limits of the FACU ancillary control circuitry. In addition, the Technician must compare the contact rating of the ancillary relay contacts to ensure it is compliant with the incoming voltages and current of the ancillary control circuit. If the ancillary equipment circuit is displayed on the annunciator, then the colour of the indication should be checked for conformity with the colours permitted in the standard.

In the case of new construction, all such ancillary systems are, themselves, subjected to inspection and test procedures performed by the manufacturers, installers and municipal inspectors prior to the issuing of a Building Occupancy Permit. These people should issue their own verification or commissioning reports documenting all of their test procedures and confirming the total acceptability of their systems under the construction contract.

Now comes the very important last step – verifying the interconnection between the FAS and the Ancillary system and actually performing operational tests. This requires the presence of both the Fire Alarm Technician and the Ancillary Technician, as well as the AHJ and the Building Owner. Discussions should lead to an agreed sequence of test operation. The Fire Alarm Technician should then initiate an alarm condition per the agreed sequence and the Ancillary Technician should observe the results, and confirm that all Ancillary systems operated as required. Several such different tests may be necessary. The Building Owner and the AHJ should then accept (or not accept) the results.

The Fire Alarm Technician should include a note on the Verification Report to confirm the occurrence of such tests, noting the names of the personnel attending the tests.

### 12.10.2  Retrofit Verifications

In a retrofit Fire Alarm System situation, the ancillary systems may have been in operation for years, presumably in full working order and not compromised during the years. (Whether or not this is the case, depends upon the building owner and the service companies maintaining the elevators, the fan systems, etc).

As stated above, the Fire Alarm Technician is bound by *CAN/ULC-S537 Verification of Fire Alarm Systems*. The Technician must confirm that the replacement system FACU provides the necessary ancillary control contacts to handle the existing ancillary systems. The Owner should arrange to have the ancillary systems technician present, and a test of the interconnections between the Fire Alarm System and the ancillaries should be activated. The FAS Annual Report should state that the test was completed successfully.

### 12.10.3  Simple Situations

In many buildings, the ancillary device may be just a single air-circulating fan, corridor smoke control door, or perhaps a single mag-lock on an exit door. In such situations it is a simple thing to perform a test that confirms the shutdown of the fan, the releasing and closing of the corridor door, or the un-locking of the exit door. If the Fire Alarm Technician feels comfortable in performing and observing the tests, and the resetting of the specific devices, then there is no good reason not to do so. It becomes a corporate decision rather than a 'standards' question.

### 12.10.4  Reporting

Without doubt, the factual reporting of the extent of the testing is vitally important. If the Owner thinks that all systems have been fully tested and are functional, then there may well be a future containing litigation

©

if systems do not function and a fire death or injury occurs. Although testing of ancillary equipment is not required by the standard, ancillary systems are part of the overall building life safety systems. If a Technician notices that an ancillary device or system appears not to function as intended (for example a fan does not shut down) then the Technician should make note of this and advise the building owner so that appropriate repair action can be taken by the appropriate service provider.

Therefore report carefully on the specifics not only of the testing that was performed, but also the testing that was not done!! In this manner, the Owner will be fully aware of any additional testing that must be performed to ensure that all systems are functional.

## 12.11   Integrity is everything

Even the most experienced designers and fire alarm technicians come under pressure from 'customers' and their representatives from time to time to undertake the absolute minimum in re-testing after a modification, in order to minimize cost, disruption and delays. Fantastic 'rationalizations' are proposed to these professionals to justify omitting certain tests or re-tests because of other forces at work.

It is squarely on the shoulders of the fire alarm professional to apply the Verification Standard both per its written requirements and its intent of ensuring zero probability that something doesn't work when it has to. It also rests with the A.H.J. to satisfy her/himself that the standard has been fully and properly applied.

A little extra time and cost up front can save many lives down the road, which cannot be valued in dollar or scheduling terms.

## 12.12  Chapter Summary

1.  The *ULC standard CAN/ULC-S537 Verification of Fire Alarm Systems* tells us, in detail, what must be done in a complete Verification.

2.  The same *ULC standard* requires that a complete report be written that covers all aspects of the Verification. The report must document all observations and test results.

3.  Unfortunately, the standard cannot stipulate who is to do the work. Usually the AHJ will demand that a CFAA-Registered Technician perform the work. If the system is a technically involved system such as a network system, then a CFAA Technician who has received factory-authorized training on the specific system equipment should perform the Verification. CFAA Technicians should perform only the work for which they feel qualified.

4.  Visual inspection of each device is as important as the actual testing. Both must be performed and reported.

5.  Technicians should equip themselves with all of the appropriate test gear needed to perform all tests on the devices and overall system. Technicians should be knowledgeable about the design and operating parameters of all the devices on the system to be verified, and ensure their compatibility.

6.  If verifying a partial system, ensure that the installation work that continues after the partial has been performed, does not affect the 'existing' system. Otherwise the partial might have to be redone.

7.  The completed installation should be quickly reviewed to ensure that all shorts, opens and grounds have been cleared from the system wiring, before beginning the Verification. A Verification is not intended to find wiring faults – it is intended to prove that all is well with the system wiring.

8.  A Verification Report should have no deficiencies.

9.  A Verification should be witnessed, and signed off by the system Designer.

10. A properly conducted Verification helps to ensure that the Fire Alarm System will protect the building and its occupants.

## 12.13   Review Questions

| # | ? | Question | Section |
|---|---|----------|---------|
| 12-1 | | **Operation of the device or system to determine that it will perform in accordance with its intended operation is:** | |
| | A | a verification | |
| | B | a test | |
| | C | an inspection | |
| | D | Is an option to a physical observation | |
| 12-2 | | **The actual operation of the device or system to ensure that it performs in accordance with its intended operation or function:** | |
| | A | check | |
| | B | inspect | |
| | C | test | |
| | D | All of the Above | |
| 12-3 | | **A visual observation to determine if the device or system will apparently perform in accordance with its intended function** | |
| | A | a verification | |
| | B | an inspection | |
| | C | a test | |
| | D | All of the Above | |
| 12-4 | | **Fire Alarm Systems are a bit like parachutes, or air bags in cars...they simply MUST work when they are needed...they are 'mission-critical'.** | |
| | A | True | |
| | B | False | |
| 12-5 | | **Verifying Technicians may find themselves under the gun, and from time to time may be asked to "speed things up" or even to "cut corners". It is critical that Verifiers adamantly insist that they be allowed to do a complete, thorough verification, and to document it fully. It can be a matter of life and death.** | |
| | A | True | |
| | B | False | |

| # | ? | Question | Section |
|---|---|---|---|
| 12-6 | | The Canadian Standards Association, in Ottawa, oversees the development of the National Building Code. The Building Code is then either adopted, or it is adopted when modified somewhat, by each Province and Territory. | |
| | A | True | |
| | B | False | |
| 12-7 | | CAN/ULC S537 itself refers to other ULC standards, including CAN/ULC S524 Installation of Fire Alarm Systems, | |
| | A | True | |
| | B | False | |
| 12-8 | | Fire officials performing a full verification of a system will be effectively putting the software and firmware through their paces, and so their familiarity with how that software is configured for the application in question is essential. | |
| | A | True | |
| | B | False | |
| 12-9 | | Reliability in verifying the integrity of a Fire Alarm System is critical, since a Life Safety System is involved, and lives are at stake. Therefore it is important that the verifier not only be qualified, but totally impartial as well. | |
| | A | True | |
| | B | False | |
| 12-10 | | It is squarely on the shoulders of the fire alarm professional to apply the Verification Standard both per its written requirements and its intent of ensuring zero probability that something doesn't work when it has to. It also rests with the A.H.J. to satisfy her/himself that the standard has been fully and properly applied. | |
| | A | True | |
| | B | False | |

©

# Chapter 13: Inspection and Testing, and Maintenance

## 13.1    Chapter Overview and Key Concepts

Upon the successful completion of Verification procedures, a Fire Alarm System is known to be in perfect working order. The *Fire Code* demands that that system remain in perfect working order. The building owner must maintain the system in full working order through appropriate system maintenance (as required) and periodic inspection and testing.

Such effort over the continuing life of the system is carried out by technically-capable personnel who understand Fire Alarms Systems, the rules and regulations, and the design and operation of the specific system.

Annual inspections are a legal requirement just about everywhere in Canada. They must be performed as directed by the National or Provincial *Fire Code*. The *Fire Code* contains certain specific requirements, and also dictates that systems must be tested in accordance with the *ULC standard CAN/ULC-S536 Inspection and Testing of Fire Alarm Systems*.

Results of the inspection procedures must be documented at length and in full detail. The Technician responsible for the work must sign off the written report.

## 13.2    Learning Objectives

After studying the contents of this chapter, the reader should be able to do the following;

- Understand the importance of continuing periodic inspections.
- Understand how a high work ethic leads to improved performance
- Understand the structure of the Inspection standard
- Identify the proper methods of system and device testing procedures.
- Perform adequate tests of the installed wiring
- Determine precisely what tests to apply to the detection devices
- Measure the acceptability of audibility and intelligibility
- Understand the importance of accurate and complete written test documentation

## Language Defined - Chapter Glossary (Also see Main Glossary)

Terms that are important to the understanding of this chapter are included below. For a complete listing of such words, expressions and terms, refer to the Main Glossary near the end of this manual. This glossary is not intended to replace or supercede any officially-published glossary. It is simply our intent that these be used as a training aid in understanding the contents of this manual. Always refer to the specific code or standard, and to the Authority Having Jurisdiction for the applicable official interpretation.

| Term | Definition |
|---|---|
| **Active Field Device** | A device that can be uniquely identified by the control unit to determine its presence and operating status, and which may be commanded to operate or to change its operating parameters independently of other field devices that share a common circuit |
| **Addressable Device** | A device that can be individually and uniquely identified by a control unit. The address is set using binary/hexadecimal/decimal methods using dipswitches, rotary switches or solid-state memory |
| **Alarm Signal** | An audible signal transmitted throughout a zone or zones to advise occupants that a fire emergency exists; also called an EVACUATION signal |
| **Alert Signal** | An audible signal intended to advise designated persons of a fire emergency |
| **Ancillary Device** | A device that performs a life safety related function, but that is not part of the fire alarm system |
| **Authority Having Jurisdiction** | The organization, office, or individual responsible for approving equipment, an installation, or a procedure. Most often, it is the municipal Fire Department |
| **Basement** | A storey or storeys of a building located below the first storey |
| **Check, Inspect And Test** | **CHECK** - A visual observation to ensure the device or system is in place and is not obviously damaged or obstructed; |
| | **INSPECT** - A physical examination to determine that the device or system will apparently perform in accordance with its intended function; |
| | **TEST** - the actual operation of the device or system to ensure that it performs in accordance with its intended operation or function |
| **Electromagnetic Door Release** | A device used to hold doors in the open position, and to release the doors to close automatically when signalled to do so by a fire alarm system or other means |

©

| Term | Definition |
|------|-----------|
| **Fire Damper** | A closure which consists of a normally held open damper installed in an air distribution system or in a wall or floor assembly and designed to close automatically in the event of a fire in order to maintain the integrity of the fire separation |
| **Fire Detector** | A device that detects a fire condition and automatically initiates an electrical signal, and includes heat and smoke detectors |
| **Fire Detector - Heat** | A device for sensing an abnormally high air temperature or an abnormal rate of increase of temperature |
| **Fire Detector - Smoke** | A device for sensing the presence of visible or invisible particles of combustion, the concentration of which exceeds a pre-determined level |
| **Ground Fault** | A circuit impedance to ground sufficient to prevent normal operation |
| **Inspect** | See definition under CHECK, INSPECT and TEST |
| **Open-Circuit Fault** | Means a circuit series resistance increase of 10 kOhm or more, unless otherwise stated, resulting from an abnormal condition |
| **Short-Circuit Fault** | A resistance shunt of 0.1 Ohm or less across a circuit, unless otherwise stated, resulting from an abnormal condition |
| **Sprinkler Supervision** | A method of electrically monitoring critical elements of an automatic sprinkler system to detect potentially disabling abnormal conditions, and provide a warning signal |
| **Supporting Field Device** | An active field device that monitors other field devices on a separate circuit and reports the status of that separate circuit to the control unit |
| **Test** | See definition under CHECK, INSPECT and TEST |
| **Trouble Signal** | A signal (usually a buzzer and an amber lamp) indicating a fault or an off-normal condition in a fire alarm system |

## 13.3 The Nature and Purpose of Fire Alarm System Inspections and Testing

Once a fire alarm system has been installed, verified and accepted by its Owner, the Designer and the Authority Having Jurisdiction, it begins its life protecting lives, property, and even the continuing business missions of the building occupants. There has been a great deal of painstaking 'check and double-check' in the design, installation and verification phases of the system, so for the Authorities, the Building Owner and the Fire Alarm Community in general to stop being concerned with it afterward, would constitute both negligence and huge wasted effort.

It is of course critical that all fire alarm systems in service, no matter how old, be kept fully functional at all times, and in order to ensure this, on-going fully documented testing and inspection of those systems is mandated just about everywhere in Canada. Such inspections and tests are carried out daily, monthly, and yearly in different degrees, and involve ensuring that everything is working properly through visual examination of the system's components, and through testing of just about all those components, at least annually. While legislation varies across Canada as to the specific qualifications for personnel doing this work and the penalties for breaking the rules, local Authorities pretty universally require that the stipulations of the applicable regulations and standards be followed religiously.... so all CFAA-trained Technicians must be familiar with those documents!

Just as for Verifications, the thoroughness, depth and quality of the inspection and test work, and the documentation of that test work, must be no less than absolutely first class. Lives depend upon it!

## 13.4 The Applicable Regulations — National and Provincial Fire Codes

In all jurisdictions in Canada, the continuing care of fire protective systems and devices within buildings is governed by either the *National Fire Code of Canada,* or a provincial *Fire Code.* The *Fire Codes* state that ' ... the owner or the owner's authorized agent shall be responsible for carrying out the provisions of this *Code.*'

The *Fire Code* regulations are enacted to provide an acceptable minimum level of fire safety to the occupants of any building falling within the regulatory scope. The legal owner must be aware of any and all regulations concerning fire safety. By accepting the regulations and abiding fully by them, the owner of any building has established a good defense against any claim of negligence of any kind arising from any source.

It is the responsibility of every building owner to ensure that the required 'checking', 'testing' and 'inspecting' of all fire protection equipment, warning and life safety systems are carried out as required by the *Fire Code.*

Very importantly, the *Fire Code* further requires that "Fire protection installations shall be maintained in operating condition." This of course means that faults found during any inspection procedures should be immediately scheduled for correction. Typically, the Inspection Service Company would be paid for the inspection and completion of the report. If faults have been found, the Owner should issue another contract, to some service provider, to have the faults corrected.

The owner is also responsible for maintaining adequate documentation of all tests, inspections and corrective actions in accordance with the regulations. These records may be presented to the appropriate authorities as proof of compliance or to the courts if needed. The owner or his agent is further required to identify the individual or individuals responsible for carrying out the check, test and inspect requirements as set out in the *Code*.

One can say that, generally, Fire Codes make four statements relating to the continuing care of Fire Alarm Systems:

- Fire Alarm Systems must be maintained in operable condition (at all times),

- Access to Fire Alarm System components requiring inspection or servicing must be kept unobstructed,

- A record must be kept of all required tests, and such records must be retained for examination by the Authority Having Jurisdiction, and

- Fire Alarm systems must be inspected and tested in conformance with standard *CAN/ULC-S536 Inspection and Testing of Fire Alarm Systems*.

## 13.5 CAN/ULC- S536 Inspection and Testing of Fire Alarm Systems

In describing the requirements for Fire Alarm Systems, the *Fire Code* refers to related and applicable Regulations and Standards, such as those from ULC and NFPA. The date of the applicable Standard is not necessarily given in the actual *Fire Code* paragraph or clause, but is generally specified in Part 1, under Referenced Documents.

The Underwriters Laboratories Standard *CAN/ULC S536 Inspection And Testing Of Fire Alarm Systems* lists the exact requirements of the work that must be performed, including the necessary documentation.

## 13.6 Qualifications of Personnel Undertaking Tests & Inspections

The Preface to *CAN/ULC–S536* simply states that it pre-supposes that '..the inspection and testing shall be conducted by qualified personnel acceptable to the Authority Having Jurisdiction'. It refers to its Appendix A, which in turn states:

'Any person who performs the annual test and inspection of a fire alarm system should be knowledgeable about this Standard, and have received suitable formal training or sufficient experience acceptable to the Authority Having Jurisdiction.' What does this really mean?

Different provinces have different specific legislation in place, and different *Fire Code* references concerning requirements for qualifications for people working on fire alarms.

Some provinces now include in their respective *Fire Code*, a reference to the qualifications of personnel working on fire alarm systems. In general they state that:

- any person who performs the annual tests or annual inspections of a Fire Alarm System required by the *Fire Code*, and any person who repairs, replaces or alters components of a Fire Alarm System, must have successfully completed a program or course acceptable to the Provincial Fire Marshal.

You must determine the specific requirements for qualification in your province and in your local jurisdiction,(your local CFAA Chapter, where established, can help you with that).

Typically, a person who has not successfully completed the required program or course may perform the work, provided that the work is performed under the guidance of a person who has successfully completed a program. Some jurisdictions require that no more than two such persons may be supervised by one person in this manner. The supervising technician must be at the work-site and must take complete responsibility for the work.

Typically the training courses that are 'acceptable to the Fire Marshal' are generic. They don't provide information on the specifics of each manufacturer's product. However, common sense dictates that, in addition to generic fire alarm theory and practice, Technicians must know enough about the particular fire alarms being tested with regard to the specific design, configuration and operation of the hardware, software, controls and annunciation, in order to plan and execute proper and complete tests.

Therefore the minimum qualification requirements of an AHJ may not be enough to equip you to understand all facets of the system you are inspecting and testing. If you do not possess system-specific knowledge yourself, you will need to have a source of such information readily available to you.

## 13.7    Inspection and Test – Initial Procedures and Processes

The Fire Alarm Technician should obtain a (legitimate) copy of the currently applicable *CAN/ULC-S536 Standard*, and should become very familiar with its contents before undertaking any inspection and testing. This is an essential pre-condition. This manual further assumes that the student has ready access to the

©

Standard, since it will be essential to refer to it regularly as the student reads and reviews this chapter

### 13.7.1  Timing of Tests and Inspections

An active fire alarm system must be given different kinds of tests each day, each month, and each year. Daily tests are quick and simple; monthly tests a little more extensive. The building owner's designated building manager or superintendent will normally undertake those tests, and although she/he must be knowledgeable about the fire alarm system, and how to respond to its signals, formal qualifications are not required for those doing the daily and monthly checks.

On the other hand, the annual tests and inspections are very comprehensive, and do require properly trained Technicians qualified per AHJ rules.

### 13.7.2  When an 'S536' Inspection and Test Isn't Sufficient

If changes are made to a Fire Alarm System such as extensions, or modifications of detection or software, or deletions of devices, or if a (complete) fire alarm control panel is replaced, then Verification procedures per *CAN/ULC S537* become applicable. The 'General Requirements' section of the *536 Standard* identifies the specific circumstances in which the *537* procedures are needed.

### 13.7.3  The Criticality of Having a Comprehensive System Description

When a fire alarm is initially designed and installed, the Designer and/or Installer provide documentation and reference materials to the Owner to allow for future review, testing, inspection, troubleshooting and repairs. It is required, as part of an annual inspection and test, that the agency doing it ensure that such documentation, in the form of a 'System Description', exists, and that the testing confirms that the system operates in accordance with that description.

Unfortunately, for various reasons, documentation originally supplied with the Fire Alarm System is sometimes lost, misplaced, or even destroyed. If this is the case, the first order of business is for the Owner to have a System Description prepared, by the 'Inspect and Test' firm, by the original Designer, or by another qualified party. The minimum requirements for a System Description are proposed in an Appendix to the S536 Standard, an AHJ will likely look for such a description to be readily available at the building, for her or his review and reference.

### 13.7.4   Documenting Periodic Test and Inspection Activity

Complete records must be made and kept safely, but available, for all checking/testing performed. This includes the Owner's daily and monthly tests as well as the annual inspection.

The format and minimum content requirements for such documentation are proposed in Appendices to the S536 Standard. Again, most AHJ's will insist that a format the same as or very similar to that in the Standard be used.

Some firms have 'automated' versions of these forms in spreadsheet programs that run on a Technician's laptop. Others require that technicians complete reports manually, and then have them typed up back at the office.... In any case, testing and inspection efforts are totally wasted if the reports are not completed clearly, carefully, and fully, as the testing is done!

## 13.8   Breaking It Down into Parts — Testing All Year Long!

### 13.8.1   Daily Inspections

Daily testing by the Owner or his/her building manager merely consists of checking that the power is on, checking the status of trouble indicators to ensure no troubles are indicated. If any part of the system is not functioning, whether because of a failure or because some portion of the system has been bypassed, trouble indicators will reflect the problem, and the Owner must have the problems fully diagnosed and rectified by a qualified Technician.

### 13.8.2   Monthly Inspections and Tests

Each month, the Owner or his representative must place the Fire Alarm System on emergency power, and then inspect and test selected parts of the system on a 'rotating basis' (meaning different elements are selected for testing each month). Monthly tests involve operating at least one initiating device, and ensuring that the correct annunciation and signals occur for, and in, the appropriate zones. They also involve testing the common audible and visual trouble signal, one firefighter's telephone, voice system paging in one zone, and an inspection of the batteries.

## 13.9   Annual Inspection and Tests

Recording and Reporting Tests of Various Kinds

Before beginning an Annual Inspection and Test (hereafter referred to as an 'Annual') the fire alarm technician should review and become familiar with the various segments of the fire alarm, ensure there is a 'System Description', and ensure he/she is familiar with each of the Report Forms in Appendix E of the S536 Standard, for which devices they apply and how they should be completed.

He/she must prepare a methodical inspection and test plan that ensures that all the required elements of the system will be checked in an organized sequence, coordinating test activity in advance with the Owner to ensure that:

- occupants are advised of the tests as they occur, and

- that alternate fire protection measures are in place when parts of the system are to be bypassed or muted.

Up front preparation and agreement concerning how an 'Annual' will be carried out can save a lot of revisiting and reworking to undertake forgotten procedures and capture missing information.

As mentioned before, and as will be mentioned again, it is critical that observations and test results are fully and neatly recorded as you go. Human memory is unfortunately a very unreliable record, especially when many complex checks and tests are carried out in relatively quick fashion!

It is just as important to be pro-actively descriptive, putting one's self in the position of the ultimate report reader, and ensuring any issues or deficiencies are very clearly described. Forms are there to ensure you capture all the minimum information needed, but they cannot cover every situation you will run across, and that is where thoughtful descriptions and details are invaluable.

Ensure that the Owner receives the report promptly after the 'Annual' is complete and take the time and trouble to go through the Report with him/her, explaining the findings, and recommending what may need to be done to bring the system up to fully functional and operational status. Make sure that a copy is kept in a safe place in case it is needed, and that the system description is preserved in the Owner's care for purposes of future inspections, tests, and problem resolutions.

## 13.9.1  Inspecting and Testing Control Units and Transponders

Even though, in offices and commercial buildings, most occupants go home at night, leaving a better and safer environment for performing 'Annuals' (involving operating signals and temporarily bypassing certain functions) sometimes such work must be done during the day. Furthermore, in multi-unit residential buildings occupants are there all the time, so technicians and service companies doing these Annuals must coordinate very carefully with Building Owners to notify occupants in advance if audible testing is to be done.

The requirements as prescribed by the *ULC S536 Standard*, anticipate and recognize that inspections and tests will be done in occupied buildings. The intent is that all functions, devices and operations of the system must be tested, but concessions are made that allow certain silent and accelerated tests to be done. For example, all initiating devices must be tested for proper effect and response, but only one field device per conventional input circuit, or one 'active field device' per 'software zone' needs the signals to actually operate (i.e. bells, horns, tones and strobes) in the appropriate zone. The balance of devices on the circuits may be tested to operate appropriate annunciation, but the field signals may be muted.

The *ULC S536 Standard* has been structured in a very organized way. WHAT must be tested as a minimum is listed in the relevant section of the main body of the Standard, each item lettered for reference. In Appendix E of the Standard where the form and format of the Test Reporting is shown for each category of test and inspection, all the same items are listed in the same order, on the form, with the same reference letter. That way, if you follow and complete the forms as shown in the Appendix, you will virtually automatically cover all the tests prescribed in the Standard.

The required inspection and testing for the entire fire alarm is divided into several sections, the first being Control Units and Transponders.

The scope of Control Unit Tests includes, but is not limited to;

- Common panel indications, all lamps, audibles, displays and (appropriate) messages,

- Operation of silence, acknowledge, reset and other panel-mounted controls,

- Trouble indications for faults of various kinds

- All automatic sequences, including transitions from Alert to Alarm, Silence Inhibits, timed functions, subsequent alarm re-activations, etc.

- Circuit supervisory functions and devices drive Trouble indications when appropriate

- The 'Sequence of Operations' and Input/Output correlations function as described in the Fire Alarm System description

- Transfer to and from Emergency Power occurs correctly without system disruption

- Communications with the (remote) Signal Receiving Centre work properly, with alarms, supervisory and trouble signals being indicated at the Control Panel and Receiving Centre in the correct circumstances and sequences, including supervision of the communication itself.

Refer to the appropriate section of the main body of the *S536 Standard* for the specific item and test descriptions, and to the corresponding section of the Appendix that proposes the forms to be used for recording observations and results.

## 13.9.2   Voice Evacuation Systems

If the Fire Alarm includes a Voice Evacuation system, it also must be thoroughly tested. The advice provided in the previous chapter concerning Voice systems applies equally to annual testing, namely, it really is important to familiarize yourself with the design, layout, configuration and operation of the Voice portion of the fire alarm so you can put it through all of its paces. Not all architectures are the same. Some systems have centralized amplifier banks with long speaker risers and runs. Others have distributed amplification with amplifiers located near or adjacent to transponders that serve several floors and/or zones of a facility. Some have multiple channels to handle concurrent tones of different types in different zones and paging in yet other zones.

So begin by understanding the Voice system, it will save you lots of time later.

Your tests must be include, but are not necessarily limited to:

- Common panel indications, all lamps, audibles
- Operation of signal silence switches, and other panel-mounted voice-related controls
- All call paging and selected zone paging functions
- Trouble indications in all appropriate circumstances
- Microphone function
- Correct response to amplifier failure
- Non-interference with "initial inhibit timer"
- Correction functions of all Emergency Telephone functions

Once again, the list above and in the Standard may not include all the functions designed into the Voice Evacuation system. Multiple channel operation, auxiliary channel operation, paging from different Control and Display Centres through "give-control/take control" functions, Stand-Alone and Degrade modes of paging and tone generation, synchronization of tones in neighbouring zones, and a variety of other operations, may apply to the system you are verifying. Again, test EVERYTHING, and record as you go....

## 13.9.3   Control Unit and Transponder Inspections

This section of the Standard lists a number of visual inspection items for Control Panels that really amount to common sense and good practice in checking out any electronic system.

- Proper and clear identification of all circuits, indications, lamps, controls etc.

- Proper mounting, securing and connection of cables, devices, boards, etc.

- Clean, secure, fully functional hardware, lock(s)

Of particular note in this section is the requirement to record the version and date of firmware and software loaded on the system. You may have to verify with the panel manufacturer's representative regarding the firmware version if it is not clearly marked on a chip or on a document accompanying the panel.

## 13.9.4   Power Supply Inspection and Testing

### General

The *Standard* requires that the Control Panel power supply be inspected to ensure it is properly fused and that it is 'Adequate to meet the requirements of the system'. It is important that you know how to determine the appropriate fuse or breaker ratings, and how to determine if the power supply is adequate.

These checks should have been done and properly documented at the time of the original panel verification, and again any time changes were made to the input and output circuit loads. However you should check that component ratings still match the manufacturer's data, and have not been replaced for differently rated devices without clear notation and explanation.

Protective fuses or circuit breakers will typically be sized at amperage ratings no higher than 125% of the full load current of the supply they feed. This full load current may be calculated by dividing the nominal input voltage of the power supply into the rated wattage of that supply, however it should be indicated in the manufacturer's documentation and in 'nameplate' or label data on the panel and the supply. Check that the main transformer wattage is adequate for the rating of the power supply it is feeding.

You should also refer to the Fire Alarm System Description, the battery calculations, and records of any additions of any additional inputs or outputs to the system since the design was done and/or since the circuit load documentation was last updated. Determine if additional (remotely powered) 'Booster' supplies are connected in the system.

Ensure you can measure and interpret load currents under full load alarm and standby/supervisory conditions in order to prove the adequacy of the Power Supply and batteries. You will soon clearly understand why ready availability of complete and up-to-date system documentation makes the job of the person doing annual inspections much faster and easier.

## Battery Inspections and Tests

Proper charging, maintenance and testing of system batteries is critical to ensuring a fire alarm can operate as it is required to in the event of a power failure. Battery life is strongly affected by the voltages at which it is charged under various conditions. While it is possible to "boost" charge batteries for some time after they have been depleted, such boosting must taper off and switch to 'float' charging once the battery has regained its nominal operating level. Overcharging will overheat a battery, rapidly shorten its life, and can even deform the battery and cause rupture. The fact that the power supplies and chargers of different manufacturers' panels may be of different designs (some regulated, some not, some software-controlled, some not) needs to be understood. A familiarity with battery behaviour and charging characteristics is critical to good inspection and testing. Always make sure that the battery installed is of the size, capacity and type as specified by the panel manufacturer for the specific system (otherwise ULC Listing of the system may be void). Always ensure that charging voltages under normal operation of the system fall within the range specified by the battery manufacturer.

The prescribed inspections/observations and tests as listed in the *Standard* include:

- ensuring the battery capacity matches or exceeds the rating indicated by the battery calculations,

- measuring and recording the battery terminal voltage with a/c on, then under both supervisory and full load conditions with the a/c off (with power on, the voltage will be a little above the nominal battery voltage since float charging is on, but with power off, voltage will start close to the nominal rating and then drop over time, depending upon how much load is on the system),

- measuring and recording the charging current,

- inspecting to ensure electrolyte is of the correct specific gravity, that electrolyte levels are correct, battery connections are tight, terminals are cleaned and lubricated, and that the battery enclosure (control panel) is adequately ventilated.

- verifying that disconnecting a battery causes a Trouble Signal to occur.

It is also required to test the battery capacity, to ensure it can operate for the required 24 hours under "supervisory" conditions, then under full load for times dictated by the type of building/occupancy.

Possible methodologies for doing so are well described in the Appendix to the *S536 Standard*. In order to impress loads on a battery to test its capacity, battery calculations are an up-front requirement, so that appropriately sized load resistors can be applied for "silent" or "silent accelerated" tests. A Battery- capacity meter is a far easier route to take in doing these tests and measurements, and will likely be the tool you will use. However you must ensure that any meter you use is calibrated, and that you carefully follow the meter manufacturer's instructions.

## Emergency Power Source Tests

The emergency generator must also be operated, to ensure it feeds the fire alarm system when normal power fails. Obviously the test should be coordinated with the Building Owner, and must be performed by a qualified person. This effort is NOT the responsibility of the Fire Alarm technician. The A/C fail simulation, generator start up and run, and transfer switch operation must be executed by (other) qualified personnel in the employ of the Owner or Owner's Representative.

As the Generator is tested under load, it should be verified that the Fire Alarm Panel receives A/C supply at voltage levels and frequency within the manufacturer-specified limits, that an initial 'A/C Fail' trouble signal is received, then restored to normal after the Gen Set comes up and switches over. As the standard indicates, any 'Trouble' signal originating from the Generator Set should cause an appropriate Trouble signal at the Fire Alarm panel.

## 13.9.5    Annunciators, Printers and Remote Trouble Signal Units

### Annunciators

An Annunciator is defined by the Standard to be ".. a control unit or transponder component to visually indicate signals from a fire alarm system." Annunciators may be in the form of labeled LED arrays, backlit windows with message text inscribed, or even messages on LCD/CRT screens, sometimes referred to as 'Sequential Displays'. There are specific requirements for sequential displays applied as the primary annunciator for the Fire Alarm, regarding the number of messages they must be able to show concurrently on their screens, for the priorities of different message types and for the order of their appearance, described in *CAN/ULC-S527 Standard for Fire Alarm Control Panels*.

As part of making sure the fire alarm control, display, and warning systems are all working properly, it is required to test all the annunciators, both those on control panels and remotely mounted units. Each annunciator must provide certain minimum indications, which include;

- Power On

- a common Trouble signal,

- a Lamp Test function (or the equivalent for LCD-type annunciators )

©

- visual indication of 'Alarm Signal Silence'

- visual indication of Alarm Signals

- correctly labeled alarm and supervisory input zone status indications, and

- visual indicators for ancillary functions

As well, there must be switches and controls to allow manual activation of alarms, alarm acknowledgement, alarm silencing (as well as a full complement of display controls where LCD or CRT type displays are used). In addition, the Design or System Description should be reviewed and checked for the requirements for other control and switch functions such as ancillary device operation, fan and damper operation, bypass functions, etc.

## Multiple Annunciators

The S536 Standard prescribes the minimum testing required in circumstances where multiple annunciators provide the same indications of the same events, simply in different locations. Because observing the annunciation of every type of event at every annunciator can be extremely time consuming, the Standard allows some relief if it can be demonstrated by the nature of the system design that like events will cause identical indications at separated locations.

## Remote Trouble Signal Units

In addition to Annunciators, it is required that Remote Trouble Signal Units operate correctly, including both visual and audible trouble indications, and trouble signal silence functions.

## Summary – Annunciation

Nothing can replace the Test & Inspect Technician studying the Design or the System Description and learning in detail the intended operation of each fire alarm system he/she tests. The fire alarm system response to a complete range of possible events and conditions needs to be simulated and proper annunciator indications verified. This is often very difficult to do while a building is partially occupied, because of the need to trigger alarm, trouble and supervisory events in order to ensure the right annunciations take place. It also requires at least two and sometimes more people to undertake the testing, and to observe responses at each system annunciator of each type of event in each zone.

### 13.9.6 <u>Printers</u>

Fire alarm systems often have system logging/event printers, whether built into the FACP or separately connected. It must be verified that the printer is properly connected, and supervised by the fire alarm panel where required; that it prints the correct information when events occur (a printer is in effect another form of annunciation, and deserves the same degree of thorough testing as fixed indicating or LCD/CRT based annunciators). As with the other parts of the system, the operation of the printer(s) as required by the System Description or the Design must be determined and tested, including specific report generation operations.

Some larger systems have more than one printer, each dedicated to printing certain types of events, or even events that arise in certain specific zones or building areas ('vectored' printer functions).

### 13.9.7 <u>Data Communication Links</u>

A Data Communication Link is a data channel between the central processing unit (CPU) and the transponders, annunciators, active field devices and supporting field devices of a distributed type control unit or a remote receiving equipment control unit. Because these links interconnect so many devices and subsystems with the Control Panel, it is critical that they be highly resilient, well protected, and tolerant of certain failure types without leading to the disabling of a Fire Alarm System.

Before testing begins, the Design and system specifications (or the System Description) must be consulted, and the interconnections, routings and intended fail-mode operations of the various data links should be understood so that a testing plan can be properly set out.

The data link supervision functions of the fire alarm panel should be tested under conditions of open circuits, ground faults and short circuits in various parts of the 'network'. It must be verified that isolators function properly and communication continues upstream of the isolator following a short circuit downstream.

If redundant loops or channels have been installed to provide continued full operation of all communications following any kind of fault on the primary circuit or loop, that functionality should also be tested, taking into account manufacturers' design parameters, architecture, and recommendations.

Also, correct per-Design or per-System Description degraded modes of operation must be tested and results recorded (such as continued inter-panel communication in all un-faulted segments of a network, when one segment suffers a short circuit).

## 13.9.8   Field Devices - Initiating

### General

The general requirement for all field devices is to ensure that they are undamaged, clean, solidly installed, properly identified, not covered up or inhibited, and cause the right result in terms of system response.

Because annual testing of fire alarm systems (typically) takes place in occupied buildings, it can be very disruptive, which is why only one device per loop or input circuit needs to be tested with bells or tones enabled. But all the rest of the devices need to be tested for correct indications and sequence operations even if bells are inhibited.

Hard-to-access field devices may be tested every two years, as long as the fact that they are inaccessible and either were or were not tested during the current annual test is documented in the inspection and test report.

### Manual Stations

All stages of manual stations must be tested for proper operation and sequence

### Heat Detectors

Restorable heat detectors must be tested with an appropriate heat source that is not an open flame. Non-restorable ones must be tested via simulating electrical operation.

### Smoke Detectors

Smoke detector testing and inspection is perhaps the most controversial area of the requirements of annual tests. While inspecting for cleanliness and proper identification are not typically found difficult, testing smoke detectors by introducing smoke or equivalent aerosols, and measuring detector sensitivity, are typically opportunities for misunderstanding or incorrect procedure.

It is therefore recommended that the fire alarm technician periodically undergo "refresher" on the theory of smoke detectors, the definitions of "obscuration" and "sensitivity", and review the dynamics of introduction of aerosols into a detector chamber, and the typical time lags one can expect for response, depending on the types of aerosol introduced. In addition, it is important for the technician to refer to the detector manufacturer's recommended test procedures and the correct means of determining detector sensitivity.

For simple conventional and single-sensor, single-criterion addressable smoke detectors, referring to the manufacturer's instructions for testing, and introduction of a manufacturer-approved test gas in appropriate quantities, is enough to verify that the detector is functioning (sensitivity must still be measured and recorded).

For multi-sensor, algorithm-based advanced-function detectors, a simple introduction of test gas may not trigger an alarm or even pre-alarm activation. This is because such detectors, either standalone, or in concert with intelligence in the FACP, are typically designed to discriminate between real fire phenomena and "deceptive" or non-fire-related phenomena, such as dust infusion, welding-related emissions or water vapour. Test gas introduction is not a true fire-related phenomenon, so an advanced detector may not respond. Such devices often simply require their algorithms be turned off at the control panel before introducing test gas to verify chamber response.

Likewise, smoke detector sensitivity measurements are often the source of confusion and frustration for the tester. Some models of smoke detectors require very specific test apparatus to be used to measure sensitivity, and for older devices, it may be very difficult for a testing firm to determine what the appropriate meter is, much less be able to get hold of one. The manufacturer's instructions typically specify the appropriate testing device and test method. Where that information is not directly available, the CFAA Website may be consulted.

Detector sensitivities must be measured and recorded for each device. The interpretation of the measurement should be made clear by the tester to the prospective reader of the report, so the reader can see clearly that the measurement implies sensitivity in the required operating range, and how far from the upper and lower limits the sensitivity is.

Fortunately, on most modern fire alarm systems, detector sensitivity can be measured and even adjusted at the FACP. This speeds up the work of the inspector/tester dramatically, and often provides readings directly in % per foot obscuration.

The use of third party pre-calibrated smoke-simulator test instruments to test sensitivity of any type of smoke detector has been accepted by authorities in some jurisdictions, and such devices are referred to in the *ULC Standard for Smoke Detectors for Fire Alarm Systems, CAN/ULC–S529*. However there persists some controversy as to the legitimacy of such devices, since they do not duplicate exactly the test methods, conditions and processes carried out by the manufacturers in their factories, nor those in the ULC testing laboratory. So while there is some recognition that these devices introduce a "gas" at some known rate of obscuration build-up, it is not universally accepted that the sensitivity results they yield match those that would be found in the factory or at ULC.

Finally, it is required that should sensitivity be found to lie outside the required operating range, IF the detector is amenable to cleaning, it may be cleaned and re-tested. If it fails to "pass" after a cleaning, it must be replaced.

If there is no way at all to measure the sensitivity of a smoke detector, it must be replaced with one whose sensitivity can be measured.

Remote Status Indicators for smoke detectors must be inspected and tested to operate properly and to be visible where appropriate.

The definition of 'Status Change Confirmation'/'Alarm Verification' in the Standard is "Confirmation of a normal to off-normal status change for a smoke detector input circuit". Typically this function, designed to avoid false alarms through nuisance activation of smoke detectors, may only be activated when approved by the Authority Having Jurisdiction. When this function is permitted, it is important that the implied delayed response by the FACP to a smoke detector state change not operate for state changes of other devices such as manual stations, and that such devices cause immediate panel/alarm response per the design.

In addition to testing activation and measuring sensitivity of Duct Smoke Detectors, airflow past or through such detectors must be measured and verified to be in the allowable range.

## Other Detectors

The manufacturer's documentation must be consulted and its recommendations applied, when testing and measuring sensitivity on Beam Smoke Detectors, and for Flame Detectors. Great care should be taken to ensure that the tester understands the operating principles of these devices, and that the devices and test procedures are applied including all manufacturer pre-cautions, requirements and installation conditions.

## Water Extinguishing System Alarm Devices

It is important that devices used to detect water flow be tested by triggering them with actual water flow. This work must be performed by personnel who are qualified to do so. In order to do this, the inspecting/testing firm must arrange to be able to safely operate the sprinkler/water system. This requires careful coordination with the building owner or facility manager, and should, if possible, be coordinated with the periodic sprinkler or extinguishing system tests that must be done several times per year.

Flow switches often have time-delayed contact actuation to avoid false alarms or false control device actuations under conditions of variable or intermittent water flow or pressure change. The time delay should be checked and recorded in the inspection report.

## Water Extinguishing System Supervisory Devices

Water extinguishing system supervisory devices must each be tested to ensure they trigger trouble signals when they are activated or become 'off-normal'. Valve position switches must activate upon 20% valve travel or more (or upon two full turns of the stem). Pressure switch trip points must be observed and corresponding trouble signals verified. Water level switches must be tested and proven to initiate trouble signals at appropriate water levels by actually changing the water level if possible. These and other switches such as low temperature devices may be tested through electrical contact operation simulation, if it is not possible to vary the actual level or temperature. Power loss to compressors and fire water pumps should be simulated by (authorized) opening of the appropriate feeder circuit breaker and verifying initiation of a trouble signal.

## 13.9.9   Field Devices - Signalling

### General

Signalling devices include bells, horns, sirens, speakers, strobes and any other kind of audible and/or visible device used to notify building occupants of an alert, an alarm or other condition. All of them need to be inspected for proper, solid, un-obstructed installation, with their shells or housings properly tightened, and proper labeling/identification as appropriate.

All of them need to be operated and it must be ensured that;

- audibility of signals (alert, alarm) is adequate throughout the zone served,
- voice messages are audible and intelligible throughout the zone(s) served by the speaker array(s),
- strobe light operation is visible and unobstructed throughout the zone(s) served,

### Residential Suites

It must be ensured that all speakers, horns or other signals are solidly and properly installed and are unobstructed and undamaged, and that tones are at adequate audibility levels throughout the suite, and voice messages are clearly audible and understandable.

©

Many residential suites will have a silencing means provided for the occupant(s) to silence signals for ten-minute periods. Where applicable, it should be ensured the silencing switches are visible, accessible and functional. If after ten minutes an original alarm signal has not been acknowledged and silenced at the FACP, or if a subsequent alarm occurs after the initial silencing, the in-suite tones must re-sound.

In newer residences, it may be that in-suite silencing means are not provided, that the Fire Alarm system automatically silences the in-suite tones after an initial period, and resounds the in-suite alarms if an alarm condition still exists or occurs after the initial silencing. It must be ascertained if such operation is applicable to the residence being inspected, and that "automatic" sequence is tested. The number of suites in each building or per floor requiring such a test will be that required to ensure that the operation is the same in all suites.

### Emergency Telephones

Each telephone must be inspected and tested for clear two-way voice communication, appropriate indication at the FACP that a handset has been lifted, that the 'in use' or 'system operable' tones are heard in each remote handset, and that the enclosures, locks, instruction labels and other "mechanical" arrangement for each telephone are per design and in good working condition.

## 13.9.10 End of Line Devices

End of line devices for conventional input and output circuits must be tested to ensure that if they are open-circuited, grounded on either side, or short-circuited ("jumpered out"), the appropriate trouble/fault signal initiates at the Control Panel. A short circuit on an initiating circuit will cause an alarm or supervisory indication, but on a signal circuit will result in a trouble condition. In versions of the *Standard* previous to 2004, this was not a requirement for Annual Test and Inspections; it is important to note that such tests are now required.

## 13.9.11 Appendices to *CAN/ULC S536*

The Appendices to the *Standard* provide comprehensive and very helpful details about each phase of an Annual Inspection and Test, and the Fire Alarm Technician should acquaint herself/himself with their contents and applications. Doing so will answer a lot of questions for the novice technician, and will virtually guide her/him through the processes and the documentation requirements. Methodology is provided there for tests of various kinds, and guidelines are provided for limits and levels for various signals and operations.

However purely moving through the Standard and its Appendices only serves as a checklist process in carrying out the Test and Inspection. It is as critical for the Technician to understand how the system is intended to work, how to spot problems, deficiencies and threats to reliable operation, and how to document her/his findings in a way that will be clear to the Owner, the AHJ, and future service people who will refer to the Report.

### 13.9.12 Documenting The Annual Inspection and Test

In addition to the above, examples of the contents of suitable forms used for documenting the outcomes of all the types of inspections and tests carried out are also in (related) Appendices in the Standard. It is likely most practical to obtain sets of prepared forms from the CFAA or from any other recognized organization that offers them.

Following are some examples of good reports, and of not-so-good reports, from actual fire alarm tests and inspections, with the particular positives and negatives highlighted. You should review them, and satisfy yourself that you have a good idea how you will make sure you will prepare first class, professional reports for your customer, your supervisor and for the local AHJ.

### 13.9.13 Rules of Thumb

Rules of thumb for Inspection and Test Reports that will serve you and your customers well include;

- Take the trouble to neatly record your results, observations, and notations as you go along with the Inspection and Test. Don't do a lot of tests in rapid succession then go and tick off boxes on pages and pages of pre-made forms. Accuracy and completeness of information is critical for anything related to a life safety system.

- Put yourself in the position of the reader of the report when making notes, describing problems, recording sensitivities or recommending service or deficiency repairs.

- Take pride in the entire Inspection and Test process, and in the quality of the report that is prepared as a result. Many firms type their inspection reports from hand-written documents supplied by the inspecting technician, to ensure the customer receives a clear, professional-looking document. You may wish to request a copy of the Report after it is typed to review it for completeness and quality before it goes to the customer.

- Be prepared to explain any comment or entry in the report should questions arise later on. The more completely and clearly you 'document' up front, the less difficulty you will have doing later reviews of your findings.

©

- Take a personal interest in making sure that the customer or building owner receives their report promptly after the inspection is done. If possible, meet with the Owner or Building Manager during the inspection and test process to keep them informed as to what is going on, and to develop an on-going relationship with them. This way, you will be able to explain your findings openly at the time or down the road, and make it easier for your customer to maintain a highly reliable life safety system.

- In the end, it is up to you to ensure the integrity, completeness and reliability of the inspection and test you do. No amount of prescribed procedures or long check-lists of items to test can replace your judgment, experience, common sense and integrity in ensuring your customer is well served and safe after you have given his/her building its "annual check-up".

## 13.10   Ancillary Devices and Systems

During the study of this chapter you have come to understand the role that an Annual Inspection plays in ensuring that the Fire Alarm System continues to function in accordance with its original design documents and the Fire Safety Plan.

Upon completion of the Inspection procedures, every single aspect of the Fire Alarm System should have been exercised and found to be completely functional and compliant. This includes the functional testing of the ancillary (relay) contacts in the Fire Alarm Control Unit (FACU). The contacts were tested and found to 'reverse' from normally open to normally closed and/or vice-versa.

From reading previous chapters in this Manual, you will understand the importance of ancillary devices and systems, and therefore you will understand how essential it is that all such systems continue to operate appropriately.

We need to look at these situations in detail.

### 13.10.1  Test Together

*CAN/ULC-S536 Inspection and Testing of Fire Alarm Systems* does not require that the Fire Alarm Technician test/verify any ancillary devices or systems. In fact a statement to that effect is found in the standard. There is also a cautionary note, to that effect, on the suggested report format. It really can be no other way, because the Fire Alarm Technician cannot be expected to be knowledgeable on the intricate workings of the air-handling systems within a hospital, the elevator controller in a high-rise condominium, or the mag-locks security system in an office tower.

Therefore, it is very important that all players in this situation (building owners, Authorities Having Jurisdiction etc) understand that the Fire Alarm Technician has no further responsibility than to confirm that the ancillary controls/contacts in the FACU operate as required, that the interconnection wiring entering the FACU from the ancillary device/system is acceptable and is properly terminated in the FACU, and that the voltage appearing on the ancillary control conductors is acceptable and within the electrical limits of the FACU ancillary control circuitry. In addition, the Technician must compare the contact rating of the ancillary relay contacts to ensure it is compliant with the incoming voltages and current of the ancillary control circuit.

To do this properly requires the presence of both the Fire Alarm Technician and the Ancillary Technician, as well as the AHJ and the Building Owner. Discussions should lead to an agreed sequence of test operation. The Fire Alarm Technician should then initiate an alarm condition per the agreed sequence and the Ancillary Technician should observe the results, and confirm that all Ancillary systems operated as required. Several such different tests may be necessary. The Building Owner and the AHJ should observe and then accept the results.

The Fire Alarm Technician should include a note on the Inspection Report to confirm the occurrence of such tests, noting the names of the personnel attending the tests.

## 13.10.2 Simple Situations

The Technician might well ask: 'If I do not test the actual control of the ancillary equipment...who will?' In many buildings, the ancillary device may be just a single air-circulating fan, corridor smoke control door, or perhaps a single mag-lock on an exit door. In such situations it is a simple thing to perform a test that confirms the shutdown of the fan, the releasing and closing of the corridor door, or the un-locking of the exit door. If the Fire Alarm Technician feels comfortable in performing and observing the tests, and the resetting of the specific devices, then there is no good reason not to do so. It becomes a personal/corporate decision rather than a 'standards' question.

Obviously, it is important that the Technician advise the Owner of the intended test, to make sure that the Owner is in complete agreement with the event itself and the timing. The Owner may even offer to be of assistance!

## 13.10.3 Reporting

Without doubt, the factual reporting of the extent of the testing is vitally important. If the Owner thinks that all systems have been fully tested and are functional, then there may well be a future containing litigation if systems do not function and a fire death or injury occurs. Although testing of ancillary equipment is not required by the standard, ancillary systems are part of the overall building life safety systems. If a Technician notices that an ancillary device or system appears not to function as intended (for example a fan does not shut down) then the

Technician should make note of this and advise the building owner so that appropriate repair action can be taken by the appropriate service provider.

Therefore report carefully, and in writing, on the specifics not only of the testing that was performed, but also the testing that was not done!! In this manner, the Owner will be fully aware of any additional testing that must be performed to ensure that all systems are functional.

## 13.10.4  Record Keeping

Records must be kept for a period of two years.

## 13.10.5  Service

On occasion, a fire alarm system will require service. If the system is not completely functional, a Fire Watch may need to be instituted while repairs are effected.

When replacing system circuit boards, care must be taken to de-energize the system while the board is removed or installed.

When determining the cause of a fault, an effective way to locate a fault condition (especially on circuits) is to do a Boolean search (sometimes referred to as "half-splitting"). This method separates a circuit into halves and then determines whether the fault is on the panel side or the EOL side. This process is repeated until the source of the problem is found. This method can also be used to find faulty boards in the FACU.

## 13.11   Chapter Summary

1.    The *ULC Standard CAN/ULC-S536 Inspection and Testing of Fire Alarm Systems* tells us, in detail, what must be done during an annual inspection.

2.    The same *ULC Standard* requires that a complete report be written that covers all aspects of the Annual. The report must document all observations and test results.

3.    Unfortunately, the standard cannot stipulate who is to do the work. Usually the AHJ will demand that a CFAA-Registered Technician perform the work. If the system is a technically involved system such as a network system, then a CFAA Technician who has received factory-authorized training on the specific system equipment should perform the Annual. CFAA Technicians should perform only the work for which they feel qualified.

4.    Visual inspection of each device is as important as the actual testing. Both must be performed and reported.

5.    Technicians should equip themselves with all of the appropriate test gear needed to perform all tests on the devices and overall system. Technicians should be knowledgeable about the design and operating parameters of all the devices on the system, and ensure their compatibility.

6.    All field devices must be inspected and operationally tested. Smoke detectors must be inspected (and cleaned if necessary), and alarm test operated. The results must be documented individually.

7.    It is very important to confirm that the zone labeling of sprinkler devices is accurate.

8.    The report of an Annual Inspection may have deficiencies. The owner must then ensure that the deficiencies are corrected.

9.    Many building owners like to receive a Certificate after completion of the Annual. A certificate is fine, but the owner must be given a copy of the complete report.

10.    A properly conducted Annual Inspection and Test procedure (and complete report) helps to ensure that the Fire Alarm System will continue to protect the building and its occupants.

©

## 13.12   Review Questions

| # | ? | Question | Section |
|---|---|----------|---------|
| **13-1** | | **It is critical that all fire alarm systems in service be kept fully functional at all times, and in order to ensure this, on-going fully documented testing and inspection of those systems is mandated just about everywhere in Canada.** | |
| | A | True | |
| | B | False | |
| **13-2** | | **The Fire Code regulations are enacted to provide an acceptable maximum level of fire safety to the occupants of any building falling within the regulatory scope.** | |
| | A | True | |
| | B | False | |
| **13-3** | | **The Preface to CAN/ULC—S536 states that it pre-supposes ..”the inspection and testing shall be conducted by qualified personnel acceptable to the Authority Having Jurisdiction’.** | |
| | A | True | |
| | B | False | |
| **13-4** | | **Fire Alarm Technicians typically do not require a copy of the currently applicable CAN/ULC-S536 Standard, and they do not need to become very familiar with its contents before undertaking any inspection and testing.** | |
| | A | True | |
| | B | False | |
| **13-5** | | **Each month, the Owner or his representative must place the Fire Alarm System on emergency power, and then inspect and test selected parts of the system on a ‘rotating basis’ (meaning different elements are selected for testing each month).** | |
| | A | True | |
| | B | False | |
| **13-6** | | **The requirements as prescribed by the ULC S536 Standard, anticipate and recognize that inspections and tests will be done in mainly in un-occupied buildings.** | |
| | A | True | |
| | B | False | |

| # | ? | Question | Section |
|---|---|---|---|
| **13-7** | | **If the Fire Alarm includes a non code required Voice Evacuation system on the fire alarm system it does not have to be tested.** | |
| | A | True | |
| | B | False | |
| **13-8** | | **The ULC S536 Standard requires that the Control Panel power supply be inspected to ensure it is properly fused and that it is 'Adequate to meet the requirements of the system'.** | |
| | A | True | |
| | B | False | |
| **13-9** | | **A Data Communication Link is a data channel between the central processing unit (CPU) and the transponders, annunciators, active field devices and supporting field devices of a distributed type control unit or a remote receiving equipment control unit.** | |
| | A | True | |
| | B | False | |
| **13-10** | | **When determining the cause of a fault, an effective way to locate a fault condition (especially on circuits) is to do a Boolean search this is sometimes referred to as "half-splitting".** | |
| | A | True | |
| | B | False | |

# Glossary

| Term | Definition |
| --- | --- |
| **Access-To-Exit** | Those parts of a building, such as aisles, hallways or corridors that provide access to an exit serving that floor area |
| **Active Field Device** | A device that can be uniquely identified by the control unit to determine its presence and operating status, and which may be commanded to operate or to change its operating parameters independently of other field devices that share a common circuit |
| **Addressable Device** | A device that can be individually and uniquely identified by a control unit. The address is set using binary/hexadecimal/decimal methods using dipswitches, rotary switches or solid-state memory |
| **Alarm Signal** | An audible signal transmitted throughout a zone or zones to advise occupants that a fire emergency exists; also called an EVACUATION signal |
| **Alert Signal** | An audible signal intended to advise designated persons of a fire emergency |
| **Ancillary Device** | A device that performs a life safety related function, but that is not part of the fire alarm system |
| **Authority Having Jurisdiction** | The organization, office, or individual responsible for approving equipment, an installation, or a procedure. Most often, it is the municipal Fire Department, although in some cases it may be the Building Department. |
| **Basement** | A storey or storeys of a building located below the first storey. |
| **Bonding** | The permanent low-impedance path obtained by joining all non-current-carrying metal parts to ensure electrical continuity, and with the capacity to conduct safely any current likely to be imposed on it |
| **Building Area** | The greatest horizontal area of a building above grade within the outside surface of exterior walls or within the outside surface of exterior walls and the centre line of firewalls. |
| **Building Height (In Storeys)** | The number of storeys contained between the roof and the floor of the first storey. An elevator machine room, sitting atop an office building, would not generally be considered a storey in this application. |
| **Candela** | The SI or metric unit of measure for luminous intensity or candlepower of a light or strobe |

| Term | Definition |
|---|---|
| **Check, Inspect And Test** | **CHECK** - A visual observation to ensure the device or system is in place and is not obviously damaged or obstructed |
| | **INSPECT** - A physical examination to determine that the device or system will apparently perform in accordance with its intended function |
| | **TEST** - the actual operation of the device or system to ensure that it performs in accordance with its intended operation or function |
| **Closure** | A device for shutting off an opening through a fire separation. Example: a door, shutter or fire damper |
| **Compatible** | The correct electrical, electronic or mechanical interaction between a series of system components that depend on individual unique characteristics that are connected together to meet the requirements of this Standard (e.g. Control Unit and/or Transponder and field devices) |
| **Contained-Use Area** | A supervised area containing one or more rooms in which occupant movement is restricted to a single room by security measures not under the control of the occupant |
| **Control Unit** | A device with the necessary circuits or components needed to provide acceptable operating power for a fire alarm system, receive signals from alarm initiating devices, cause audible alarm signals to operate, and electrically monitor the installation wiring and device placement against certain faults and/or removal |
| **Conventional Field Device** | A field device that is usually connected to a control unit and/or transponder on a common wiring circuit with other devices so that all devices on the circuit provide a common status change information (e.g. fire alarm detection or signalling). Such devices cannot be uniquely identified by a control unit and/or transponder unless there is only one device on the circuit. (Refer to active field device) |
| **Decibel** | A unit of measurement for comparing levels of sound power, based on a logarithmic scale. Generally expressed in deciBels (dB) |
| **Dwelling Unit** | A suite operated as a housekeeping unit, used or intended to be used, as a domicile by one or more persons and usually containing cooking, eating, living, sleeping and sanitary facilities |
| **Electromagnetic Door Release** | A device used to hold doors in the open position, and to release the doors to close automatically when signaled to do so by a fire alarm system or other means |

| Term | Definition |
|---|---|
| **Exit** | A facility such as a door, stairs or ramp that leads from the floor area that it serves to an open public thoroughfare, or to a protected exterior open space that has access to an open public thoroughfare. Once in an exit facility, a person should have a continuous path leading to the building exterior |
| **Fire - Flame Stage** | A phase in the development of fire in which flame has occurred. |
| **Fire - Heat Stage** | The most dangerous phase in the development of fire in which uncontrolled heat and rapidly expanding air complete the development of the fire |
| **Fire - Incipient Stage** | The earliest phase in the development of fire in which invisible products of combustion are given off. No visible smoke, flame or appreciable heat is present |
| **Fire - Smouldering Stage** | The stage in the development of fire where combustion products are now visible as smoke. Flames or appreciable heat are still not present |
| **Fire Alarm System** | A system comprising both manually operated devices and automatic fire detectors, alarm signaling devices and a control unit, all electrically interconnected in order to detect fire conditions and to warn the occupants of the building |
| **Fire Compartment** | An enclosed space, separated from all other parts of the building by fire separations having the required fire-resistance rating |
| **Fire Damper** | A closure which consists of a normally held open damper installed in an air distribution system or in a wall or floor assembly and designed to close automatically in the event of a fire in order to maintain the integrity of the fire separation |
| **Fire Detector** | A device that detects a fire condition and automatically initiates an electrical signal, and includes heat and smoke detectors |
| **Fire Detector - Heat** | A device for sensing an abnormally high air temperature or an abnormal rate of increase of temperature |
| **Fire Detector - Smoke** | A device for sensing the presence of visible or invisible particles of combustion, the concentration of which exceeds a pre-determined level |
| **Fire Rated Assembly** | Commonly used term for an assembly with a fire resistance rating. It may or may not have a fire separation requirement on it |
| **Fire Resistance Rating** | The time, in hours, that a material or a construction assembly withstands the passage of flame or transmission of heat in accordance with established test procedures |

| Term | Definition |
|------|------------|
| **Fire Separation** | A construction assembly that acts as a barrier against the spread of fire. A fire separation may or may not have a fire resistance rating |
| **First Storey** | The uppermost storey having its floor level not more than two metres above grade. In certain jurisdictions, it is the storey with its floor closest to grade and having its ceiling more than 1.8 m above grade |
| **Flame Detector** | A detector that is designed to sense the radiation emanating from a flame. Two common types of flame detectors are 'infrared' and 'ultraviolet' detectors |
| **Floor Area** | The space on any storey of a building between the exterior walls and required firewalls, including the space occupied by interior walls and partitions, but not including exits and vertical service spaces that pierce the storey |
| **Ground Fault** | A circuit impedance to ground sufficient to prevent normal operation |
| **Heat Transfer — Conduction** | Heat transfer from one object to another of different temperature, by means of direct contact of the two objects |
| **Heat Transfer — Convection** | Heat transfer by the motion of particles within a medium (air, gas, liquid) |
| **High Building** | A building where the floor level of the top storey of the building is above grade more than that allowed in 3.2.6 of the Building Code |
| **Impeded-Egress Zone** | A supervised area in which occupants have free movement but require the release, by security personnel, of security doors at the boundary before they are able to leave the area, but does not include a contained use area |
| **Inspect** | See definition under CHECK, INSPECT and TEST |
| **Interconnected Floor Spaces** | Superimposed floor areas or parts of floor areas in which floor assemblies that are required to be fire separations are penetrated by openings that are not provided with closures |
| **Major Occupancy** | The principal occupancy for which a building or part thereof is used, or intended to be used, and shall be deemed to include the subsidiary occupancies that are an integral part of the principal occupancy. |
| **Manual Station** | A device that initiates an alarm condition in a fire alarm system, when actuated manually. The station will remain in the operated condition until it has been reset to normal using a special tool. Previous editions of standards used the terminology "Manual Pull Station". |

©

| Term | Definition |
|------|------------|
| **Means Of Egress** | A continuous path of travel provided for the escape of persons from any point in a building or contained open space to a separate building, an open public thoroughfare, or an exterior open space protected from fire exposure from the building and having access to an open public thoroughfare. Means of egress includes exits and access to exits |
| **Occupant Load** | The number of people for which a building or part of a building is designed, on a square-metre basis for each person. This figure is set by the authorities, is different for different occupancies, and is quite likely different than the actual occupant load the building may eventually experience. |
| **Open-Circuit Fault** | A circuit series resistance increase of 10 Kohms or more, unless otherwise stated, resulting from an abnormal condition |
| **Owner** | Any person, firm or corporation controlling the property under consideration |
| **Plenum** | A chamber forming part of an air-duct system |
| **Public Corridor** | A corridor that provides access to exit from more than one suite |
| **Return Duct** | A duct for conveying air from a space being heated, ventilated or air-conditioned back to the heating, ventilating or air-conditioning appliance |
| **Self-Closing** | An approved device which will ensure closing after having been opened |
| **Service Room** | A room provided in a building to contain equipment associated with building services |
| **Short-Circuit Fault** | A resistance shunt of 0.1 Ohm or less across a circuit, unless otherwise stated, resulting from an abnormal condition |
| **Smoke Alarm** | A combined smoke detector and audible alarm device designed to sound an alarm within a room or suite in which it is located, upon the detection of smoke within that room or suite |
| **Smoke Barrier** | A continuous membrane, either vertical or horizontal, such as a wall, floor, or ceiling assembly that is designed and constructed to restrict the movement of smoke. A smoke barrier may or may not have a fire resistance rating. Such barriers may have protected openings |
| **Smoke Compartment** | A space within a building enclosed by smoke or fire barriers on all sides, including the top and bottom |

| Term | Definition |
| --- | --- |
| **Sprinkler Supervision** | A method of electrically monitoring critical elements of an automatic sprinkler system to detect potentially disabling abnormal conditions, and provide a warning signal |
| **Storey** | That portion of a building which is situated between the top of any floor and the top of the floor next above it, and if there is no floor above it, that portion between the top of such floor and the ceiling (roof) above it. |
| **Suite** | A single room or series of rooms of complementary use, operated under a single tenancy, and includes: |

(a)  dwelling units,

(b)  individual guest rooms in motels, hotels, boarding houses, rooming houses and dormitories, and

(c)  individual stores and individual or complementary rooms for business and personal services occupancies.

| Term | Definition |
| --- | --- |
| **Supply Duct** | A duct for conveying air from a heating, ventilating or air-conditioning appliance to a space to be heated, ventilated or air-conditioned |
| **Supporting Field Device** | An active field device that monitors other field devices on a separate circuit and reports the status of that separate circuit to the control unit |
| **Test** | See definition under CHECK, INSPECT and TEST |
| **Trouble Signal** | A signal (usually a buzzer and an amber lamp to LED) indicating a fault or an off-normal condition in a fire alarm system |
| **Vertical Service Space** | A shaft oriented essentially vertically that is provided in a building to facilitate the installation of building services including mechanical, electrical and plumbing installations and facilities such as elevators, refuse chutes and linen chutes |
| **Waterflow Switch** | A device used to detect the flow of water through some portion of the automatic sprinkler system piping, as will occur when one or more sprinkler heads has operated, and will operate a set of electrical contacts for interconnection to a fire alarm system. An adjustable time delay mechanism may be installed between the paddle-operated stem and the contacts to keep brief water movements from initiating an alarm signal |